Other Books by Drs. Freedman and Kaplan

COMPREHENSIVE TEXTBOOK OF PSYCHIATRY
Alfred M. Freedman and Harold I. Kaplan, EDITORS   1967

PSYCHOPATHOLOGY OF ADOLESCENCE
Alfred M. Freedman (with Joseph Zubin), EDITOR   1970

COMPREHENSIVE GROUP PSYCHOTHERAPY
Harold I. Kaplan (with Benjamin J. Sadock), EDITOR   1971

STUDIES IN HUMAN BEHAVIOR
Alfred M. Freedman and Harold I. Kaplan, GENERAL EDITORS
DIAGNOSING MENTAL ILLNESS: EVALUATION IN
PSYCHIATRY AND PSYCHOLOGY   1972
INTERPRETING PERSONALITY: A SURVEY OF
TWENTIETH-CENTURY VIEWS   1972
HUMAN BEHAVIOR: BIOLOGICAL, PSYCHOLOGICAL,
AND SOCIOLOGICAL   1972
TREATING MENTAL ILLNESS:
ASPECTS OF MODERN THERAPY   1972
THE CHILD: HIS PSYCHOLOGICAL AND
CULTURAL DEVELOPMENT   1972
VOL. 1: NORMAL DEVELOPMENT AND
PSYCHOLOGICAL ASSESSMENT
VOL. 2: THE MAJOR PSYCHOLOGICAL DISORDERS
AND THEIR TREATMENT

INTERPRETING
PERSONALITY

INTERPRETING PERSONALITY

A Survey of
Twentieth-Century Views

ALFRED M. FREEDMAN, M.D.

Professor and Chairman, Department of Psychiatry,
New York Medical College

AND

HAROLD I. KAPLAN, M.D.

Professor, Department of Psychiatry, New York Medical College

EDITORS

Studies in Human Behavior

New York   ATHENEUM   1972

The editors express their appreciation to the following publishers and publications for permission to reprint portions of the works cited.

Heinz L. Ansbacher: H. Ansbacher from his Introduction to *Problems of Neurosis* by A. Adler, P. Mairet, editor, Harper & Row, New York, 1964.

Basic Books, Inc., Publishers: Sigmund Freud, "Instincts and Their Vicissitudes," in Volume IV of *The Collected Papers of Sigmund Freud*, edited by Ernest Jones, M.D., New York, 1959.

Grune & Stratton, Inc.: Sandor Rado, "Mind, Unconscious Mind, and Brain," in *Psychoanalysis of Behavior*, Vol. 1, New York, 1956.

International Universities Press, Inc.: C. Brenner, *An Elementary Textbook of Psychoanalysis*, New York, 1955.

W. W. Norton & Company, Inc.: Sigmund Freud from *An Outline of Psychoanalysis*, translated and edited by James Strachey. Copyright 1949 by W. W. Norton & Company, Inc. Copyright © 1969 by The Institute of Psychoanalysis and Alix Strachey.

Princeton University Press: *The Collected Works of C. G. Jung*, edited by G. Adler, M. Fordham, and H. Read, translated by R. F. C. Hull, Bollingen Series XX, Vol. 9, *The Archetypes and the Collective Unconscious* (copyright © 1959 & 1969 by Princeton University Press), Vol. 11, *Psychology and Religion* (copyright © 1958 & 1969 by Princeton University Press), Vol. 17, *The Development of Personality* (copyright © 1954 by Princeton University Press).

Preface

This book is one of a series of volumes based on the First Edition of the *Comprehensive Textbook of Psychiatry,* which we edited for use in medical schools. Dr. Helen S. Kaplan served as Assistant to the Editors of that edition. The *Comprehensive Textbook* resulted from our part in setting up the undergraduate and graduate programs in psychiatry at New York Medical College. New articles have been written for these volumes, and certain subjects have been updated or eliminated, in an effort to reach a wider audience.

The responsibility for teaching psychiatry has made us acutely aware of the whole spectrum of current progress in the continuing search for the causes of mental disorders. Recent scientific research has placed at the disposal of the clinical practitioner new knowledge that must be incorporated into existing theoretical and therapeutic methods. Our aim is to include in these volumes all such major contributions in the basic and social sciences that have an influence on the teaching and practice of psychiatry. We have attempted to derive a balanced and current summary of psychiatric thinking in a variety of fields.

The interaction with distinguished and creative colleagues in the preparation of the material contained in these volumes has been most gratifying. We have had a unique opportunity to engage in a stimulating exchange of ideas and to establish rewarding personal relationships as well.

Many people have given us dedicated and valuable help, and we wish to express our deep appreciation to them. We would mention in particular Lois A. Baken, Elaine Cohen, Pauline DeMarco and Marian Hailey. And we give special thanks to Joan Welsh for her invaluable help in editing and stylizing this series.

A. M. F.
H. I. K.

Contents

AREA C

Other Psychoanalytic and Psychodynamic Theories

AREA D

Personality Theories Derived from Psychology

Introduction

One might assume that a book entitled *Interpreting Personality* offers somewhere within its pages a single definition of personality and, perhaps, of psychoanalysis. But such is not the case. No one theory of personality adequately explains or predicts normal or abnormal functioning. Nevertheless, the practice of psychiatry exists, and its insights into the causes of mental illness and into the methods of cure rest on the various theories presented in this book.

In 1900 Sigmund Freud published *The Interpretation of Dreams*, in which appeared a discussion of the Oedipus complex. The study was ignored; only a general book reviewer had anything good to say about it. Freud condensed his scientific treatise, renamed it *On Dreams*, and published it the following year for the general public, thereafter trusting in lay readers rather than in his competitive and established medical colleagues for a readiness to examine the workings of the mind in a new way. Thirty years later Freud was recognized as the founder of psychoanalysis and was treated with such awe and deference that the authoritarian letter of his statements rather than their questioning, unorthodox spirit was frequently adopted by scientists and lay readers alike.

Freud read for his degree in medicine in Vienna during the 1870's, a decade when the biological conclusions of Darwin and the physical and physiological ideas of the Helmholtz school excited students. Helmholtz's advocates postulated that the same two basic forces in chemical matter—attraction and repulsion—also operated in biology.

Freud eventually described an unconscious area of the mind that is a realm of wishes and pleasures and that forms the motivational force behind human action. The infant is born in a state of yearning, full of id. He grows through an age of oral longing to an anal stage, when he learns to control the elimination of body wastes while he is, as a person, being controlled by his parents. In the oedipal stage his longing turns to a desire for sexual union with his mother until he finally accepts the fact that he will not be allowed this pleasure. Then he begins to repress from the preconscious (linking part) and conscious level of his mind the forbidden sexual wishes. With this repression, neurosis begins.

It was Freud's wish to describe the physiological underpinnings of mental events, to give the study of personality a physical basis, but the mechanical model he chose to clarify these events was one tied to the still basically Newtonian physics of his century. Freud's libido was a basic psychic energy, a life force, an instinct for union, a force that is attracted and attracting. Libido moves chronologically from one orifice of the body to another, since the individual makes contact with the world at orifices. In light of relativity physics, many dropped Freud's libido theory.

In Freud's system the way to health was to isolate repression and to relieve the pressure by expressing the forbidden wish in words. First, however, the repression had to be located in the normally inaccessible unconscious. Encouraging the patient to associate ideas freely until they led to the site of the repression was the method Freud selected after testing and rejecting hypnosis. Free association, in league with the correct psychic relationship between doctor and patient, was the basis of his psychoanalysis.

Later in his studies, Freud considered the infant to be born with a second instinct, that of aggression. This instinct was linked with a rage at frustrated mastery and with a physiological tendency, like that of cell tissue, not to hold together in attraction but to return to an inanimate state. This death wish stood in contradistinction to the earlier-expressed life or sexual wish, which leads physiologically to a uniting of cells.

Freud's ideas changed and evolved; as a result, his terminology is somewhat inconsistent. For instance, he early saw anxiety as arising only from the repression of sexual wishes. Later, he distinguished nonsexual anxieties arising from such dangers as birth itself. Anxiety can also emerge in anticipation of real danger, but neurotic anxiety comes from the anticipation of an unreal danger so strongly feared that the patient projects its reality outward from the mind to the external world. This projection results from a miscalculation of reality and increases the likelihood of further such miscalculation.

Reality is that province of the ego that protects the id's wishes by adjusting them to reality. The superego is the internalized parental demands and is developed during the phallic phase. Freud's focus was not on ego or superego but on id, libido, and instinct. Some followers, however, selected the ego as the focus for the further study of human personality, especially of the healthy personality. A notable expounder of a basically Freudian ego psychology is Erik Erikson.

Erikson elaborated on Freud's trio of id-ego-superego and on his theory of infantile sexuality. He examined the modes of approach that an infant uses at each developmental stage, and he showed the dangers that can develop if one of the modes or one of the bodily zones is emphasized out of the normal sequence. Erikson also extended the theory of development into a lifelong chronology; eight stages present eight conflicts and eight chances to activate a ratio of positive-negative ego power. Throughout Erikson's writing is the sense that adults continue to grow in ego capacity, that the inadequacies of the past can be corrected. He emphasized the societal aspect of child rearing far more than Freud did in his early family-oriented studies. A group of people share a common past and dream of a common future; they transfer this past-future to children in legends and to infants by the manner in which mothers nurse, dress, and regulate. Even newborns are being prepared for frustration or fulfillment, freedom or limitation. Erikson considered the infant to be born with anxiety—uncomfortable, helpless, and small—with ample time for anxiety to ferment in the long dependence of the human young.

Erikson had known Freud. So had Alfred Adler, Carl Jung, Wilhelm Reich, Sandor Rado, and others whose innovations produced schisms within the Freudian movement and in some instances led to the establishment of new schools of psychoanalysis. Most of those who disagreed with Freud rejected the idea that sexuality is the prime force in the making of personality. Cultural determinants, not biological drives and instincts, would be the area of their focus.

Alfred Adler spent nine years attending Wednesday night discussions at Freud's quarters in Vienna before he branched out on his own. Adler fixed on therapy itself, whereas Freud had focused on the cause of illness. The infant is born helpless and inferior; from this sense of inferiority comes his propelling anxiety and his drive for superiority, after which he can realize himself as an individual with a life style of his own. He may become side tracked into sick modes of behavior, which Adler termed ruling, getting, or avoiding. Normally, he will have a social feeling, a need and happiness in reacting to others; if not, he will be neurotic, clinging to inferiority, full of self-deception and self-defeating attitudes. The therapist helps by encouraging him to encounter and outgrow these attitudes.

Carl Jung described an unconscious different from Freud's depository of wishes and repressions. First called the collective unconscious and later the objective unconscious, it is present in the newborn and is independent of his life experience. Within it are archetypes, which are pictures or senses of The Mother, The Father, The Child, The Hidden Treasure, and others. The individual projects these archetypes onto real people, and inevitable discrepancies result. The rationality of the ego is then swamped in emotions generated by the archetypes, and anxiety is produced. The complexes that result from a mismatch of archetype and reality are also stored in the unconscious. And the unconscious contains, preformed, the individuality of the infant that unfolds as he grows. The goal of therapy, indeed of life, is individuation.

Interpersonal factors were especially important to Karen Horney, who left Europe in the 1930's. Horney did not give credence to Freud's theory of zones or to the importance of the family romance. Nor did she look back at childhood to remove repressions that cause disease. Neurosis has to be outgrown in the present, having originated in distorted parent-child relationships that have become self-perpetuating. A neurotic child learns to move away from or against others rather than toward; and neurosis is present whenever there is a significant discrepancy between achievement and potential. Because of a parent's rejecting attitude, the child becomes self-effacing, too expansive, or completely resigned. He comes to hate the self that is the poor total of his experiences, and he glamorizes his undeveloped traits and potentials—building himself a psyche that is vulnerable to humiliation.

Harry Stack Sullivan, an American, never studied with Freud. He brought to psychoanalysis a strong scientific orientation, insisting that such givens as the Oedipus complex, mother love, and man's aggressive instinct be reexamined in the light of the observable rather than the dimness of what could be remembered on the psychoanalytic couch. Each person is an individual, but his individuality is the subject of literature. His standardness belongs to science. Sullivan held all behavior to derive from conditioning in the interpersonal medium. There is no mother instinct, he decided, only tension in an infant that produces a cry that, in turn, provokes a response of tenderness in any mothering figure within hearing. When physiological needs are met, an infant feels satisfaction. When interpersonal needs are met, he feels security. When little security is forthcoming, his sense of powerlessness fails to diminish, and he does not develop self-esteem. For example, if a significant adult offers continual disapproval, the infant responds with anxiety, lack of security. This is the first step toward mental illness. The growing person may try to deal with an anxious insecurity by selecting a neurotic or psychotic solution as he moves through five epochs—birth, speech, peers, same-sex intimacy, and opposite-sex intimacy.

Erich Fromm, who came from Europe in 1933, also saw human behavior as culturally rather than biologically determined. Individuals relate to the world in two major ways—by assimilating or acquiring, and by socialization. The society's manner of assimilating may be by hoarding or marketing, and it may be receptive, exploitative, or—best of all—productive. The manner of socialization may be masochistic, sadistic, destructive, conforming, or one of love. Humans are lonely, being removed from nature and from other animals. Their loneliness causes them to look for meaning among other humans. The infant belongs to his mother and to his home, but he goes through a process of separation and individuation that produces anxiety. However, it is the sick society that produces the pathological man, driving him into self-destructive and antisocial stances. He learns his society's manner of assimilation through the values of his parents, who are molded by it.

Sandor Rado studied with Freud and was considered a classical psychoanalyst until he gradually formed his clinical observations into a new theory he called adaptational psychodynamics, the "introspectional branch of human biology." Like Freud, he tried to pull together a theory of human mental behavior that would satisfy the demands of the larger field of biology and fit into it. But he turned to Darwin rather than to Helmholtz. He looked to see what had been vital to man in survival. What he settled on had little to do with body orifices or sexuality. He followed the physiological concepts of Cannon in dividing the emotions into two classes—the emergency emotions, which deal with the presence or anticipation of pain, and the welfare emotions, which accompany pleasure or its anticipation.

The human being's central integrative apparatus had developed through the evolutionary history of the species and is composed of four layers. Hedonic self-regulation, an ability to turn away from pain and toward pleasure, can be seen in protozoa. This self-regulation requires an awareness of what is dangerous and, therefore, an ability to refer to past experience. In the second layer, metazoan development, preverbal brute emotion emerges in a creature that can control its muscles with brain power, delay its response to a stimulus, and have some slight sense of future as well as of past. The emergency emotions of fear, rage, shame, guilty fear, and guilty rage are adaptive devices against danger; the welfare emotions of desire, joy, affection, love, and pride are connected with survival and group communication. At the third level, emotional thought, there is trial action, symbols can be manipulated, and language develops. There is a true past, present, and future. Thoughts are selective and self-justifying rather than objective. The mother regulates by reward and punishment, as does the society, and finally the individual becomes self-punishing and self-rewarding. The fourth layer is that of unemotional thought, which is rational and objective. Through the layers rises the axis or the action self, at first primordial and all-powerful, then tested and adjusted to a decreased omnipotence, bringing adults to heel.

Overproduction of emergency emotions underlies all emotional disorder. Treatment begins after fears have been relieved by the undoing of repression. The psychiatrist attempts to build up the patient's welfare emotions; his capacity for pleasure, assertion, and real competition are enhanced by realistic successful performance. The patient should avoid transference, an act of magic and dependence that Rado rejects in favor of a regard for the therapist as an expert in personal relations.

Other theories were propounded separately from those of Freud; still others were further redactions of or elaborations on his ideas. One begins to see a pattern of study where certain areas are filled in and agreed on, while others remain blank or controversial. There is an accompanying sense that a new discovery or approach will turn the known material into new perspectives.

Adolf Meyer, a Swiss, was already working and writing in America when he said in 1906 that Freud's ideas would be important, although they were too focused on pathology and hypothesis. Meyer considered mental illness to be a regression to infantile behavior as a means of self-cure or defense. The person who becomes mentally ill is one who develops an imbalanced personality by having chosen and put into use habits that do not lead to an effective adaptation to life. A cure should follow retaining of habits. Each patient's individual history is important—much more so than the classification of illness or the description of symptoms. Because of Meyer's ideas, the one-word diagnosis of "schizophrenia," for instance, was listed as "schizophrenic reaction" in the American Psychiatric Association's first presentation of standard nomenclature. Meyer is known as the father of psychobiology.

Otto Rank considered anxiety to be born with the baby. In the womb there is effortless gratification, which birth interrupts. The infant separates from the umbilical cord, from the womb, from the mother—and thereby experiences birth trauma. A primal anxiety leads to a primal repression of it. After birth, any change from pleasure to pain or from pain to pleasure evokes the anxiety. Life is a process of individuation, during which the person may stop growing at stage one, where he becomes normal or like others. If he grows beyond that to stage two, he wishes to go against others all the time and becomes neurotic. Those who reach the third stage can maintain their separate individuated values without having to impose them on others; they are creative. The unifying emotions, such as love, stand in contrast to the separating emotions, such as hate. Therapy should be short, with an end set, and should be focused on the present; the therapist should be flexible and dynamic.

Melanie Klein found environmental factors to be only of small importance in mental illness. She stayed with the Freudian theory but believed that the Oedipus situation is known to the child as early as the first year. A baby can adopt a paranoid posture at two to three months, and everyone goes through a depressive episode at weaning. Anxiety in infant boys stems from the imagined sexual act, in which the infant imagines that the male penis is incorporated by the female.

Before venturing beyond the limits of legality, Wilhelm Reich contributed to the general knowledge of psychiatry by identifying particular kinds of resistance to therapy that occur in particular pathological types—the hysterical, compulsive, phallic narcissistic, masochistic, and neurotic. He emphasized character analysis.

Jules Masserman believed that what is being learned in animal studies can be applied to human behavior. Many physiological needs, rather than a few instincts, impel motivation. Reality is relative by species and by individual—that is, perception differs according to particularities of body design. The human mind is highly individual, depending on individual memory. Displacement activities among animals show that they are constantly trying new ways to satisfy old desires. Humans are not different in this regard. Conflict presents mixed good and bad stimuli to both animals and humans, and a piece of candy coupled with electric shock is a dilemma all species recognize. He warns against taking away the three origin- or ur-defenses: belief in personal immortality, in the omnipotence of authorities, and in the well-meaning of society. These defenses should, perhaps, be deflected into realistic channels but never attacked. Without them intolerable anxiety emerges.

A generation and a half before Freud, Kierkegaard had written on the basic anxiety of all men, an existential anxiety that nothing can fully remove. European and American existentialists hold diverse views, but all are concerned with clarifying the anxiety-laden relationship between the solitary individual and what he perceives to be outside himself, be it called object, Thou, or world. Even with a clear relationship between the self and the world, there is a horror of nothingness. Dread and fear follow a man as he struggles between self-interest on the one hand and responsibility on the other hand. Mental illness is withdrawal into a private world, where communication between the perceived world and the perceiver breaks down. For some, the withdrawal is solipsistic or autistic. For others, withdrawal, if eventually shared, can be creative.

Additional theories of personality have been derived from the field of psychology. Quantitative measurement has contributed a measuring tool called the Sixteen-Factor Personality Test. Results from this test can be put into equations to predict such things as a teenager's reform from delinquency and an adult's response to therapy. Factor analysis has shown that anxiety alone is not the key to neurosis, for neurotics differ from normal persons in at least seven of sixteen primary factors. Computer aid should speed discoveries in this young science, and Raymond B. Cattell urges the study of such things as the change in traits due to aging and the physiological events corresponding to mental events.

Personality learning theory studies adjustment path analysis. What are the basic standard outcomes of any given situation? Make a certain choice, and the path opens to neurosis. The matrix analysis of multi-dimensional learning expresses the value of intersection theory; it binds personality with situation but takes into account the multiple dimensions of both. Other theories by psychologists include Henry Murray's system of needs and complexes; Theodore Sarbin's personality as an integration role and self; Gardner Murphy's canalization and conditioning; Gordon W. Allport's minimalization of individual history in favor of forward-striving toward goals; Kurt Lewin's differentiation, boundary properties, and integration. Andras Angyal's theory of personality is rigidly or plastically conjoined with the environment at two poles, a social pole and a psychological pole; Kurt Goldstein offers an elaboration of the figure and ground concept; Abraham H. Maslow's theory of healthy self-actualization arranges motivation into priorities; O. Hobart Mowrer's personality development sequence runs from infantile indulgence through socialization and negativism to adolescence, when the nonintegrative personality, with its too lenient superego, may turn to delinquency or may assuage guilt by neurotic behavior.

AREA A

Orthodox Freudian Psychoanalytic Theories

CHAPTER ONE

Classical Freudian Psychoanalysis

JOHN E. MACK, M.D., &
ELVIN V. SEMRAD, M.D.

INTRODUCTION

CONCEPTS DERIVED from psychoanalysis are applied so widely in psychiatric training and practice that they have become a fundamental part of our approach to mental and emotional disorders. Obviously, then, it is imperative that the student develop a clear understanding of classical psychoanalytic theory and the work of its founder, Sigmund Freud. Unfortunately, discussions aimed at residents, medical students, and other students of psychiatry that attempt to facilitate such understanding, are typically impeded by problems arising from the student's lack of familiarity with the principal investigative tool of classical psychoanalysis—free association—and, concomitantly, his limited contact wth the data derived therefrom, upon which psychoanalytic theory is based. In fact, the study of psychoanalysis requires a fundamental change in orientation; in contrast to the planned, organized pursuit of data that is characteristic of most fields of medicine, the psychoanalyst does not deliberately solicit specific information from his patient. Rather, psychoanalytic data consist of the patient's spontaneous and uncensored verbal expressions. In addition, the student's efforts to understand psychoanalytic theory may be further complicated by the apparent disparity between the formal terminology Freud employed to describe mental and emotional phenomena and the technical language used in other medical and paramedical disciplines. Throughout this discussion, an attempt has been made to define in detail the methods and terminology that are fundamental to classical psychoanalytic theory in order to avoid confusion and misunderstanding.

Scientific Orientation

As a result of his early training, Freud came to his work in psychology imbued with the belief, held by most scientists of his day, that scientific law and order would ultimately permit an understanding of the apparent chaos of mental process and that brain physiology was the most promising avenue of approach to this objective. By 1897 Freud no longer shared this illusion; however, all his life he continued to believe that there was a close interrelationship between physical and psychical processes, that mind and brain did not exist as separate entities. In addition, he maintained that physical processes preceded psychological phenomena. All information that reached the mind began as physical excitation, whether such information emanated from the external world and was transmitted through the sense organs, or whether it came from the chemical stimuli provided by the body. In his efforts to correlate mental processes with physiological ones, Freud was able to note similarities in the way both operated. However, although he was thoroughly familiar with the language of physiology, he found the task of translating psychological processes into physiological terms an insurmountable one. Nevertheless, he made several attempts to describe mental phenomena in terms of the functioning of the nervous system before he eventually suspended these efforts and decided instead to approach psychological problems on a level of investigation appropriate to their study.

Definition

Traditionally, classical psychoanalysis has referred primarily to Freud's libido and instinct theories; recently, it has come to include the concepts of ego psychology as well. Essentially, it is based on the free association method of investigation that yielded the data used by Freud to formulate the key concepts of unconscious motivation, conflict, and symbolism, which formed the basis for his broader theoretical system.

Basic Hypotheses

Psychoanalytic theory, like all personality theory, is concerned primarily with the elucidation of those factors that motivate behavior. Psychoanalysis is unique, however, in that it considers these motivating forces to derive from unconscious mental processes. Freud's demonstration of the existence of an unconscious mind and his concept of psychic determinism are generally regarded as his greatest contributions to science, and these remain the fundamental hypotheses of psychoanalytic theory. When it is considered within this theoretical framework, behavior that is inexplicable otherwise can be attributed to specific psychic determinants or goals.

These hypotheses lead, in turn, to the elaboration of a third concept that is central to psychoanalytic theory: the mechanism of repression, the selective forgetting of what is too painful or objectionable for the conscious mind to accept. Initially, on the basis of his early clinical experiences, Freud maintained that the significance of repression resided in its relationship to psychopathology; he believed that there was a relationship between the repression of sexuality and the development of neurosis. Although this insight, in itself, was of dramatic import for the future development of psychoanalysis, its true value lies in the fact that it opened new avenues of investigation, which, in turn, gave rise to more complex theoretical constructs of greater significance. Thus, Freud's subsequent study of infantile sexuality and his knowledge of adult perversions led him to hypothesize that the sexual instinct may find many forms of expression apart from its final aim of genital union, coitus—that, in fact, the sexual instinct must pass through a rather complicated developmental sequence before it achieves what Freud called "genital primacy."

Psychoanalytic theory deals with mental structure and the economics of mental functioning as well as its dynamics. Thus, Freud divided the mind, in a regional or topographical fashion, into the unconscious proper, the preconscious, and the conscious. The study and formulation of these systems of the mind and of the tripartite model of ego, id, and superego, which represent its structural components, form the basis for the Freudian theory of personality.

Throughout his lifetime, Freud continued to modify and elaborate his original concepts of the psychic apparatus, the dynamics and economics of mental functioning, and the origins and nature of psychopathology. And the open-ended nature of psychoanalytic theory has permitted further modification and elaboration of these constructs by those who followed in his path. The boundaries of classical psychoanalytic theory have not been sharply defined in this section. Rather, an attempt has been made to describe in detail those concepts that are currently accepted by psychoanalysts who have been trained in the classical tradition and that have particular relevance for students of psychiatry—that is, Freud's concept of the topography of the mind, the libido and instinct theories, concepts pertaining to the mechanisms of defense and to the nature of anxiety, the psychology of dreams, the significance of early childhood experiences, and, finally, formulations in ego psychology. At the same time, however, it is generally agreed that these formulations can be fully understood only if one traces their historical development. The following discussion and further elucidation of these basic concepts have been guided by this premise.

HISTORICAL BEGINNINGS OF PSYCHOANALYSIS

Sigmund Freud was born of Jewish parents on May 6, 1856, in Freiburg, a small town in Moravia, which has since become part of Czechoslovakia. When he was four, his father, a wool merchant, brought the family to Vienna. And it was in Vienna, a city he both loved and hated, that Freud was educated, practiced, and lived his entire life until he was forced to flee to England in 1938, when the Nazis annexed Austria.

MEDICAL TRAINING

Because his education followed a somewhat erratic course, it took Freud three years longer than the usual time to earn his medical degree. However, the fact that he was a medical student in the years from 1873 to 1881 is significant. For during this period the research in biology of Darwin and his associates and the investigations in physiology and physics by Helmholtz and his school were producing a new scientific climate, which played a significant role in Freud's intellectual development. This new orientation emphasized natural law, the unity of science, and scientific exactitude as opposed to the romanticism and mysticism that pervaded scientific thought in central Europe after the Napoleonic Wars. For five years while he was at medical school, Freud studied in the physiological laboratory of Ernst Brücke, a founder of the scientific movement known as the Helmholtz school of medicine, which postulated that the only forces active in biological organisms were the physicochemical forces inherent in matter, "reducible to the force of attraction and repulsion." In a broader sense, according to the Helmholtz school, all biological organisms were phenomena of the physical world: systems of atoms, governed by forces, according to the principle of conservation of energy that had been described by Robert Mayer in 1842 and was applied by Helmholtz twenty years later. Freud was strongly influenced by these principles and by Brücke himself, who epitomized the qualities he most admired—scientific discipline and intellectual integrity.

MEDICAL CAREER

Freud continued to work in Brücke's laboratory for a year after he graduated from medical school, and it was there that he developed the physiological framework into which he later tried to cast his psychological theories. Nor did Brücke's influence diminish throughout Freud's lifetime; his consistent, overriding goal was to apply Brücke's principles to the study of the nervous system and then to the mind. As mentioned above, Freud made a number of attempts to do so before he became resigned to the fact that the lack of relevant physiological data precluded the explanation of mental phenomena in terms of the physicochemical nature of brain function. Although he never renounced Brücke's principles, thereafter he limited his theory of the mind to the psychological parameters of mental functioning. Nevertheless, it would seem useful at this point to digress briefly to describe the essay entitled "Project for a Scientific Psychology," which represented Freud's most ambitious attempt to explain the physical roots of mental phenomena. Space limitations preclude a detailed outline of this remarkable document, which was written over a two-year period from 1895 to 1897 and published posthumously. Its essential features may be summarized as follows.

Writing in the language of physics and brain physiology and drawing upon contemporary neurophysiology and neuroanatomical concepts, Freud attempted to conceptualize psychology as a natural science. To do this, he combined two theories. One, which may be attributed to the influence of the Brücke-Helmholtz school, stated that the laws that governed physics and chemistry were equally applicable to psychology. Second, the theory of neurons, which derived from Freud's neurohistological studies, was the basis for his attempt to describe the mind in terms of their neurones and their synapses.

According to the "Project," the functioning of the nervous system could be described in terms of two closely allied principles. The first principle, of inertia, stated that neurones tend to discharge nervous excitation. Pain was related to excessive nervous excitation and pleasure to its discharge; this discharge of excitation was the primary function of the neuronic system. Its secondary function, which Freud explored in the "Project," concerned the choice of specific paths for the discharge of quantities of excitation that impinged on the nervous system from the external world or from within the organism in order to maintain psychic equilibrium. Second, Freud maintained that the functioning of the nervous system was governed by the principle of constancy. This concept may be traced to the principle of the conservation of energy (Mayer and Helmholtz), which held that the sum of forces remains constant in every isolated system, and to Herbart's hypothesis that mental processes tend to strive for equilibrium (an idea that is similar to what Cannon later described as homeostasis). In 1892, Freud (with Breuer) defined constancy as follows: "The nervous system endeavors to keep constant something in the functional condition that may be described as the 'sum of excitation.'"

Despite the fact that many of the speculations advanced in the "Project" regarding the functioning of the nervous system were confirmed by subsequent neurophysiological investigations, clearly, the "Project" was premature in its effort to link mental and physiological phenomena. However, it did anticipate many of Freud's subsequent purely psychological concepts; for example, the physiological principle of inertia was later translated into the psychoanalytic pleasure-unpleasure principle. But, most important, it demonstrated Freud's deep commitment to discovering a biological basis for his psychological theories.

To return to our chronological account of Freud's medical career, during the year he spent at Brücke's institute, he did several highly creditable pieces of histological and neuroanatomical research. He found research particularly congenial, and he hoped to continue with his theoretical work. But financial considerations made this impossible. Despite a deep aversion to the practice of medicine as such, Freud was forced by his personal economic situation to leave the laboratory setting in 1882 and to begin work in the General Hospital in Vienna, first on the surgical service and then in

Theodor Meynert's Psychiatric Clinic. As a student, only Meynert's medical lectures had aroused Freud's interest; while he was assigned to his service, he shared the general opinion that Meynert was the most gifted brain anatomist of his time. Freud was not quite so enthusiastic about Meynert's qualifications as a psychiatrist, however. He felt that the emphasis on neuroanatomy and neuropathology (which, in fact, was characteristic of psychiatry during this period) diminished Meynert's clinical competence. Nevertheless, as a result of his study of Meynert's amentia (acute hallucinatory psychosis), Freud obtained a vivid impression of the mechanism of wish fulfillment, which later became a basic part of his theory of the unconscious.

Interest in neurology. In Meynert's service, Freud increased his knowledge of brain disorders; concurrently, he received Meynert's permission to use his laboratory for an extensive study of the brain of the neonate. These events coincided with his decision to specialize in neurology rather than engage in general practice. When he received a highly coveted traveling grant in 1885, he used it to go to Paris, where he studied at the Salpêtrière for nineteen weeks under the great French neurologist, Jean-Martin Charcot. This was a crucial period in Freud's career. During the time he spent in Charcot's clinic, Freud was able to observe a wide variety of neurological syndromes. However, he was most impressed by Charcot's radical approach to hysteria. As a result of Charcot's influence, Freud became deeply interested in the problem of hysteria and firmly convinced that hysterical phenomena were genuine.

In fact, Charcot's teachings were in marked contrast to the view that had been prevalent up to that time, according to which hysterical phenomena were viewed either as deliberate pretense or as the product of the patient's imagination and, as such, were not to be taken seriously. As a result of Charcot's systematic and thorough study of the manifold manifestations typical of hysteria, it was recognized as a legitimate disease of the nervous system and, as such, a possible subject of serious study and understanding.

The psychological explanation for hysterical phenomena was not investigated by Charcot. However, the possibility that such phenomena might be psychological in origin did occur to Freud when Charcot was able to precipitate hysterical paralyses, seizures, and other characteristic symptoms artificially through hypnotic suggestion. Thus, by means of his experiments in hypnosis, Charcot distinguished hysterical phenomena from organic neurological entities. Although he believed that hysteria had a neurological basis and, in fact, was due to congenital degeneration of the brain, the symptoms manifested in hysteria were psychogenic in origin; that is, they were produced by specific ideas held by the patient. And, by the same token, hysterical symptoms could be cured by ideas.

The Austrian physician, Anton Mesmer, who died in 1815 at the age of 81, is generally credited with the discovery of hypnotism, which was to play such a crucial role in the development of psychoanalysis. Mesmer used the special power he called "animal magnetism" to "cure" people (often in dramatic public exhibitions) of afflictions that in all probability would be diagnosed today as hysterical symptoms. A century later, A. A. Liébault, a kindly French country doctor in Nancy, used hypnotic sleep to relieve countless peasants of their neurotic symptoms via the technique of suggestion. It remained for psychoanalysis to provide a rational scientific explanation of the psychological mechanisms operant in the psychoneuroses; however, psychotherapy, as a form of medical treatment, may be said to have had its beginning in Liébault's clinic. Freud was particularly interested in the work of Hippolyte Bernheim, an associate of Liébault, who used hypnosis as a therapeutic modality. On the basis of his careful study of the characteristics of suggestibility, Bernheim concluded that this phenomenon was not limited to hysterics. In fact, it was present in patients with a wide range of neurotic disorders and in normal individuals as well. Bernheim's attempt to account for a wide variety of normal and abnormal social reactions through suggestion or autosuggestion may well have represented the first attempt to understand human behavior and its motivation on the basis of data derived from clinical study.

Freud spent several weeks in Nancy during the summer of 1889. His visit was a profitable one, in several respects. He was deeply impressed by the relationship Liébault established with his patients and by the dramatic effects Bernheim was able to produce in his hospitalized patients through the use of hypnotic suggestion. Most important, as he observed Bernheim's experiments, Freud became profoundly aware of the possibility that powerful mental processes, which were hidden from consciousness, were operative in the minds of men.

In summary, then, Freud's approach to mental and emotional disorders and psychological phenomena up to this point can be traced to two principal influences. From the Helmholtz school, from his teachers, Brücke, Meynert, and Charcot, he had learned to emphasize rational scientific understanding, careful empirical study, and clinical observation. From the French doctors Liébault and Bernheim, he learned that the physician himself may play a useful role as an instrument of psychotherapeutic change. In addition, in the course of his visit to the Liébault clinic, he gained the impression that deeper psychological forces, not immediately accessible to consciousness, were operative in human motivation and behavior. Initially, he was inclined to defend the orientation of the Helmholtz school, and of Brücke and Charcot in particular. Ultimately, his ability to integrate these diverse influences, together with the extraordinary psychological sensitivity and insight that characterized Freud's genius, enabled him to create a new science that represented a unique approach to the study and resolution of human conflict.

Freud returned to Vienna from Charcot's clinic in Paris in 1886 with the avowed intention of giving up his laboratory studies so that he might devote all his time to the clinical practice of neurology. Nevertheless, in 1891 he wrote a short book, entitled *Aphasia,* in which he challenged Wernicke's and Lichtheim's minute localization schemes of this disorder and instead offered a functional explanation that accounted for the subvarieties in terms of disruptions of the radiating associational pathways. Freud's work, which was the only one of the period to cite the genetic view of Hughlings Jackson, received little attention at the time; however, the validity of its basic principles has since been recognized. In 1891 and 1893, he published two exhaustive clinical studies of the paralyses of children. The first of these, written in collaboration with Dr. Oscar Rie, a pediatrician, dealt with unilateral paralysis in children. It was widely acclaimed by neurologists, and even today it is considered a classic. The second presented an equally comprehensive study of central diplegias in children.

EVOLUTION OF PSYCHOANALYSIS

Psychoanalysis as a method of investigation, a therapeutic technique, and a scientific discipline with a growing body of basic propositions and findings may be said to have evolved in the decade from 1887 to 1897, first through Freud's collaboration with Breuer and then through his independent efforts.

COLLABORATION WITH BREUER

Even at the time the two works on childhood paralyses were written, Freud had already become deeply interested in clinical psychopathology. In part, this may be attributed to the fact that the cases seen by a neurologist in private practice were largely psychoneurotic rather than neurological. To an even greater extent, however, Freud's growing interest in psychopathology may be attributed to his association with Josef Breuer, a prominent Viennese physician with whom he formed a close friendship while he was working at Brücke's Institute of Physiology. Breuer's treatment of the famous case of Frl. "Anna O." or, more specifically, his communication to Freud of the details of that case, was one of the factors that led to the development of psychoanalysis. Breuer treated "Anna O." (Bertha Pappenheim) from December 1880 to June 1882. The patient was an intelligent girl of 21 who had developed a number of hysterical symptoms in association with the illness of her father, of whom she was passionately fond. These included paralysis of the limbs, contractures, anesthesias, disturbances of sight and speech, inability to take food, and a distressing nervous cough. Her illness was further characterized by two distinct phases of consciousness. During one, she was normal; during the second, she took on another personality. The transition between these states of consciousness was effected by autohypnosis, which Breuer subsequently supplemented with artificial hypnosis. Anna had shared with her mother the duties of nursing her father until his death. During her altered states of consciousness, she was able to relate the vivid fantasies and intense emotions she had experienced while tending her father. And to the great amazement of the patient—and Breuer—her symptoms could be made to disappear if she could recall, with an accompanying expression of affect, the scenes of circumstances under which they had arisen. Once she had become aware of the value of this "talking cure" or "chimney sweeping," Anna proceeded to deal with each of her manifold symptoms, one after another. For example, she recalled that on one occasion when her mother was absent and she had been sitting at her father's bedside, she had had a daydream in which she imagined that a snake was coming to bite her sick father. When she tried to ward off the snake, her arm, which had "gone to sleep" over the back of a chair, seemed paralyzed. Moreover, the arm had remained paralyzed until the patient recalled the scene under hypnosis. Quite understandably, the case of Anna made a profound impression on Freud; it provided convincing evidence of the power of unconscious memories and suppressed affects in the production of hysterical symptoms.

Still another aspect of Breuer's treatment of Anna was of crucial significance for the future development of psychoanalysis. In the course of treatment, Breuer had become increasingly preoccupied with his unusual patient, and his wife had grown increasingly jealous and resentful. When he realized this, Breuer abruptly terminated treatment. Only a few hours had elapsed, however, before he was recalled to Anna's bedside. He found the patient, who he believed was greatly improved, in a state of acute excitement. Anna, who had never alluded to the forbidden topic of sex during the course of treatment, was now experiencing a hysterical childbirth (pseudocyesis), the logical termination of the phantom pregnancy she had developed in response to Breuer's therapeutic efforts, of which he had been quite unaware. Breuer managed to calm her through hypnosis. However, the experience unnerved him and served to restrict his further participation in Freud's investigations into the unknown (and therefore unpredictable and dangerous) sphere of the mind.

INDEPENDENT INVESTIGATIONS: THERAPEUTIC TECHNIQUE

Use of hypnosis. Late in 1887, Freud began to use hypnosis intensively in his own practice. At first, he used hypnosis for the single purpose of getting the patient to deny the reality of his symptoms. It was evident, however, that even though the patient might deny his symptoms under hypnotic suggestion, he was well aware of their reality in waking life. Freud found the contradiction and general superficiality of this approach a source of increasing dissatisfaction. Partly as a result of his interest in Breuer's treatment of "Anna O.," Freud was eager to learn what lay behind his patients' symptoms, to investigate them in depth, and it is this goal that continues to distinguish the more arduous psychoanalytically oriented treatment methods from those psychiatric treatment techniques that seek merely to suppress overt symptoms.

Accordingly, in 1889, Freud turned to the cathartic method (in conjunction with hypnosis) in order to retrace, as Breuer had in the case of Anna O., the history of the symptom. The first time he employed this method, in the case of Frau Emmy von N., he adhered quite strictly to the concept of the traumatic origin of hysterical phenomena. Accordingly, the goal of treatment was limited to the removal of symptoms through recovery—and verbalization—of the suppressed feelings with which they were associated, a procedure that has since been described as abreaction. In his account of this case, Freud also hinted that inhibited sexuality may have played a role in the etiology of the patient's symptoms.

Once again, however, he was dissatisfied with the results he achieved. The beneficial effects of this hypnotic treatment were transitory; they lasted only as long as the patient remained in contact with the physician. Freud suspected, therefore, that they were, in fact, dependent upon the personal relationship between patient and physician. Freud's suspicion was confirmed when one day a patient awoke from a hypnotic sleep and suddenly threw her arms around his neck. Breuer had told him earlier of the events that followed the termination of his treatment of Anna O. Now Freud himself had an opportunity to observe a similar reaction in a patient he had been treating. Fortunately, unlike Breuer, he was not frightened by this experience. Rather, it aroused his scientific interest.

From this point on, Freud understood that the therapeutic effectiveness of the patient-physician relationship, which had so mystified him, could be attributed to its erotic basis. Many years later, he said that he had also regarded these transference phenomena as definitive proof of the sexual etiology of the neuroses. In any event, these experiences served to underscore his dissatisfaction with hypnosis. At a later state in the development of psychoanalysis, Freud described hypnosis as a mask that concealed and therefore precluded investigation of the transference and resistance phenomena that are central to psychoanalytic theory and practice. In essence, his decision to make the crucial transition from Breuer's cathartic method to another more suitable technique was based on similar, albeit less sophisticated, considerations. He wanted to be free of hypnosis because it had become increasingly apparent that the hypnotic method owed its success to the fact that the patient acted out of love for her doctor—that is, she remembered traumatic experiences and feelings at his command and appeared to recover from her illness in order to please him. Obviously, a cure that did not involve some understanding on the part of the patient of the origins and significance of her symptoms could only be temporary at best. Freud's decision was based on other considerations as well; he had found that many of the patients he encountered in private practice were refractory to hypnosis. Later, he recognized that his inability to hypnotize a patient might be due to the patient's reluctance to remember, and he identified this as resistance. At the time, however, he was eager to develop a treatment method that might be applied whether or not the patient was hypnotizable. Freud continued to use hypnosis, where indicated, until he had refined the technique of free association to his entire satisfaction. He reached this point in 1896, and he never used hypnosis again.

Concentration method. In 1892, Freud undertook the treatment of Frl. Elisabeth von R., a patient whom he had earlier found to be refractory to hypnosis, and for the first time abandoned this therapeutic tool. His decision to make this attempt was based largely on a statement made by Bernheim to the effect that, although they appeared to be forgotten afterward, the experiences recalled under hypnosis could once again be recalled in states of consciousness if the physician asked the patient leading questions and urged him to produce these crucial memories. Concentration was based on this premise. The patient was asked to lie down on a couch and close her eyes. She was then instructed to concentrate upon a particular symptom and to try to recall memories. Concurrently, Freud pressed his hand on her forehead in order to facilitate the emergence of such memories, even as he urged her to remember and continued to question her.

Free association method. The use of free association as a therapeutic technique evolved very gradually from these beginnings over the three-year period from 1892 to 1895. The first step in its development came about when the patient, Elisabeth von R., remarked that she had not expressed her thoughts because she wasn't sure what Freud wanted to hear. From this point on, Freud no longer tried to direct the patient's thinking but encouraged her to ignore all censorship and to express every idea that occurred to her, no matter how insignificant, irrelevant, or shameful it might seem. At a later point in treatment, the patient complained that Freud had interrupted her train of thought by his persistent questions and that she found his habit of pressing his hand on her forehead an unnecessary distraction.

In brief, by the late 1890's both Freud and his patients had come to feel that the urging, pressing, and questioning that were part of the concentration method actually interfered with the free flow of thought. Accordingly, these procedures were abandoned, and eventually patients were no longer instructed to close their eyes. However, the use of the couch continues to play a central role in classical psychoanalysis, and the fundamental rule of the free association method has remained unchanged.

THEORETICAL CONTRIBUTIONS

Etiological propositions. The application of free association as a treatment method served to illuminate aspects of mental functioning that had never been observed previously. For one thing, Freud discovered that a patient's train of memory extended well beyond the traumatic event that had precipitated the onset of his illness. He found that his patients were able to produce memories of their childhood experiences, of scenes and events that they thought had long been forgotten. This discovery led, in turn, to the conclusion that frequently these memories had been inhibited because they involved sexual experiences or painful incidents in a patient's life. Moreover, he learned that the recollection of such experiences in the present could evoke intense excitement, moral conflict, feelings of self-reproach, or fear of punishment. Since these childhood experiences remained so vivid, obviously they must exert a predisposing influence in relation to the development of psychoneurosis. Inevitably, this led to extensive modification in the view prevalent at the time and shared by Freud that heredity must be accorded a major role in the predisposition to neurosis. Freud continued to acknowledge the role of heredity in determining an individual's future susceptibility to neurosis, an opinion most psychoanalysts share today. However, he assigned much of the responsibility for the etiology of the psychoneuroses, which had hitherto been attributed to heredity, to unfavorable childhood experiences. He further postulated that hysteria might be acquired as well as congenital. Emotionally disturbing experiences played a major role in the etiology of acquired hysteria, and hereditary factors were of minor importance.

Concept of resistance. As mentioned above, Freud discovered early in his practice that his patients were often unwilling or unable to recount memories that later proved to be etiologically significant. He defined this reluctance, as it manifested itself in the treatment setting, as resistance. However, his initial observations were supplemented later by data derived from his clinical investigations. He found that, in the majority of patients he treated, resistance could not be attributed to a reluctance to cooperate —that is, to obey the rule of free association. Nor were they unwilling to get well, for frequently those patients who were most distressed and embarrassed by their illness were most hampered in treatment by this phenomenon. Rather, resistance was due to active forces in the mind, of which the patients themselves were often unaware, that led to the exclusion from consciousness of painful or distressing material. Freud described this active force as repression, and this concept remains one of the cornerstones of psychoanalytic theory.

Repression. In a broad sense, Freud considered repression to be at the core of symptom formation. He described the mechanism as follows. A traumatic experience or series of experiences, usually of a sexual nature, that had occurred in childhood had been forgotten or, more accurately, repressed because of their painful nature. However, the excitement associated with the event has not been extinguished, and its traces persist in the unconscious in the form of repressed memories. These memories remain without pathogenic effect until some contemporary event, such as a disturbing love affair, revives them. At this point, there is a breakdown of the successful repression and what Freud termed "the return of the repressed"; this signals the onset of the period of illness proper. The original sexual excitement is revived and is now forced to find a new path or outlet. The clinical manifestation or symptom results from a compromise between the repressed desire and what Freud called the "dominant mass of ideas constituting the ego."

Cases of conversion hysteria were considered of particular relevance in this connection and were studied carefully by Freud during the 1890's. In such cases impulses that were not allowed access to consciousness followed the path of somatic innervation, resulting in such symptoms as paralysis, blindness, disturbances of sensation, and less disguised hysterical attacks. However, despite his emphasis on conversion hysteria as the prototype of repression, Freud believed that the basic proposition—that symptoms resulted from a compromise between a repressed impulse and the repressing forces in the personality—applied to obsessive-compulsive phenomena as well and even to paranoid ideation. As a logical consequence of this hypothesis, psychoanalytic treatment during this period consisted of helping the patient to recall repressed sexual experiences so that the excitation that had accompanied such experiences could find its way to consciousness and be discharged through verbalization with accompanying remembered affect.

Theory of infantile sexuality.   One final but fundamental modification of these early ideas had still to be made before psychoanalysis could come into its own as a depth psychology that presented a new science of the human mind. During the middle 1890's Freud's clinical experience had led him to devote increasing attention to the importance of sexual seduction in the etiology of the psychoneuroses, especially when such seduction had occurred prior to puberty. He had even distinguished obsessional neurosis from hysteria on the grounds that in the former the subject actively and aggressively pursued the precocious sexual experience, while in hysteria the subject remained passive during the trauma. The important point was that until this time he had taken literally his patients' tales of outrage committed by their fathers, nursemaids, etc., but had devoted little attention to the role of the child's own psychological life in the elaboration of these tales. The specific factor that precipitated a radical change in this view has not been clearly delineated. There are several possibilities, however. For one, he had gained additional insight as a result of his clinical investigations of the role of fantasy in childhood. Secondly, his own self-analysis had clearly demonstrated the child's inclination to distort reality to conform with his wishes. There is a third possibility that he simply began to doubt there could be so many wicked fathers in middle-class Vienna. In any event, in a letter to his friend Wilhelm Fliess in September 1897, he expressed his doubts as to the veracity of his patients' reports of seduction and suggested instead that "sexual fantasy regularly makes use of the theme of the parents."

At first, the obvious validity of this new insight seemed to threaten the very foundation on which his theories rested, but his depression did not last. He sensed that this discovery offered new possibilities for the study of psychological factors. In attempting to distinguish psychic reality and fantasy from actual events and psychoneurosis from perversion, psychoanalysis had taken on a new dimension. A dynamic theory of infantile sexuality, in which the child's own psychosexual life played a dominant role, could eventually replace the static concepts in which the child represented an innocent whose erotism was prematurely and consistently disrupted at the hands of unscrupulous adults. Writing to Fliess, he recalled a quote from a story that was applicable to these new developments in psychoanalysis: "Rebecca, you can take off your wedding-gown, you're not a bride any longer. . . . In the general collapse only the psychology has retained its value." In fact, however, for psychoanalysis there would never be a honeymoon. After an initial period of rejection by the medical world, it entered a period during which it assumed its full responsibilities as a psychological science. The fact that Freud himself turned to the study of dreams, to his self-analysis, to his theory of the mind, to further studies of infantile sexuality, and to the origins and nature of the psychoneuroses, was additional evidence of its maturation. It was the end of the beginning.

SUMMARY: THERAPEUTIC AND THEORETICAL CONTRIBUTIONS (1887–1897)

By 1897 the fundamental concepts of psychic determinism and the operation of a dynamic unconscious were established, and a theory of psychoneurosis based on psychic conflict and the repression of the memories of disturbing childhood experiences was clearly outlined. Sexuality, especially in early childhood, was revealed to play an important role in the production of psychological symptoms that had not been recognized hitherto. Above all, a technique, a method of investigation had been developed that could be used to explore a wide range of mental phenomena that had been poorly understood before Freud's time. Nor were the applications of psychoanalysis restricted to the systematic study of psychopathological conditions; it provided an approach to the understanding of dreams, creativity, wit, and other normal mental phenomena as well.

FRAMEWORK OF PSYCHOANALYTIC THEORY: THE THEORY OF THE INSTINCTS AND THE PSYCHIC APPARATUS

Throughout his lifetime, Freud's thinking was characterized by a tendency to describe various aspects of mental functioning as successive series of contrasting phenomena. Moreover, he suggested that mental life, in general, was dominated by three polarities: the first, subject (ego) versus object (outer world), represented the polarity of reality; the second, pleasure versus unpleasure, was designated as an economic polarity; and the third, activity versus passivity, was identified as a biological polarity. In fact, this dualistic view reflects the essential nature of the instrument studied, the human mind. Yet it is possible that we are straitjacketed by this view in our attempt to understand the mind; in that event, a strict adherence to the dualistic approach should be seriously questioned. Psychoanalytic theory is founded on dualisms to so great an extent, however, that it cannot be discussed accurately without thinking in such terms, and this discussion will not be an exception. Nevertheless, the possibility that a dualistic approach might provide a distorted view of the phenomena under consideration should be taken into account.

Basically, the body of psychoanalytic theory may be divided into the theory of the instincts or drives on the one hand and the psychic apparatus as it deals with these instincts on the other. This part of the chapter is concerned with that part of the psychoanalytic theory that deals with the development of the sexual and aggressive instincts in terms of their source, aim, impetus, and object and with related phenomena. The next part of the chapter will focus on the formation and function of the psychic apparatus, or what is currently known as ego psychology.

All human beings have similar instincts. The actual discharge of instinctual impulses is organized, directed, or, if necessary, suppressed by the individual ego, which serves as the mediator between the organism and the external world. Historically and logically, the detailed attention to the instincts in psychoanalysis preceded the preoccupation with ego psychology. Obviously, one would not attempt to investigate an apparatus whose function it is to organize, direct, and suppress without prior understanding of the precise nature of the phenomena that were organized, directed, and suppressed. However, to an increasing extent, the study of the ego as a product of the interplay of unconscious instinctual demands and environmental influences has become a dominant concern of psychoanalysts and behavioral scientists in allied disciplines, to the degree that several workers feel that there has been a concomitant de-emphasis on the study of the deeper forces of the mind. The question is open to argument.

With specific reference to this presentation, no attempt has been made to order the discussion of these concepts on the basis of their importance. Nor will it be possible to discuss these concepts in strict chronological sequence, although their historical evolution will be indicated where this is possible. Finally, certain areas of psychoanalytic study—such as anxiety, symptom formation, the phenomenon of narcissism, the theory of the mind, and character development—may be discussed appropriately from two vantage points: In this part of the chapter these phenomena will be discussed in relation to the formation of the basic—and universal—instincts and drives. The following part of the chapter will focus on their relationship to the structure and function of the psychic apparatus, which permits psychoanalysis to understand individual differences among human beings from a causal and genetic point of view.

DEVELOPMENT OF THE INSTINCTS

LIBIDO THEORY

There is some confusion as to what Freud meant by the term "libido." In brief, Freud regarded the sexual instinct as a psychophysiological process, as did everyone else, that therefore had both mental and physical manifestations. Essentially, he used the term "libido" to refer to "that force by which the sexual instinct is represented in the mind," and it is used here in this accepted sense—that is, as referring specifically to the mental manifestations of the sexual instinct.

As mentioned earlier, Freud recognized that the sexual instinct did not originate in finished form—that is, as represented by the stage of genital primacy. Rather, it underwent a complex process of development, during which it had many manifestations apart from the simple aim of genital union. The libido theory referred to the investigation of all these manifestations and the complicated paths they might follow in the course of development.

INFANTILE SEXUALITY

Of all Freud's theories, the concepts he advanced with regard to the erotic life of infants and young children undoubtedly aroused the most violent and continued opposition. Indeed, even today, many sophisticated psychiatric residents react with complete incredulity to the elucidation of sexual material in a clinical demonstration of a case of childhood neurosis. Freud's theory of infantile sexuality threatened to undermine one of the most cherished ideals of the nineteenth century, the innocence of children. Moreover, the belief that children, and especially infants, are somehow above sexual longings persists today; nor is this belief confined to the uneducated. Under the circumstances, the theory of infantile sexuality is certainly an outstanding example of the courage Freud demonstrated in his pursuit of scientific truth in the face of the most adverse public opinion.

Freud had become convinced of the relationship between sexual traumata experienced in childhood and later psychopathology as a result of his early investigations of the actual neuroses—hypochondriasis, neurasthenia, and anxiety neurosis. These studies had, in turn, led to awareness of the importance of sexual factors in the etiology of the psychoneuroses. With increased clinical experience, Freud was able to reconstruct the early sexual experiences, responses, and fantasies of his patients. These data provided the framework for a developmental theory of childhood sexuality, which in the years since has been corroborated in many respects by direct observation. Apart from the data he had extracted from his clinical experience, Freud based his theory on the self-analysis he began in 1897 and continued for an undetermined period. The insights he acquired in the course of the analysis regarding his own erotic longings in childhood and his conflicts in relation to his parents clearly suggested that, in all likelihood, these phenomena were not restricted to the neuroses, that normal individuals underwent similar developmental sequences.

Freud had completed his formulations concerning all the essential phases of sexual development before the turn of the century. Nevertheless, *Three Essays on the Theory of Sexuality*, containing a full account of his startling views, was not published until 1905. Even more surprising is the fact that his detailed discussion of the sexual development of children, including the pregenital organization of the libido, and the libido theory itself appeared for the first time in the third edition of the *Three Essays*, ten years later.

In essence, although Freud used the term sexuality in these essays in the familiar sense, to refer to the erotic life of the individual, he extended the general concept concerning those sensations and activities that are typically considered sexual and those parts of the body that are usually associated with erotism. Freud noted that infants were capable of erotic activity from birth, and he described the various stages of sexual development during the first four years of life. The fifth year marks the beginning of the latency period, at which point sexual development comes to a halt, although this depends on the individual, until the child reaches puberty when he is approximately 11 years old. At puberty there is renewed growth of the genital organs and a resurgence of the sexual drive, and the child begins his final preparations for the adult sexual role.

PHASES OF PSYCHOSEXUAL DEVELOPMENT

The earliest manifestations of sexuality arise in relation to bodily functions that are basically nonsexual, such as feeding and the development of bowel and bladder control.

The oral phase.   Erotic activity during this phase, which extends into the second year of life, centers on the mouth and lips and is manifested in sucking, biting, and chewing.

The anal phase.   As a concomitant of the child's increasing preoccupation with bowel function and control, the dominant erotic activity then shifts from the oral to the anal and rectal regions from ages 2 to 4.

The genital or phallic phase.   The genital phase of sexual development begins sometime during the third year of life and continues until approximately the end of the fifth year. Initially, erotic activity is linked both psychologically and physiologically with the activities and sensations associated with urination. However, Freud postulated that in boys phallic erotic activity was essentially a preliminary stage for adult genital activity. In contrast to the male, for whom the principal sex organ remains the same throughout, the female has two leading erotogenic zones—the clitoris and the vagina. The clitoris is pre-eminent during the infantile genital period of development. However, development is complicated by the fact that during or after puberty the transition must be made to vaginal primacy.

Karl Abraham, one of the most gifted psychoanalytic pioneers, whose premature death was considered a great loss to psychoanalysis, further subdivided these phases of libido development. He divided the oral period into a sucking and biting phase and the anal phase into destructive-expulsive and mastering-retaining phases. Finally, he hypothesized that the phallic period comprised an early phase of partial love, which was designated as the true phallic phase, and a later, more mature genital phase.

Freud suggested, in connection with this elucidation of sexual development, that there were three phases of genital masturbatory activity: during early infancy, at the highest point of infantile sexuality, and during puberty. During the earliest months of life the genital region in both boys and girls may be stimulated inadvertently by the mother. However, masturbatory activity—that is, stimulation of the penis in boys and the clitoris in girls—reaches its peak sometime during the third year of life and continues until the end of the fifth year.

As indicated earlier, for each of the phases of psychosexual development described above, Freud delineated specific erotogenic zones, various regions of the body that might be the source of erotic sensation.

Vicissitudes of Infantile Sexuality

The part instincts.   During infancy and early childhood, for the most part, erotic sensation emanates from the mucosal surfaces of a particular body part or organ. More specifically, during the earliest years of life, the mucous membranes of the mouth, anus, or external genitalia are the appropriate primary focus of the child's erotic life, depending on his phase of development. Subsequently, in normal adult sexual activity, the genital zone becomes predominant. However, the pregenital or prephallic erotogeneity of the oral and anal zones still retains a place in preliminary mating activities—that is, in the foreplay or forepleasure that precedes coitus, which, ideally, culminates in end pleasure, orgasm.

Freud described the erotic impulses that arise from the pregenital zones as component or part instincts. Kissing, stimulation of the area surrounding the anus, or biting the love object in the course of lovemaking are examples of activities associated with these part instincts. Early genital excitement may undergo displacement to the eyes, for example, and looking and being looked at (scoptophilia) may be a source of pleasure. Ordinarily, in the course of development, these component instincts undergo repression or retain a restricted role in sexual foreplay. Normally, the young child is characterized by polymorphous perverse sexual instincts; that is, his total sexuality is undifferentiated and encompasses all the part instincts. However, in the adult these part instincts are expected to become subordinate to the primacy of the genital region. The failure to achieve genital primacy may result in various forms of pathology. If, for example, the libido becomes too firmly attached to one of the pregenital erotogenic zones or a single part instinct is predominant, a perversion, such as fellatio or voyeurism, which ordinarily would be limited to the preliminary (preparatory) stages of lovemaking, replaces the normal act of sexual intercourse. The persistent attachment of the sexual instinct at a particular phase of pregenital development was termed a fixation.

Neurosis and perversion.   Freud further discovered that in the psychoneuroses only a limited number of the sexual impulses that had undergone repression and were responsible for creating and maintaining the neurotic symptoms were of a normal kind. For the most part, these were the same impulses that, in the perversions, were given overt expression. The neuroses, then, were the negative of perversions. However, the relationship between psychoneuroses and perversions is not nearly so simple as it might seem at first glance. Its more complex aspects are elaborated on in detail below. For example, at this point in its development, Freud's theory could not account for the fact that in one case a part instinct might be repressed and contribute to neurotic symptom formation, while in another case the part instinct retained overt dominance over the individual's sexual activity in the form of a perversion. In other words, although the theory of sexuality encompassed the concept of fixation of the libido, insofar as it was limited to the description of various potential zones of libidinal stimulation and excitement, it was unable to explain the outcome of fixation in a particular case. The resolution of the problem had to await the development of later theories concerning the defense mechanisms, the functions of the ego and the superego, and the nature and role of anxiety in mental functioning.

SOCIAL AND CULTURAL IMPLICATIONS OF THE THEORY OF INFANTILE SEXUALITY

Despite the anger and general sense of outrage they evoked initially, Freud's investigations of the sexual development in early childhood had important social and cultural consequences. For one thing, they have given rise to a more enlightened approach to the child's sexual explorations and a more respectful attitude toward his expressions of sexual curiosity. Moreover, our greater sexual freedom and the development of a more rational morality can be attributed to Freud's discoveries. Under the circumstances, it is rather ironic to realize that even today Freud's theory of infantile sexuality evokes strong resistance. Indeed, it is even more ironic that such resistance should persist among professionals and laymen alike in view of Freud's elucidation of its origins and nature as a concomitant of his investigations in this area. Nevertheless, apparently his vivid case histories did successfully demonstrate the possible repercussions of undue sexual restrictions and harshness, especially in the critical stages of development. As a result, he was able to influence the sexual attitudes of successive generations, even where there was no real acceptance of the theoretic principles involved.

DEVELOPMENT OF OBJECT RELATIONSHIPS

Current theories in psychoanalytic psychiatry have focused increasingly on the importance for later psychopathology of disturbances in early object relationships—that is, the relationship of affect to an object outside one's self. Those workers who emphasize the importance of cultural factors in development have criticized Freud for setting forth a timetable of infantile sexual development in a social vacuum without taking into account the impact on the child of the adults with whom he comes into contact. In fact, however, the criticism that has been leveled against Freud on this score is patently unjust. Even the most cursory examination will disclose that Freud's early writings on sexual development incorporated his basic concepts of object relationships as they evolved in relation to the sexual instinct and that he considered these phenomena closely interwoven. Nor is this surprising when one considers that the libido theory evolved from the crucial insight Freud acquired early in his clinical experience that the sexual fantasies of his adult patients typically centered on their early relationships with their parents. Throughout his descriptions of the libidinal phases of development, Freud made constant reference to the significance of the child's relationships with crucial figures in his environment. He postulated that the choice of a love object in later life, the love relationship itself, and object relationships in other spheres of activity depend largely on the nature and quality of the child's object relationships during the earliest years of life.

Object relationships during the pregenital phases of development. At birth, the infant has no awareness of the external world of objects. At most, he is capable of an undifferentiated sensitivity to pain and pleasure. Hunger, cold, and pain give rise to tension and to a corresponding need to seek relief from these painful stimuli in sleep. At the same time, the human infant is more helpless than other mammals, and his helplessness continues for a longer period of time. He cannot survive unless he is cared for, and he cannot achieve relief from painful stimuli without help from outside. Object relationships of a primitive kind are established when the infant begins to grasp this fact. Because he is aware only of his own tension and relaxation and unaware of the external world, longing for the object exists only as long as disturbing stimuli persist and the object is absent. Once the object appears and the infant's needs are gratified, the longing disappears.

ORAL PHASE. The infant's first awareness of an object, in a psychological sense, comes from his longing for something that is already familiar, for something that gratified his needs in the past but is not immediately available. Essentially, it is hunger that compels the infant to recognize the outside world. In this context, the infant's primitive reaction to the first objects—that is, his desire to put them in his mouth—becomes understandable. Moreover, this reaction coincides with his first recognition of reality; the infant judges reality in terms of whether something will provide satisfaction (and should, therefore, be swallowed), or whether it will create tension (and, consequently, should be spit out).

It is at this point that the mother becomes more than an anonymous agent whose ministrations keep the infant alive. She is recognized as the source of nourishment and, beyond this, as the source of the erotogenic pleasure the infant derives from sucking. As such, she becomes the first love object. From the oral phase onward, sexual development—that is, the focus on successive erotogenic zones and the emergence of associated component instincts—reflects the child's attachment to the crucial people in his environment and his feelings of love or hate or an admixture of both toward these important persons. For example, if a fundamentally warm relationship between mother and child has been established during this period, theoretically at least the stage is set for the development of trusting and affectionate ties to others in later life.

At first glance, this formula for success appears to be relatively simple and clear-cut. However, in fact, the oral stage is not without its possible perils in terms of the course of future development. Apart from the adverse consequences that are typically associated with the mother's rejection or undue frustration of the infant's needs, distortions in the early mother-child relationship may have more subtle but equally severe repercussions. As mentioned earlier, Abraham subdivided the oral stage into a sucking and biting phase. Inevitably, the frustration associated with the latter part of the oral period, and particularly with the weaning process, which to the child signifies the imminent loss of oral gratification, evokes biting and cannibalistic impulses toward the object. When such impulses are excessive, they may be a prelude to later serious impairment of object relations.

ANAL-SADISTIC PHASE. In a broad sense, the infant's role during the oral phase of development is a passive one. The onus is on the mother to gratify or frustrate his demands. In contrast, during the anal period the child is expected for the first time to relinquish one aspect of his freedom; he is expected to accede to his mother's demand that he use the toilet for the evacuation of feces and urine. The primary aim of anal erotism is the enjoyment of the pleasurable sensation of excretion. Later on, the stimulation of the anal mucosa through retention of the fecal mass may be a source of more intense pleasure.

The connection between anal and sadistic drives may be attributed to two factors. First, the object of the first anal-sadistic activity is the feces themselves, and their pinching off is perceived as a sadistic act. Subsequently, people are treated as feces were previously. The sense of social power that evolves from sphincter control constitutes the second sadistic element; in training for cleanliness, the child exerts his power over his mother by giving up or refusing to give up his feces.

The first anal strivings are autoerotic. Pleasurable elimination and, at a later point, pleasurable retention do not require the outside help of an object. At this stage of development, defecation is invested with omnipotence, and the feces, which represent the agent of such pleasure, become a libidinal object, so to speak, by virtue of their narcissistic evaluation. Although they have become external, they have ego quality, for they represent part of what was once one's own body. Hence, there is a tendency to reintroject what was once eliminated in order to restore narcissistic equilibrium. Thus, the feces become an ambivalently loved object. They are loved and retained or reintrojected on the one hand; and they are hated and pinched off on the other hand.

Certain pleasurable anal sensations are associated with the mother's ministrations, such as diaper changes. This maternal care, in combination with the conflicts that surround toilet training, subsequently alters the direction of object strivings. However, as mentioned above, people are treated in much the same way feces were earlier. The compulsive neatness that is typical of patients who have regressed to this pregenital phase of development is an expression of their wish to dominate. They exert power over things and people and force them into a rigid and pedantic system. Their feelings are characterized by the ambivalence referred to earlier—that is, the tendency to control and retain the object, together with a desire to expel and destroy it.

The connection between anal erotism and the physiological basis for ambivalence derives from the fact that during this stage in his development the child treats the object, feces, in a contradictory manner. He alternately expels the matter from his body and retains it as a loved object.

Abraham considered his subdivision of the anal-sadistic stage cited earlier of crucial importance, for at the dividing line between these two phases a decisive change occurs in the individual's attitude toward the external world. It is at this point that the tendency to preserve the object becomes pre-eminent and the capacity for object love begins, albeit in a restricted sense.

Phallic or genital phase: the Oedipus complex.   Although some progress is made toward finding a love object during the pregenital phases of development, for the most part, the child's libidinal activity is autoerotic; sexual impulses are directed toward his own body and discharged through masturbatory activity. The fundamental task of finding a love object belongs to the phallic or genital period, at which time the pattern for later object choices is set down; for now the child discovers the anatomical differences between the sexes. The events associated with this genital phase set the stage for the developmental predisposition to later psychoneuroses. Freud used the term "Oedipus complex" to refer to the intense love relationships formed during this period, together with their associated rivalries, hostilities, and emerging identifications. The Oedipus complex represents the climax of infantile sexuality. The transition from oral erotism via anal erotism toward genitality and the various associated stages in the development of object relations culminate in oedipal strivings. An overcoming of these strivings, which are then replaced by adult sexuality, is a prerequisite for normal development; conversely, the neuroses are characterized by an unconscious clinging to oedipal tendencies.

The Oedipus complex evolves during the third to the fifth years in children of both sexes. However, there is some discrepancy in the development. Freud explained the nature of this discrepancy as follows. In boys, under normal circumstances, the Oedipus complex is *resolved* by the castration complex; oedipal strivings are given up because of castration anxiety. In girls, the Oedipus complex is *evoked* by the castration complex; the girl turns to her father out of disappointment over the lack of a penis.

CASTRATION COMPLEX. In boys, the development of object relationships is relatively simple because the boy remains bound to his first object, the mother. Moreover, the primitive object choice that first develops in response to the mother's fulfillment of the infant's basic needs takes the same direction as that which arises later in response to the attraction of the opposite sex. Thus, in the phallic period, in addition to the child's interest in the mother as the source of nourishment, he develops a strong erotic interest in her and a desire to possess her exclusively. These feelings usually become manifest at the age of 3 and reach a climax in the fourth or fifth year of life.

With the initial appearance of the Oedipus complex in the phallic phase of development, the boy begins to court his mother almost as a lover would, expressing his wish to sleep in her bed, proposing marriage, and taking advantage of any opportunity to watch her dress or undress. Competition from his siblings for the mother's affection is, of course, intolerable. But, above all, he wants to eliminate his arch rival—her husband and his father. The child anticipates retaliation for his aggressive wishes toward his father, and these in turn give rise to severe anxiety. He begins to feel that, if he continues to show sexual interest in his mother, his penis will be removed. The idea of such deprivation in association with the male organ was identified by Freud as the castration complex. In "The Passing of the Oedipus Complex," Freud further suggested that in the phallic period the narcissistic fear about the penis is, in fact, stronger than the object relationship, the erotic attachment to the mother. Gratification of the boy's passionate love for his mother would endanger his penis. Confronted by the threat of castration, especially from his father and the anxiety it evokes, the boy must finally renounce his oedipal love for his mother. And now he identifies with his father and incorporates within himself his father's prohibitions. In so doing, he manages to internalize, to cover up the castration complex, and it remains free from external authority until it is reactivated at puberty.

The boy's love for his mother remains the dominant striving during this period of infantile sexual development. However, love and competition are not mutually exclusive; the boy loves his father too, and, at times, when he has been frustrated by his mother, he may hate her, or he may love both parents at the same time. In fact, the situation becomes even more complex in the light of the psychoanalytic hypothesis concerning the bisexual nature of the libido. Thus, on the one hand, the boy wants to possess his mother and kill the hated father-rival; and, on the other hand, he loves his father and reacts to his mother with hostility when her demands on her husband interfere with the exclusiveness of the father-son relationship. The negative Oedipus complex refers to those situations where the boy's love for his father is prevalent and the mother is hated as a disturbing element in this love. Obviously, under certain circumstances the reversal of the typical oedipal triangle may have serious implications for future development. It must be emphasized, however, that the negative Oedipus complex is normally present to some degree, along with its positive, familiar orientation. Under normal conditions, these conflicting feelings are able to coexist for a temporary period without provoking undue conflict.

THE GIRL'S SITUATION. Understanding of the little girl's more complex oedipal situation came later, for it raised a number of questions that proved more difficult of solution. Despite the validity of Freud's basic propositions in this area, the further elaboration and clarification of his concepts had to await the researches of his able female colleagues, notably, Helene Deutsch, Ruth Mack Brunswick, and Jeanne Lamplde Groot.

As in the boy's case, the little girl forms an initial attachment to her mother as the source of fulfillment of her vital needs. However, unlike the boy, for whom the mother remains the love object throughout, the girl is faced with the task of shifting this primary attachment from the mother to the father in order to prepare herself for her future sexual role. Thus, Freud was concerned first with elucidating the factors that influence the little girl to give up her pre-oedipal attachment to the mother and form the normal oedipal attitude toward the father. Secondly, he was preoccupied with the factors that led to the dissolution of the Oedipus complex in the girl so that it might be replaced by adult sexuality.

The girl's renunciation of the pre-oedipal attachment to the mother could not be satisfactorily explained as a consequence of the ambivalent or aggressive qualities that characterize the mother-child relationship at certain phases of development, for boys participate in the same type of relationship. Rather, the crucial precipitating factor was found to lie in the anatomical differences between the sexes or, more specifically, the girl's discovery of these differences during the phallic period. Until this discovery, apart from constitutional differences and depending on the extent to which these are accentuated by variations in the parents' early attitudes toward a daughter in comparison with a son, the girl's development parallels that of the boy. Fundamental differences emerge when she discovers during the phallic period that the clitoris with which she is endowed is inferior to its male counterpart, the penis. Typically, the little girl reacts to this discovery with an intense sense of loss and injury and with envy of the male. And at this point, the mother, who had previously been an object of love, is held responsible for bringing her into the world less well equipped and engenders hostility so intense that it may persist. With the further discovery that the mother lacks this vital organ as well, her devaluation becomes even more profound. In an attempt to make up for her inadequacy, the little girl turns to her father, in the hope that he will give her a penis or a baby in place of the missing penis. The factors that lead to the dissolution of the Oedipus complex in girls, Freud's second concern, now appeared to be the following: the diminution of the girl's sexual love for her father because of his failure to satisfy her demands and fear of the mother's disapproval.

SIGNIFICANCE OF THE OEDIPUS COMPLEX. Freud regarded the Oedipus complex as the nucleus for the development of later neurosis and symptom formation. Furthermore, the various admixtures of libidinal fixations, object orientations, and identifications with which the child emerges from the Oedipus situation exert a profound influence on the development of character and personality. This is a current concern of psychoanalytically oriented psychiatry. As such, the processes that enable the resolution of the Oedipus complex as the child emerges into the latency period clearly merit more detailed discussion than has been provided here. These processes are so intimately bound up with the development of the psychic apparatus and its structural components that it was considered appropriate to defer this discussion for presentation in the following part of the section, which is devoted to these areas of psychoanalytic theory. However, it should be emphasized here, once again, that in puberty there is a resurgence of incestuous oedipal feelings in both sexes, and the task of withdrawing libido from the parents and attaching it to other, more suitable love objects becomes of critical importance. And, with parenthood, the father and mother re-experience their early relationships with their own parents through identification with their child.

NATURE AND ORIGINS OF ANXIETY

Initial formulations. Freud's first theory of anxiety emphasized its biological genesis in the sexual instinct. Thus, as a result of his early clinical studies in the 1890's, pathological anxiety was uniformly attributed to disturbance in sexual function. However, Freud distinguished between the etiological factors that produce anxiety in specific clinical entities. On the one hand, in those syndromes that he classified as the actual neuroses—neurasthenia, hypochondriasis, and anxiety neurosis—the causative factors have a physical basis. In contrast, he attributed the psychoneuroses, such as hysteria, primarily to psychological factors.

According to Freud, an increase in sexual tension as a physiological phenomenon leads to an increase in its mental representation, libido, together with various associated ideas and emotions. In the normal course of events, this sexual tension is discharged somatically through sexual intercourse and, concurrently, its mental representations as well. However, in the actual neuroses, such as anxiety neurosis, abnormal sexual practices, such as coitus interruptus, prevent the proper somatic discharge of sexual tensions or toxins and the adequate expression of the psychic elaboration of these sexual tensions. Freud maintained that it is this interference with the adequate discharge of the psychic component of sexual tension, i.e., its libidinal aspects, that gives rise to anxiety. Anxiety is also characteristic of psychoneurotic states, such as hysteria or obsessive-compulsive states, but here the interference with normal sexual functioning was attributed to psychic conflict or repression.

Freud held to this theory in its essential outlines until 1926, when he proposed certain fundamental revisions.

Modifications. Many workers have based their objections to Freud's first theory of anxiety on the fact that his postulates concerning the somatic or toxic aspects of sexual functioning or malfunctioning were naive. In fact, however, in the years since, endocrinological investigations have confirmed the existence of a variety of sexual substances—hormones. Moreover, research findings in this area have disclosed that some of these substances are even related chemically to the hormones that are involved in fight-flight or anxiety reactions.

Nevertheless, this theory does have certain inherent limitations. First, it contradicts a basic aspect of the psychoanalytic concept of the psychoneuroses. Freud postulated that in the psychoneuroses anxiety is the result of sexual repression, which implied that repression precedes anxiety. But what causes repression? Freud had also stated that repression arose in response to unbearable affects, which would certainly include anxiety. This implies that anxiety precedes repression and represents the basic contradiction that was the source of considerable controversy.

Second, the theory did not take into account anxiety that arises in response to realistic danger, so-called objective anxiety. Obviously, in certain situations the anticipation of external danger may cause somatic phenomena and subjective sensations of fear, which are indistinguishable from those that occur in neurotic states but are entirely unrelated to the accumulation of sexual tensions. Thus, anxiety can best be understood not in terms of its associated sensation or its somatic expression but in terms of whether it is precipitated by an external or an internal danger. In other words, as Freud came to realize, a comprehensive theory of anxiety must take into account its relationship to the self-preservative goals of the organism; it must consider the *function* of anxiety. In a broader sense, the deficiencies associated with Freud's early theory of anxiety serve to underscore the inevitable limitations of an approach that tries to account for a phenomenon as complex as anxiety entirely on the basis of consideration of the instincts and their fate, without reference to the functions of the psychic apparatus or its relationship to the outside world.

Accordingly, in his later theory of anxiety, Freud dealt specifically with the limitations inherent in his early effort. His later theory did not discard the important relationship between frustrated sexuality and anxiety in certain neurotic conditions. Nor did it rule out the possibility that there was a direct somatic relationship between sexual conflict and anxiety, the precise nature of which had not yet been defined. However, these economic considerations were included within a broader theoretical framework.

CONCEPT OF NARCISSISM

The concept of narcissism holds a transitional position in the development of psychoanalytic theory. On the one hand, it necessitated important modifications in the libido and instinct theories; on the other hand, it precipitated a detailed examination of the ego and its functions. Moreover, this concept has further implications that have not yet been fully explored for the understanding of psychotic patients and other patients who fail to respond to treatment.

Theoretical basis. Prior to the psychoanalytic application of the concept of self-love, the term narcissism was applied in a restricted sense to designate a sexual perversion of the type demonstrated by the Greek youth Narcissus, who fell in love with his own reflection. The first systematic discussion of narcissism appeared in Freud's writings in 1914 in his classic paper "On Narcissism." The phenomenon had provoked his interest as early as 1909, however. On the basis of his clinical experience and his observations of the psychopathology of everyday life, Freud had become aware of the need to expand his libido theory in order to accommodate the concept of narcissism.

In 1908 Freud observed that in cases of dementia praecox (schizophrenia) libido appeared to have been withdrawn from other persons or objects and concluded that this might account perhaps for the loss of contact with reality that was typical of such patients. He then speculated as to where this libido had been invested instead. The megalomanic delusions of these patients appeared to indicate that the libido they had withdrawn from external objects was now invested in themselves, in their own egos. Concomitantly, Freud became aware of the fact that the phenomenon of narcissism was not limited to the psychoses; it might occur in neurotic and normal individuals as well under certain conditions. He noted, for example, that in physical illness and hypochondriasis investment, or what he called "cathexis," of the libido was frequently withdrawn from other objects or persons and from external activities and events. Similarly, he speculated that in sleep libido was withdrawn from outside objects and invested in the person's own body. It may be that in dreams the more-intense-than-real-life quality of the emotional experience results from libidinal cathexis of the fantasy representations of the persons who compose the dream images.

Freud was aware, of course, of the significant role of narcissism in the myths and beliefs of primitive people who attributed the occurrence of external events to the omnipotence of their own thoughts. Above all, even the most casual observation of young children reveals the extent of their narcissism, their exclusive dedication to their own self-interest, and the tenacity with which they cling to the magical omnipotence of their thoughts.

Narcissism and the development of object relationships. Freud's observations of the narcissistic behavior of young children provided incontrovertible evidence of the role of narcissism in development and, in turn, led him to incorporate such considerations into his libido theory, outlined earlier in this chapter.

To begin with, although for obvious reasons the hypothesis is not testable by direct observation, Freud postulated that a state of primary narcissism exists at birth. That is, the neonate is entirely narcissistic; his libidinal energies are devoted entirely to the satisfaction of his needs and the preservation of his well-being. The libido thus invested in the infant himself was termed narcissistic or ego libido. Later, as the infant gradually begins to recognize the person immediately responsible for his care as a source of tension relief or pleasure, libido is released for investment in that person, usually the mother. Freud called the libido that becomes available for attachment to others "object libido." Thus, the development of object relations parallels this shift from primary narcissism to object attachment —that is, from infancy, when narcissistic libido is pre-eminent, to later childhood, when object libido predominates. However, it should be pointed out that some narcissistic libido is normally present throughout adult life; this is considered healthy narcissism and finds expression in the individual's sense of well-being. Moreover, Freud observed that in a variety of traumatic situations, physical as well as psychological—such as actual injury or the threat of injury, object loss, or excessive frustration— libido is withdrawn from objects and reinvested in the self. He called this renewal of libidinal investment in the individual's own body or self "secondary narcissism."

Applications to infantile sexuality. Discussion of the concept of narcissism inevitably gives rise to the central question of whether it differs essentially from autoerotism. In fact, the difference between the two is a fundamental one: Autoerotism refers to erotism in relation to the subject's own body or its parts; narcissism refers to the love of something more abstract—the self or the subject's ego.

Apart from such considerations, it should be noted that Robert Waelder has made an initial attempt to apply levels of self-love or narcissism to the developmental schemata of erotogenic zones within the framework of Freud's theory of infantile sexuality. As it applies to the oral period, narcissism is expressed in the wish for affection and is defined as receptive narcissism; phallic narcissism designates the wish for admiration, which is said to characterize this stage of psychosexual development.

Narcissism and choice of love object. Reference was made earlier to the crucial role of early object relationships in the later choice of love object. Freud found that further application of the concept of narcissism facilitated understanding of the basis for the choice of a love object in adult life. Thus, a love object might be chosen according to the narcissistic type—that is, because she resembles the subject's idealized self-image or his fantasied self-image—or the object chosen might be an anaclitic type, in which case the object would resemble someone who took care of the subject during the early years of his life. Persons who themselves have an intense degree of self-love, especially certain beautiful women, have, according to Freud, an appeal over and above their aesthetic attraction. Such women supply for their lovers the lost narcissism that was painfully renounced in the process of turning toward object love. Finally, a homosexual object relationship represents still another example of a narcissistic object choice. In this case, the individual's choice of an object is predicated on sexual resemblance.

In summary, the concept of narcissism occupies a pivotal position in psychoanalytic theory. With the introduction of the concept of narcissism, it became obvious that the concept of the individual, his body, and his ego could no longer be used interchangeably, that further understanding and advances in psychoanalytic theory would depend on a clearer definition of the concept of self or ego. Attempts to implement such understanding brought into focus ambiguities in the concept of the ego, which served to underscore the need for systematic study of its development, structure, and functions. The attention to narcissistic phenomena has also enlarged our understanding of a variety of mental disorders, as well as various normal psychological phenomena. Finally, it represents a kind of watershed in psychoanalysis for the theory of the instincts.

THEORY OF THE INSTINCTS

When he began his work, Freud strove unceasingly to maintain psychoanalytic theory on a firm biological foundation. Only the lack of adequate scientific data induced him to relax his efforts on this score. His theory of the instincts represents one of his most important efforts to link psychological and biological phenomena, for Freud conceived of the instinct as a borderline concept between the mental and the organic spheres. Consequently, as mentioned earlier in connection with the term libido, Freud's use of the term instinct is not always consistent. At times libido refers to the somatic process underlying the sexual instinct and at other times to the psychological representation. It has been suggested that this confusion stems, in part, from the fact that German cannot be translated accurately into English. *Triebe* are powerful, imperative strivings, such as sexuality and self-preservation, within living organisms, which are rooted in their physical nature. In contrast, the Darwinian word "instinct" implies innate, inherent, unlearned, biologically useful behavior. Thus, the reader would do well to keep in mind the fact that Freud's *Triebe*—which has been variously translated as instinct, drive, and instinctual drive—must not be confused with the word instinct as it is used in zoology.

Freud provided his clearest definition of *Triebe* in 1915 in his paper "Instincts and Their Vicissitudes," when he wrote:

> . . . an "instinct" appears to us as a concept on the frontier between the mental and the somatic, as the psychical representative of the stimuli originating within the organism and reaching the mind, as a measure of the demand made upon the mind for work in consequence of its connection with the body.

This definition clearly points up the essential role of the instinct in psychoanalysis. Nevertheless, instinct theory remains a somewhat obscure area. The relationship between psychological and somatic processes is particularly difficult to elucidate; nor is this difficulty lessened by affirmation of the belief in the essential unity of mind and body. Psychoanalysts are, in brief, forced, just as Freud was, to delimit their theoretical constructs to the psychological parameters of human behavior. Recognition of this fact has caused an increasing number of analysts to turn to what ethologists and other students of animal behavior can teach about instincts.

Characteristics of the instincts. According to Freud, an instinct has four principal characteristics: source, impetus, aim, and object. This classification was stressed especially in his early writings, when he was most concerned with the sexual instinct. In general, the source of an instinct refers to the part of the body from which it arises, the site of its inception. The source, then, refers to a somatic process, the stimulus of which is represented in mental life as a drive or affect. In sexual life, the stimulus would refer to the process or factor that excites a specific erotogenic zone, the source. The impetus is a quantitative concept that refers to the amount of force or demand for work made by the instinct. The aim is any action directed toward satisfaction or tension release, such as the infant's activity in seeking the nipple. The object is the person or thing that is the target for this action. The object is the most variable characteristic of the instinct, insofar as it is appropriate to its task to the extent that its characteristics make satisfaction possible. The subject's own body may serve as the object of an instinct in masturbatory activity, for example.

Classification of instincts. In the early years of psychoanalysis, as might be expected, the development of instinct theory was closely related to the clinical phenomena that Freud was investigating. From the beginning, he held to his dualistic classification of the instincts. Although initially he postulated an instinct of self-preservation, at this time (1890's) Freud was primarily concerned with the sexual drive, which reflected his preoccupation with the role of sexual factors in the etiology of hysteria and the psychoneuroses. Later, this relationship between the classification of instincts and clinical work became uneven. For example, in his classification of the life and death instincts, Freud concerned himself with abstract forces in nature, and his concepts in this area were not directly supported by clinical evidence.

EGO INSTINCTS. Because Freud's predominant interest was in the sexual basis of the neuroses until approximately 1910, the self-preservative or ego instincts were rather neglected. However, his increasing interest in the phenomenon of self-love or narcissism led, in turn, to greater emphasis on the ego instincts. At this point, he saw narcissism as an essentially libidinal instinct; he called the remaining aspects "ego instincts," which he considered primarily nonsexual and devoted to self-preservation. Freud also felt that the ego instincts were closely associated with repression. Furthermore, at this time Freud also believed that mental conflict, which could produce symptom formation and neurosis, resulted from the clash between two instincts—the libido (or sexual) instinct as opposed to the ego (or nonsexual) instinct. Only after he had evolved a comprehensive theory of the mental structure, particularly the ego and the mechanisms of defense, did he abandon this conception.

NATURE OF AGGRESSION. Freud's discovery and early formulations regarding the ego instincts led him in 1915 to reconsider the nature and role of aggression. Previously, Freud had considered aggression largely in terms of sadism, which he had defined as one of the sexual part or component instincts that were manifest at every level of psychosexual development. But clearly there were nonsexual aspects of sadism, and so for a time he included sadism among the ego instincts—citing, for example, the impulse to attack in order to protect oneself. Gradually, however, Freud was forced to realize that there were both sexual and nonsexual aspects of sadism. Thus, he differentiated between aggression and hate, which he assigned to the ego instincts, and the libidinal aspects of sadism, which reverted to the sexual instinct. Sadism was further seen as the result of a fusion of sex and aggression, of love and hate, which might occur, for example, in the case of thwarted desire.

But this classification gave rise to still another problem. On the basis of clinical evidence of the self-destructive tendencies of depressed patients and self-inflicted injury among his masochistic patients, as well as his observations of the wanton destructiveness normally manifested by small children, Freud concluded that in many instances aggression or aggressive impulses were not self-preservative; therefore, they could not be properly assigned to the ego instincts. Thus, when Freud set forth his new structural theory of the mind in the 1920's, he gave aggression separate status as an instinct with a source that was largely in the skeletal muscles and the aim of which was destruction. Aggression could come about, it was true, through the frustration of libido, but in that event it was secondarily invoked, on loan to the sexual instincts. The elevation of aggression to the status of a separate instinct on a par with sexuality dealt a severe blow to any lingering romantic notion of the essential goodness of man, whose aggressive impulses were stimulated only if he was sufficiently thwarted or abused. This new formulation had other implications as well. Attention then had to be given to the specific role of aggression in mental disorders and to tracing the steps through which it is neutralized or detoxified. These processes have been investigated by Hartmann and Waelder, respectively, only in the past two decades.

LIFE AND DEATH INSTINCTS. Freud introduced his theory of the dual life and death instincts, eros and thanatos, in 1920. This classification of the instincts is more abstract and has broader applications than his previous concept of libidinal and aggressive drives. The life and death instincts were considered to represent the forces that underlay the sexual and aggressive instincts. As such, they represented the trends of biological organisms in general. Although Freud conceded that the death instinct was not, in itself, clinically verifiable, he felt that the validity of this concept was substantiated by certain observable phenomena. He pointed in particular to the tendency of individuals to repeat past behavior, a phenomenon he described as the "repetition compulsion," even if such behavior had proved to be ill-advised. Further evidence was to be found in the many examples of the individual's inexplicable need to suffer.

Freud defined the death instinct as the tendency of organisms and their cells to return to an inanimate state. In contrast, the life instinct, or eros, referred to the tendency of particles to reunite, of parts to bind to one another to form greater unities, as in sexual reproduction. These forces are, therefore, analogous to catabolism and anabolism. Inasmuch as the ultimate destiny of all biological matter, with the exception of the germ cells, is to return to an inanimate state, the death instinct was thought to be the dominant force.

Apart from the fact that it implies a rather gloomy view of life, the concept of the death instinct is the aspect of Freudian theory that has been criticized most severely, both by psychoanalysts and by workers in related disciplines. This criticism has been based on the fact that, although there is an undeniable tendency toward cellular deterioration, it cannot be assumed from this that the total organism possesses a drive or instinct in that direction.

PLEASURE AND REALITY PRINCIPLES. In Freud's early formulations, the instincts were thought to be governed by certain regulatory principles, which were applied to all stimuli impinging on the organism, whether these stimuli emanated from within or without. Even at the time he wrote the "Project" in 1895, Freud had recognized the significance of the constancy principle, the tendency of the organism to maintain a particular level or state of equilibrium. And, along with the concept of the death instinct, Freud developed the nirvana principle, which postulated a tendency on the part of the organism to discharge internal tension and seek a state of rest. In 1911 he described two basic principles of mental functioning that derived from this need to maintain a state of equilibrium —the pleasure and the reality principles.

The pleasure principle, which he considered largely inborn, referred to the tendency of the organism to avoid pain and seek pleasure through tension discharge. In essence, the pleasure principle persists throughout life, but, inevitably, it must be modified by the reality principle. The demands of external reality, called the reality principle, necessitate the delay or postponement of immediate pleasure, with the aim, perhaps, of achieving even greater pleasure in the long run. The reality principle is largely a learned function; therefore, it is closely related to the maturation of ego functions and may be impaired in a variety of mental disorders that are the result of impeded ego development. Thus, here again, we come upon one of the theoretical propositions of Freud's middle period that underscored the need for a systematic psychology of the ego and its functions.

THEORY OF DREAMS

First recognition of the significance of dreams. Today, dreams occupy a central position in psychoanalytic practice and theory and are the subject of expanding research interest. Nevertheless, their application in psychoanalytically oriented psychiatry and the value of dream interpretation in psychiatric treatment have not been clearly elucidated.

Freud first became aware of the significance of dreams in therapy when he realized that in the process of free association his patients frequently described their dreams of the night before or of years past. He then discovered that these dreams had a definite meaning, although it was disguised. And Freud found that encouraging his patients to freely associate to dream fragments was more productive than their associations to real life events, insofar as it facilitated the disclosure of unconscious memories and fantasies.

Freud's monumental publication in 1900, *The Interpretation of Dreams*, included much of the data derived from his clinical experience in this area as well as the insights he acquired by free association to his own dreams. On the basis of these data, he concluded that a dream, like a psychoneurotic symptom, is the conscious expression of an unconscious fantasy or wish that is not readily accessible to the individual in waking life. Thus, although dreams were considered one of the normal manifestations of unconscious activity, they were shown later to bear some resemblance to the pathological thoughts of psychotic patients in the waking state. The dream images represent the unconscious wishes or thoughts disguised through symbolization and other distorting mechanisms. Earlier, Freud had postulated the existence of a censor, which excluded unconscious wishes during conscious states and which in sleep compelled the transformation of unconscious wishes into the disguised conscious form of the dream as experienced by the sleeper. Freud assumed that this censor was in the service of the ego; that is, he considered it a self-preservative function, which was in accord with his belief that reason and volition presided over these functions. With the development of ego psychology, the activities of the censor, along with the manifestations of repression, displacement, and symbolism in waking life, have been included among those functions of the ego and superego that may lie outside the individual's conscious awareness.

Analysis of dream content. The analysis of dreams elicits material that has been repressed or otherwise excluded from consciousness by the defensive activities of the ego. The dream, as it is consciously recalled, is but the end result of the unconscious mental activity that occurs during sleep and that, because of its intensity, threatens to interfere with sleep itself. But, instead of waking, the sleeper dreams. We call the conscious experience during sleep, which the sleeper may or may not recall after waking, the "manifest dream" and refer to its various elements as the "manifest dream content." The unconscious thoughts and wishes that threaten to waken the sleeper are described as the "latent dream content." The term "dream work" is used to designate the unconscious mental operations by which the latent dream content is transformed into the manifest dream. Thus, the meaning of a dream actually refers to the latent dream content. The latent dream content that gives rise to the manifest dreams may be categorized as follows.

NOCTURNAL SENSORY STIMULI. Sensory impressions—such as pain, hunger, thirst, and urinary urgency—may play a role in initiating a dream. To illustrate, a sleeper in a cold room who urgently needs to urinate may, instead of disturbing his sleep and leaving his warm bed, dream that he has wakened, voided, and returned to bed.

THE DAY'S RESIDUE. The second category of latent dream content comprises thoughts and ideas that are connected with the activities and the preoccupations of the dreamer's current waking life. Because of their continued activity in his unconscious, these thoughts, like sensory stimuli, tend to force waking. Instead, the sleeper may incorporate these thoughts and ideas into the manifest dream.

REPRESSED ID IMPULSES. In essence, however, the latent dream content derives from one or several impulses from the repressed part of the id—that is, from wishes that have their origin in the oedipal and pre-oedipal phases of development. Thus, nocturnal sensations and the day's residue play only an indirect role in initiating a dream. A nocturnal stimulus, however intense, must be associated with one or more repressed wishes to give rise to a dream. Similarly, unless there is a strong link with the repressed, the concerns of waking life cannot in themselves give rise to a dream, however compelling their claim on the sleeper's interest and attention.

By virtue of the fact that in early childhood the psychic apparatus is still relatively immature, the relationship between latent and manifest dream content is best illustrated by the dreams of this stage of development. At this point we cannot distinguish between infantile and current conflicts, for they are one and the same. Nor is it possible to distinguish sharply conscious impulses from those that have been repressed, for the very young child's ego has not yet developed to the point where it has erected permanent defenses against the impulses emanating from the id. Thus, the classifications of latent and manifest content have less relevance with regard to the dreams of early childhood, insofar as latent content refers to unconscious material, and manifest content to that which is consciously perceived.

Significance of dreams. Throughout *The Interpretation of Dreams,* which is generally considered to be one of Freud's greatest contributions, he maintained that every dream represents a wish fulfillment. And this hypothesis is documented by extensive clinical data, including the first complete analysis he made of one of his own dreams in 1895. As mentioned earlier, manifest dreams are most clearly representative of the imaginary fulfillment of a wish or impulse in early childhood, before such wishes have been repressed. However, in later childhood and in adulthood the ego defends itself against the unacceptable instinctual demands of the id, and these demands are repressed to the degree that they appear in the manifest dream in disguised form. Nevertheless, in essence, the dream remains the same—the gratification of an id impulse in fantasy. Or, more accurately, since motility is blocked by the sleep state, the dream enables partial but safer gratification of the repressed impulse.

Because this crucial wish fulfillment aspect of the dream is usually obscured by extensive distortions and disguises, it cannot be readily identified on superficial examination. And inevitably, just as Freud's theory of neurosis has been rejected by those workers who have not accepted his findings concerning infantile sexuality on which it is based, his theory of dreams has been rejected by those critics who have restricted their own investigations to the manifest elements of the dream.

Nature of dream work. Dream work comprises several processes, which create the disguises and distortions that permit the translation of latent content into the manifest dream.

DREAM FORMATION. The latent content must find some means of representation in the manifest dream. Sleep brings a relaxation of repression, and latent wishes and impulses press for discharge and gratification. Since motility is blocked, these repressed wishes and impulses must find some means of representation through mechanisms of thought and fantasy. Latent content achieves representation in one of two ways. First, thoughts, impressions, or memories must be found that can adequately serve to represent in visual terms these latent wishes or impulses. The individual's experiences in the course of any single day provide an ample supply of such material. As mentioned earlier, when current psychological experiences are linked with repressed material, they are incorporated into the content of the dream as the day's residue. Second, less frequently, nocturnal stimuli—such as hunger, pain, thirst—may be associated with repressed impulses and wishes and give rise to their representation in auditory, tactile, olfactory, or gustatory terms.

The unconscious wishes and impulses that press for discharge have been repressed because of their unacceptable nature. Because there is continued resistance to their discharge, these wishes and impulses must attach themselves to more neutral or innocent images in order to pass the scrutiny of the dream censor. This is achieved by the selection of apparently trivial or unimportant images from the individual's current psychological experience, images that nevertheless are linked or associated dynamically with latent images, which they resemble in some respect. In order to facilitate the economic expression of the latent contents and at the same time to maintain the disguise that is essential to escape the censor, the dream work employs several further mechanisms to enable these neutral images to represent repressed impulses and wishes.

SYMBOLISM. For certain body parts or other highly cathected objects, the dreamer substitutes innocent images that resemble the original part in one or more essential features. For example, the snake is a familiar symbol for the penis; or a house may symbolize the female genitalia or womb.

DISPLACEMENT. The mechanism of displacement refers to the transference of emotions (cathexes) from the original object to which such emotions are attached to a substitute or symbolic representation of that object in the dream. Because it is neutral—that is, less invested with affect—this substitute object is more acceptable to the dream censor. Thus, whereas symbolism refers to the substitution of one object for another, displacement facilitates the distortion of unconscious wishes through the transference of affect from one object to another. At the same time, the aim of the unconscious impulse remains unchanged. For example, although the mother may be represented visually in the dream by an unknown woman or one who has less emotional significance for the dreamer, the latent content of the dream continues to derive from the dreamer's unconscious attitudes of love and hate toward his mother. The greatest part of the distortion that enables the translation of latent impulse and wishes into manifest dream content is accomplished through the mechanism of displacement.

PROJECTION. Through the process of projection, the dreamer's unacceptable impulses or wishes are perceived in the dream as emanating from another person. Moreover, the person to whom these unacceptable impulses are ascribed in the dream is often the one toward whom the subject's own unconscious impulses are directed. For example, the individual who has a strong, albeit repressed, wish to be unfaithful to his wife or sweetheart may dream that his love object has been unfaithful to him. He has thereby projected his own unacceptable wishes onto another person and made possible their expression in the manifest dream.

CONDENSATION. Condensation is the mechanism by which several unconscious wishes, impulses, or attitudes are combined and find expression in a single image of the manifest dream. To illustrate, in a child's dream an attacking monster may represent not only the dreamer's father but also some aspects of his mother, and the monster may stand for his own primitive impulses as well. Conversely, a single latent wish or impulse may be given multiple representations in the manifest dream content. Clearly, then, condensation provides the dreamer with a highly flexible and economic device for facilitating, compressing, or expanding the manifest dream that is forged out of latent or unconscious wishes and impulses.

AFFECTS IN DREAMS. The affects or emotions that are associated with the latent dream content are also subjected to a variety of vicissitudes. They may not appear in the manifest dream at all or may be experienced in somewhat altered form. For example, repressed rage toward another person may take the form of annoyance or a mild dislike in the manifest dream or may even be represented by the dreamer's awareness that he is not annoyed. Or affect associated with the latent dream content may be transformed into its opposite in the manifest dream. A repressed longing may thereby be represented by a manifest repugnance or vice versa; sadness may masquerade as joy, etc. In any event, these transformations of affect introduce another strong element of disguise into the manifest dream.

SECONDARY REVISION. Freud stated that dream formation preserves an example of the manner in which the primitive mental apparatus worked. As such, symbolism, displacement, and condensation are characteristic of developmentally early modes of thinking or of the primary process, as described below. In contrast, secondary revision, which is the final operation employed in dream formation, is the mechanism through which the absurd, illogical, and bizarre charcteristics of the dream— which represent the distorting effects of symbolism, displacement, and condensation—acquire the coherence and rationality required by the subject's more mature ego. Secondary revision employs intellectual processes, which more closely resemble those thought processes that govern states of consciousness; in brief, logical mental operations characteristic of the secondary process are introduced into the dream work.

ANXIETY DREAMS. When Freud formulated his basic theory of dreams, he had not yet developed a comprehensive theory of the ego and of its development and functions. Consequently, his early studies of dreams emphasized their function in discharging or gratifying instinctual drives or wishes by representing their fulfillment in the dream's hallucinatory elements. However, dreams may also be approached from the standpoint of their function in avoiding tension or psychic pain. This is properly the domain of the ego, and the dream affords us an opportunity to study the structure and early development of ego functions. Freud realized only later that symbolism, displacement, condensation, projection, and secondary revision serve a dual purpose. On the one hand, they facilitate the discharge of latent impulses. On the other hand, they may be regarded as primitive defense mechanisms that prevent the direct discharge of instinctual drives and thereby protect the dreamer from the excessive anxiety and pain that would accompany such discharges.

Of course, the mechanisms that are employed to disguise latent content may fail. When anxiety pervades a dream or is so severe that it forces at least partial waking, this indicates some failure in the primitive defense operations of the ego. An element of the latent dream content has succeeded, despite extensive dream work, in forcing its way into the manifest dream in a form that is too direct or too readily recognizable for the ego to tolerate. The ego reacts to the direct expression of repressed impulses with severe anxiety.

PUNISHMENT DREAMS. In the punishment dream, which is a related phenomenon, the ego anticipates superego (conscience) condemnation if part of the latent content that derives from the repressed impulses should find direct expression in the manifest dream. In anticipation of the terrible consequences of the loss of the ego's control over the instincts in sleep, there is a compromise between the repressed wish and the repressing agency, the superego. The demands of the superego are satisfied by giving expression to punishment fantasies.

Recent research on physiological functioning during sleep and dream states has important implications for psychoanalytic theory. Obviously, a detailed discussion of these investigations lies beyond the scope of this chapter. It should be mentioned, however, that perhaps the most fundamental finding to emerge from these experiments is that dreaming is a continuous process that consumes a considerable part of the sleep period in all subjects and seems to play an essential role in the integration of normal psychological functioning. A shift in emphasis is perhaps required from regarding latent drives as initiating the dream process itself to investigation of the way the instincts and ego functions determine the form of particular dreams and shape them to their purposes.

Freud's early theory of the nature and function of the mind, which is discussed below, evolved in large measure from his study of the genesis, nature, and function of dreams.

FREUD'S EARLY THEORY OF THE MIND

Historical antecedents. The originality of Freud's theories cannot be disputed. However, it is important to recognize that his early ideas derived from the scientific and philosophical concepts of his day. It was pointed out in the introduction to this chapter that Freud's earliest theory of the mind, as set forth in the "Project,"

which was published after his death, was based on the neurophysiological concepts of brain function advanced by the Helmholtz school,
which, in turn, were derived from Newtonian physics. One of the
unique aspects of Freud's contribution to the study of the mind was
his effort to integrate empirical biological data with the kind of psychological understanding that, with rare exceptions, had previously
been left to philosophers and writers. As demonstrated in the "Project," his earliest efforts at formulating a theory of the mind were in
the language of physiology. He attempted therein to interpret sys-
tematically such phenomena as consciousness, perception, memory,
thought, judgment, motive forces, and defenses against pain or unpleasure in terms of shifts in quantities of excitation between various
systems of neurons. For reasons stated earlier, Freud was eventually
forced to abandon this effort, although he continued to believe that
psychical processes never operated independently of physiological
ones and that the latter even preceded the former. However, he concluded that, until methods were developed that would permit verification of the interplay between the two spheres, psychical processes
should be described in the language of psychology.

Although the relationship is more difficult to trace, Freud's psychological theories also have their antecedents in the contributions of
nineteenth century psychology and the then related discipline of philosophy.

For example, several authors have called attention to the resemblance between Freud's basic formulation of the dynamic unconscious and a similar concept developed seventy years earlier by the
German philosopher Johann Herbart. Moreover, while ordinarily
Freud might not be expected to be familiar with Herbart's work,
there is evidence that he was exposed to his theories during his last
year at the gymnasium. Herbart maintained that unconscious mental
processes were dominated by a constant conflict of ideas of varying
intensity. Ideas, according to Herbart, could be driven out of the
mind by opposing ideas; but, far from being lost, they continued to
assert themselves and would be treated by the subject as disturbing
elements requiring self-preservative efforts.

Freud had also studied the writings of Gustav Fechner, whom he
greatly admired and whose psychology was based on Herbart's theories. Fechner, too, believed in unconscious processes that existed below threshold and needed to attain a certain intensity before they
reached consciousness. The famous comparison of the mind with an
iceberg nine-tenths under water originated with Fechner. Fechner, in
turn, had an important influence on Brücke, who maintained that
"movements in the nervous system give rise to ideas." In all likelihood, Freud had probably read the publications of some of Herbart's
other followers as well, such as Wilhelm Griesinger, the prominent

German psychiatrist, who believed that ideas could be absent from consciousness and who associated the unconscious with impressions received from bodily organs. Other late nineteenth century writers and scholars—such as Theodor Lipps, professor of psychology at the University of Munich—wrote of the existence of unconscious mental processes. Fechner and Herbart exerted significant influence also on the ideas of Theodor Meynert, Freud's professor of psychiatry. Although, for Meynert, mind and brain were virtually interchangeable, he too was concerned with threshold and the circumstances under which ideas (excitations of brain cells) reached consciousness. Brain cells, according to Meynert, established connections through associations that were extended by means of the nutrition supplied by blood vessels. He also suggested the existence of a controlling agency that inhibited or pressed back the "bad" activity of the brain.

It is always difficult to weigh the influence of particular ideas upon the thinking of later writers. Certainly, the similarity between certain elements in Freud's early psychological theories and the earlier concepts of these men cannot be denied. The originality of Freud's contribution lies in the fact that, whereas previously these ideas were presented in the form of general theoretical statements, Freud elaborated a coherent theory of a dynamic unconscious based on detailed clinical observation of psychological phenomena and then tested the validity of his theory by applying it to other clinical problems.

Freud's Topographical Theory of the Mind

The topographical theory, as set forth in the seventh chapter of *The Interpretation of Dreams* in 1900, represented an attempt to divide the mind into three regions—namely, the unconscious, the preconscious, and the conscious—which were distinguished from one another by their relationship to consciousness. Although the working model for this theory was similar in many respects to that set forth earlier in the "Project," the physiological language had, for the most part, disappeared. Accordingly, the data upon which this later theory was based derived from dream interpretation, analysis of the psychoneuroses, and the study of the psychopathology of everyday life—such as the study of jokes, wit, slips of the tongue and other errors.

Each of the three regions of the mind—which are sometimes referred to as the "system ucs," the "system pcs," and the "system cs"—had unique characteristics that differentiated it from the others.

The unconscious. The unconscious contains repressed ideas and affects and is characterized as follows.

1. Ordinarily, its elements are inaccessible to consciousness and can become conscious only through the preconscious, which excludes them by means of censorship or repression. Repressed ideas may reach conscious-

ness when the censor is overpowered (as in psychoneurotic symptom formation), relaxes (as in dream states), or is fooled (in jokes).

2. The unconscious is associated with the particular form of mental activity that Freud called the "primary process" or "primary process thinking." The primary process has as its principal aim the facilitation of wish fulfillment and instinctual discharge; thus, it is intimately associated with the pleasure principle. As such, it disregards logical connections (which it readily short circuits), permits contradictions to coexist, knows no negatives, has no conception of time, and represents wishes as already fulfilled. Primary process thinking is characteristic of very young children, for example, who are dedicated to the immediate gratification of their desires.

The unconscious also employs the primitive mental operations of displacement and condensation, which permit rapid discharge of the mental energy attached to these repressed affects and ideas through the avenues of the preconscious and conscious systems. As defined earlier, displacement is the mechanism by which mental energy (cathexis) attached to one idea is shifted to another idea that encounters less censorship. Condensation is the process by which energy attached to more than one unconscious idea may be discharged through a single thought or image that embodies (in part, through symbolism) the characteristics of these several ideas. Condensation has thus the property of economy. The qualities of motility that are ascribed to the primary process also account for the fact that it is frequently linked to creativity.

3. Memories in the unconscious have lost their connection with verbal expression. Freud discovered in the course of his clinical work that repression of a childhood memory could occur if energy was withdrawn from it and especially if verbal energy was removed. However, when words were reapplied to the forgotten memory trace during psychoanalytic treatment, it became excessively cathected and could reach consciousness once more.

4. The content of the unconscious is limited to wishes seeking fulfillment. These wishes provide the motive force for dream and neurotic symptom formation.

5. The unconscious is closely related to the instincts. At the time this theory was developed, these were thought to consist of the sexual and self-preservative drives. Thus, it contains the mental representatives and derivatives of the instinctual drives, especially the derivatives of the sexual instincts.

The preconscious. This region of the mind is not present at birth but develops in childhood in a manner that parallels the course of ego development, as described in Freud's later structural theory. The preconscious is accessible to both the unconscious proper and the conscious. Elements of the unconscious can gain access to consciousness only by first becoming linked with words and reaching the preconscious. However, one of the functions of the preconscious is to maintain repression or censorship of wishes and desires. The type of mental activity associated with the preconscious is called "secondary process" or "secondary process thinking." In contrast to the primary process, such thinking is aimed at avoiding unpleasure, delaying instinctual discharge, and binding mental energy in accordance with the demands of external reality and the subject's moral precepts or values. It respects logical connections, and it tolerates inconsistencies less well than the primary process. Thus, the secondary process is closely allied with the reality principle, which, for the most part, governs its activities.

The conscious. The nature of consciousness was described in less detail in Freud's early theories, and certain aspects of consciousness are not yet completely understood by psychoanalysts. Freud regarded the conscious as a kind of sense organ of attention that operated in close association with the preconscious. Through attention, the subject could become conscious of perceptual stimuli from the outside world. From within the organism, however, only elements in the preconscious entered consciousness; the rest of the mind lay outside awareness. Prior to 1923, Freud also believed that the conscious controlled motor activity and regulated the qualitative distribution of psychic energy.

Dynamics of mental functioning. Freud conceived of the psychic apparatus as a kind of reflex arc, in which the various segments had a spatial relationship. The arc consisted of a perceptual or sensory end, through which impressions were received; an intermediate region, consisting of a storehouse of unconscious memories; and a motor end, closely associated with the preconscious, through which instinctual discharge occurred. In early childhood, perceptions were modified and stored in the form of memories.

According to this theory, in ordinary waking life the mental energy associated with unconscious ideas seeks discharge through thought or motor activity, moving from the perceptual to the motor end. However, under certain conditions, such as external frustration or sleep, the direction in which the energy travels along the arc is reversed, and it moves from the motor to the perceptual end. It thereby reanimates early childhood impressions in their original perceptual form and results in dreams during sleep and hallucinations in mental disorders. Freud called this reversal of the normal direction in which mental energy traveled in the psychic apparatus "topographical regression."

Although he subsequently abandoned this model of the mind as a reflex arc, the central concept of regression was retained by Freud and applied later in somewhat modified form in his theory of neurosis. This theory states that libidinal frustration results in a reversion to earlier modes of instinctual discharge or levels of fixation that were previously determined by childhood frustration or excessive erotic stimulation. Freud called this kind of reversion "libidinal" or "instinctual regression."

to the reality principle from the pleasure principle in
es a similar capacity to postpone gratification and
m with the requirements of the outside world. We
at the important relationship of libido to a self that
completely defined, as postulated in the theory of
or a clearer understanding of this self or ego. Accord-
aphical theory of the mind, the preconscious, which
accessible to consciousness, was held responsible for
h in many instances was an unconscious operation),
a new formulation of the agency performing this
er problem arose in relation to the ego or self-
ncts held responsible for repression. Presumably, the
ponsible for defense, but surely this task belonged to

preconscious nor the ego instincts were solely respon-
n or censorship, how was repression achieved? Freud
this question in 1915 by postulating that ideas are
e unconscious by the withdrawal of libido or energy
in the manner characteristic of unconscious ideas,
enew their attempt to become attached to libido and
ess. Thus, the withdrawal of libido must be con-
. Freud described this process as "anticathexis" or
." But, again, if such countercathexis is to be con-
against ideas in the unconscious, it must be perma-
self operate on an unconscious basis. Understanding
tructure—that is, the ego—that could perform this
ction was clearly called for and constituted still an-
of the need for the development of ego psychology.

h phases: development of ego psychology. During the
evolved his theory concerning the structural compo-
which was to be the foundation of ego psychology, and
f anxiety on the basis of these new formulations. The
to the major contributions to this area of psychoanaly-
wers. Both of these crucial phases in the development
re discussed in detail below.

F THE PSYCHIC APPARATUS

viewpoint, the psychic apparatus is divided into three
ted as ego, id, and superego—which are distinguished
unctions. The main distinction lies between the ego and
e locus of the instinctual drives. It is under the domina-
y process; and, therefore, it operates in accordance with
iple, without regard for reality. The ego, on the other
a more coherent organization, the task of which is to

SIGNIFICANCE OF THE TOPOGRAPHICAL THEORY

The topographical theory underscores, once again, the need for a more systematic concept of psychic structure. Its main deficiency lies in its inability to account for two important characteristics of mental conflict. First, Freud found that many of the defense mechanisms that patients employed to avoid pain or unpleasure and that appeared in the form of unconscious resistance during psychoanalytic treatment were themselves not initially accessible to consciousness. Obviously, then, the agency of repression could not be identical with the preconscious, inasmuch as this region of the mind was by definition accessible to consciousness. Second, he found that his patients frequently demonstrated an unconscious need for punishment. However, according to the topographical theory, the moral agency making this demand was allied with the anti-instinctual forces available to awareness in the preconscious.

These criticisms were among the important considerations that ultimately led Freud to discard the topographical theory insofar as it was concerned with the assignment of specific processes to specific regions of the mind. More precisely, Freud came to realize that what is more important is whether these processes belong to the primary system or the secondary system. Accordingly, the concepts included in Freud's early theory that have retained their usefulness refer to the characteristics of primary and secondary thought processes, the essential importance of wish fulfillment, the tendency toward regression under conditions of frustration, and the existence of a dynamic unconscious and the nature of its operation.

PSYCHIC APPARATUS AND EGO PSYCHOLOGY

At the outset of this discussion it must be emphasized that "id," "ego," and "superego" are abstract terms, the value of which lies in their operational referents. Each refers to a particular aspect of human mental functioning for which no more useful term has been found to date. However, unlike infantile sexuality or object relationships, id, ego, and superego are not empirically demonstrable phenomena.

Many workers have commented on the fact that Freud's attention was directed to the structure of the mind and the characteristics of ego functioning at a relatively late stage in the development of psychoanalysis. In fact, a careful review of the evolution of Freud's theoretical concepts reveals that from the beginning he associated certain aspects of mental functioning with the ego and others with the superego. However, during the years of his first great discoveries, he was concerned primarily with establishing the existence of unconscious mental processes and elucidating their nature and with demonstrating the value of psychoanalysis as a potential technique for exploring the depths of the human mind. It is not surprising, therefore, that he was less concerned with the detailed study of those aspects of mental functioning that were normally accessible to consciousness, for they were already familiar to psychology; moreover, methods had already been established for their investigation. It was only when Freud discovered that all unconscious processes could not be relegated to the instincts, that certain aspects of mental functioning associated with the ego and superego were unconscious as well, that he turned to the study of these structural components.

Freud turned to the development of ego psychology so that the progress of psychoanalysis might not be impeded by a lack of understanding of certain phenomena associated with this aspect of mental functioning. There is no question that his efforts have had important repercussions for the development of psychoanalysis and for the understanding of personality and behavior in general. Ego psychology is not, in itself, associated with new insights that might conceivably approach the magnitude of Freud's earlier discoveries. However, in the course of its development over the past thirty or forty years, particularly in the years since World War II, ego psychology has helped to refine psychoanalytic theory; it has served to organize, to codify, to place in a systematic conceptual framework the vast amount of data derived from psychoanalytic investigation. In addition, contributions to ego psychology during this period have led to significant improvements in psychoanalytic treatment techniques.

HISTORICAL DEVELOPMENT OF EGO PSYCHOLOGY

The evolution of the concept of the ego within the framework of the historical development of psychoanalytic theory can be divided into four phases. The first phase, which ended in 1897, coincided with the development of early psychoanalytic concepts. The second phase, from 1897 to 1923, spanned the development of psychoanalysis proper. During the third phase, in the years from 1923 to 1937, Freud developed his theory of ego psychology and his later theory of anxiety. Finally, the fourth phase in the evolution of the concept of ego psychology began with Freud's death and reflects the contributions of Anna Freud, Heinz Hartmann, Ernst Kris, David Rapaport, Erik Erikson, and other contemporary psychoanalysts who may be credited with the development of a general psychology of the ego.

First phase: early concepts of the ego. In the initial phase in the development of psychoanalytic theory, the ego was not always defined precisely. Rather, it referred to the dominant mass of a person's conscious ideas and moral values as distinct from those impulses and wishes that were repressed. Thus, the ego was thought to be concerned primarily with defense, a term that was soon replaced by repression, with which it was then thought to be synonymous. In the neurophysiological language of the "Project," the ego was described as "an organization . . . whose presence interferes with passage of quantities [of excitation]." Translated into the language of psychology, the ego constituted a defense that had been

---

erected against ideas that
in turn, were found to be
thought that they had be
seduction. Because the me
pleasant affects, they evok
original thoughts. Howeve
of energy and the producti
this early ego was contradi
and avoid unpleasant affec
process, it evoked another,

It will be recalled tha
counts of the traumatic
childhood. And he saw
ories of these events, as
individual's relationship
its ideational representati
theory, investigation of tl
Only recently, with incr
important role of the eg
with the outside world o
focus of study once more.

Second phase: historical
cated to the development ol
as such received little direc
concerned primarily with th
Consequently, references to
frequent. However, as indic
Freud's early theory of the ir
mind; the clarification of tl
the function of the ego and t

In regard to the sexual i
tudes to which this instin
sion. These included rev
active, sadistic impulse m
one); turning upon the su
the object might be direc
might be repressed; or the
When they are approached
these vicissitudes might be
relationship to reality is p
noted earlier, the concept
to delay discharge of the
demands of external reality

---

ego. Progression
childhood invol
thereby to confo
have seen, too, t
has not yet been
narcissism, calls
ing to the topog
by definition wa
censorship (whic
thereby requirin
function. Anoth
preservative inst
instincts were re
the ego.

If neither the
sible for repressi
tried to answer
maintained in tl
(cathexis). But
they constantly
reach conscious
stantly repeated
"countercathexi
sistently effectiv
nent and must
of the psychic
complicated fur
other indication

Third and fourt
third phase, Freu
nents of the mind
revised his theory
fourth phase refer
sis by Freud's foll
of ego psychology

STRUCTURE

From a structural
provinces—design
by their different
the id. The id is tl
tion of the primar
the pleasure princ
hand, represents

avoid unpleasure and pain by opposing or regulating the discharge of instinctual drives to conform with the demands of the external world. In addition, the discharge of id impulses is opposed or regulated by the third structural component of the psychic apparatus, the superego, which contains the internalized moral values and influence of the parental images.

The ego. It was pointed out earlier in this discussion that the conscious and preconscious functions that are typically associated with the ego—words, ideas, logic—did not account entirely for its role in mental functioning. The discovery that certain phenomena that emerge most clearly in the psychoanalytic treatment setting, repression and resistance, could themselves be unconscious, pointed up the need for an expanded concept of the ego as an organization that retains its original close relationship to consciousness and to external reality and yet performs a variety of unconscious operations in relation to the drives. Once the scope of the ego had been thus broadened, consciousness was redefined as a mental quality that, though exclusive to the ego, constitutes only one of its qualities or aspects.

No more comprehensive definition of the ego is available than the last one Freud was to give in 1938 in *An Outline of Psychoanalysis:*

> Here are the principle characteristics of the Ego. In consequence of the pre-established connection between sense and perception and muscular action, the ego has voluntary movement at its command. It has the task of self-preservation. As regards external events, it performs that task by becoming aware of stimuli, by storing up experiences about them (in the memory), by avoiding excessively strong stimuli (through flight), by dealing with moderate stimuli (through adaptation) and finally by learning to bring about expedient changes in the external world to its own advantage (through activity). As regards internal events, in relation to the id, it performs that task by gaining control over the demands of the instincts, by deciding whether they are to be allowed satisfaction, by postponing that satisfaction to times and circumstances favorable in the external world or by suppressing their excitations entirely. It is guided in its activity by consideration of the tension produced by stimuli, whether these tensions are present in it or introduced into it.

Thus, the ego controls the apparatus of motility and perception, contact with reality, and, through the mechanisms of defense available to it, the inhibition of primary instinctual drives.

The id. Freud borrowed the term "id" from Georg Groddeck, an internist who became a disciple of psychoanalysis, but suggested, in *The Ego and the Id*, that it might have originated with Nietzsche. Originally, it stood for all that was ego-alien. Thus, in contrast to his concept of the ego as an organized, problem-solving agent, Freud conceived of the id as a completely unorganized primordial reservoir of energy derived from the instincts, which is under the domination of the primary process. However, it is not synonymous with the unconscious. The structural viewpoint was unique in that it demonstrated that certain functions of the ego (the erection of defenses against the demands of the id) are unconscious and that, for the most part, the superego operates on an unconscious level as well.

The superego. The origins and function of the superego are described in detail below. In brief, the superego is the last of the structural components to develop, resulting from the resolution of the Oedipus complex. It is concerned with moral behavior, which is based, in turn, on unconscious behavioral patterns that were learned at early pregenital stages of development.

The structural model provides a useful means of expressing the nature of neurotic conflict. Essentially, neurotic conflict can be explained structurally as a conflict between the forces of the ego and the forces of the id. Most frequently, the superego participates in the conflict by allying itself with the ego and imposing demands in the form of conscience or guilt feelings. Occasionally, however, the superego may be allied with the id against the ego. This occurs in cases of severely regressed reactions, where the functions of the superego may become sexualized once more and take on the same impelling quality of the instinctual drives.

The external world may also participate in the neurotic conflict in that it may be perceived by the ego as an instinctual temptation or the voice of conscience or both.

ORIGINS OF THE ID

Freud postulated that the infant is endowed with an id, with instinctual drives that seek gratification, at birth. The infant does not, however, have the capacity to delay, control, or modify these drives. Similarly, in the matter of coping with the external world, he is completely dependent on the egos of other persons in his environment.

ORIGINS OF THE EGO

If we define the ego as a coherent system of functions for mediating between the instincts and the outside world, we must concede that the newborn has no ego. Developmental ego psychology is then faced with the problem of explaining the processes that permit the modification of the id and the concomitant genesis of the ego. Freud believed that the modification of the id occurs as a result of the impact of the external world on the drives. The pressures of external reality enable the ego to appropriate the energies of the id to do its work. In the process of formation, the ego seeks to bring the influences of the external world to bear on the id, to substitute the reality principle for the pleasure principle, and thereby contributes to its own further development. In summary, Freud emphasized the role of the instincts in ego development, particularly the role of conflict. At first, this conflict is between the id and the outside world; later it is between the id and the ego itself.

More recently, Heinz Hartmann and his co-workers have expanded and modified this theory by postulating the existence of primary autonomous ego functions, the development of which is independent of the drives and of conflict. Hartmann and his co-workers, Ernst Kris and Rudolph Loewenstein, have suggested that the ego does not differentiate from the id per se but that both develop from a common matrix. It follows, then, that the rudimentary apparatuses that underlie these primary autonomous ego functions—such as perception, motility, memory, and intelligence— are present at birth. This concept further implies that there may be congenital or genetically determined variations in ego functions. Although this hypothesis was, in fact, advanced by Freud in 1937, it has been greatly expanded and elaborated on by Hartmann and his colleagues over the past twenty-five years. Thus, a genetic view has been added to the theory of ego development.

In addition, Hartmann has elaborated on the role of these rudimentary ego apparatuses in the infant's coordinations with the object and the environment for the satisfaction of instinctual needs and drives. These early coordinations are the bases for what Hartmann has described as the adaptive function of the ego—that is, its function as mediator between external reality and the needs and demands of other psychic systems, the id and superego. The adaptive functions of the ego are related to Hartmann's concept of ego development. The optimal functioning of the organism requires the balance of these controlling forces: ego autonomy from the demands of the id and ego autonomy from the demands of the environment.

EVOLUTION OF THE EGO

The body ego.   At first, the infant is unable to differentiate his own body from the rest of the world. That is, he cannot distinguish between his own proprioceptive and other subjective perceptions and reality per se. Body and mind are one, in the sense that perceptual stimulation is a prerequisite for somatic development. The ego begins with the child's ability to perceive his body as distinct from the external world. From this point on, it is concerned with the ordering of reality into subjective and objective phenomena and with awareness of the relationship between these phenomena and of other complex relationships between current apperceptions and their memory.

Developmental determinants.   Much of contemporary psychoanalytic research has been devoted to the elucidation of those factors that facilitate or impede the development of ego functions. Investigations in this area, which have included the direct observation of infants, have provided considerable evidence of the relationship between gratification and frustration of drives and needs in the early months of life and the future fate of the ego. The crucial importance for ego development of adequate satisfaction of the infant's libidinal needs by the mother or mother surrogate has been stressed repeatedly. However, although it is less clearly understood and appreciated, a certain amount of drive frustration in infancy and early childhood is equally important for the development of a healthy ego. There is much evidence that maternal deprivation at significant stages of development will lead to the impairment of ego functions to varying degrees. But overindulgence of the child's instinctual needs will interfere with the development of the ego's capacity to tolerate frustration and, consequently, with its ability to regulate the demands of the id in relation to the outside world.

IDENTIFICATION AND INTROJECTION. Within this framework, psychoanalysis has described two psychic mechanisms that are specifically involved in the development of ego functions. The loss of the loved object or of a particularly gratifying relationship with the object is a painful experience at any stage of life, but it is particularly traumatic in infancy and early childhood, when the ego is not yet strong enough to compensate for the loss. Yet in the early years of life, the child is constantly subjected to such deprivation. In the normal course of events the young child does not suffer the actual loss of his parents, who are the primary objects at this stage of development, but he must endure constant alterations in his relationship with them. Moreover, at each stage in his development, he must endure the loss of the kind of gratification that was appropriate to the previous phase of his maturation but must now be given up.

The child attempts to retain the gratifications derived from these earlier relationships, at least in fantasy, through the process of identification. By this mechanism the aspects or qualities of the person who was once the center of the gratifying relationship are internalized and re-established as part of the developing ego. Freud believed identification played a fundamental role in the development and enrichment of the ego and called the character of the ego a "precipitate of abandoned object-cathexes."

Identification begins in the oral phase of development, and it is closely associated with the oral incorporative mode of this early period. Thus, the image of the loved object may be taken inside, much as the child first took in the food provided by the loved object. The psychological mechanism of symbolic incorporation—that is, the taking in of another person or of his or her qualities—is called introjection, and, in fact, this mechanism continues to influence character development long after the oral period.

There is some difference of opinion as to whether identification, as it applies to ego development, must be accompanied by introjection. Some authors believe, for example, that the expansion of the ego can result from direct imitation, without involving incorporation-introjection processes. On the other hand, Melanie Klein and her followers, who have studied the processes of incorporation and introjection extensively, credit very young infants with the capacity for complex processes of introjection and postulate that these mechanisms play a fundamental role at every stage of development. Clinical studies by the Kleinian group of the mechanisms of incorporation and introjection have greatly enhanced our understanding of the distortions in these mechanisms in psychosis.

Freud also suggested that identifications may occur out of love, rather than loss, simultaneously with object cathexis; that is, identification may occur before it has become necessary to give up the object. An example of this form of identification would be the hysteric who assumes the traits of her lover or the husband who takes on the characteristics of his spouse. In these instances the mechanism of identification serves to strengthen the ego, just as it does in the early stages of development. In this connection, too, increasing attention has been given in recent years to the infant's very early identification with the primary object (the mother), the close relationship between this phenomenon and the child's initial differentiation of himself from the object, and his progress from a state of primary narcissism to the beginning of early object relationships.

It must be emphasized that the types of identification described above lead to the strengthening of the ego and are compatible with the development of healthy object relationships. On the other hand, identification with the aggressor is a defensive maneuver, based on the child's need to protect himself from severe anxiety experienced in relation to the object. The child identifies with and incorporates the characteristics of the feared person, who is perceived as his attacker and on whom he is dependent, so that he may become allied with the aggressor rather than be his victim, so that he may share in his power rather than be powerless before him. Such identifications may impoverish the ego by burdening it with negative introjects; their contribution to the formation of rewarding object relationships and the development of ego skills is questionable.

Again, mechanisms such as identification with the aggressor are significant in that they direct our attention to the importance of the characteristics and qualities of the object itself for the child's ego development. Although Freud did not investigate this aspect of ego development in detail, it has been the focus of increasing attention in recent years, particularly in connection with the etiology of childhood psychosis.

A special type of identification with the parental imagoes occurs as a concomitant of the resolution of the oedipal conflict and gives rise to the formation of the superego, as described below. However, ego development does not end in the oedipal phase. The latency period, in particular, is an important growth phase for the acquisition of new ego strengths through learning, through the exploitation of motor skills, and through the development of a variety of object attachments and constructive identifications.

Significance of zones and modes in ego development.   Erik Erikson has made a major contribution to the zonal-modal model of ego development. He has postulated a parallel relationship between specific phases of ego or psychosocial development and specific phases of libidinal development, during which particular erotogenic zones are the loci of stimulation. This relationship may be projected to extend throughout the life cycle. Erikson's epigenetic theory of ego development describes the life tasks appropriate to specific phases of development. The characteristic successful or unsuccessful performance of these tasks has important implications for future development. For example, if task solution is successful in the oral period, basic trust will be established; if task solution is unsuccessful, mistrust will be the result, with concomitant impairment in ego functioning during the later stages of development. Autonomy versus shame and doubt are the extremes in the anal period, initiative versus guilt in the phallic phase, industry versus inferiority in latency, identity versus identity diffusion in adolescence, intimacy versus isolation in young adult life, generativity versus stagnation in adulthood, and integrity versus despair in maturity.

FUNCTIONS OF THE EGO

This discussion of ego functions is based on the preceding definition of the ego as a substratum of personality, comprising a group of functions that share in common the task of mediating between the instincts and the outside world. Thus, the ego is not synonymous with self, personality, or character.

Any attempt to draw up a complete list of ego functions would be arbitrary at best. Invariably, the lists of basic ego functions suggested by various authors differ from one another to varying degrees. This discussion will be limited to several functions that are generally conceded to be fundamental to the ego's operation.

Relation to reality. Freud always regarded the ego's capacity for maintaining a relationship to the external world among its principal functions. The character of its relationship to the external world may be divided into three components: (1) the sense of reality, (2) reality-testing, and (3) the adaptation to reality.

SENSE OF REALITY. The sense of reality originates simultaneously with the development of the ego. The infant first becomes aware of the reality of his own body sensations. Only gradually does he develop the capacity to distinguish a reality outside his body.

REALITY-TESTING. This refers to the ego's capacity for objective evaluation and judgment of the external world, which depends, in turn, on the primary autonomous functions of the ego, such as memory and perception. Because of the fundamental importance of reality-testing for negotiating with the outside world, its impairment may be associated with severe mental disorder. The development of the capacity to test reality (which is closely related to the progression from the pleasure to the reality principle), to distinguish fantasy from actuality, occurs gradually. This capacity, once gained, is subject to regression and temporary deterioration in children, even up to grade school age, in the face of anxiety, conflict, or intense instinctual wishes. However, this should not be confused with the breakdown of reality-testing referred to above, which occurs in adult psychopathology.

ADAPTATION TO REALITY. This refers to the capacity of the ego to utilize the individual's resources to form adequate solutions based on previously tested judgments of reality. Thus, it is possible for the ego to develop good reality-testing in terms of perception and grasp but to develop an inadequate capacity to accommodate the individual's resources to the situation as perceived. Adaptation is closely allied to the concept of mastery in respect to external tasks and to the instincts. It should be distinguished from adjustment, which may entail accommodation to reality at the expense of certain resources or potentialities of the individual. The function of adaptation to reality is closely related to the defensive functions of the ego.

Control and regulation of instinctual drives. The development of a capacity to delay immediate discharge of urgent wishes and impulses is essential if the ego is to assure the integrity of the individual and fulfill its role as mediator between the id and the outside world. The development of the capacity to delay or postpone instinctual discharge, like the capacity to test reality, is closely related to the progression in early childhood from the pleasure to the reality principle.

Furthermore, this progression parallels the development of the secondary process, or logical thinking, which aids in the control of drive discharge. Thus, the evolution of thought, from the initially prelogical primary process thinking to the more logical and deliberate secondary process thinking, is one of the means by which the ego learns to postpone the discharge of instinctual drives. For example, the representation in fantasy of instinctual wishes as fulfilled may obviate the need for urgent action that may not always serve the realistic needs of the individual. Similarly, the capacity to figure things out or anticipate consequences represents thought processes that are essential to the realistic functioning of the individual. Obviously, then, the ego's capacity to control instinctual life and to regulate thinking is closely associated with its defense function, discussed below.

Object relationships. The capacity for mutually satisfying object relationships is one of the fundamental functions of the ego. The significance of object relationships—and their disturbance—for normal psychological development and a variety of psychopathological states was fully appreciated relatively late in the development of classical psychoanalysis. The evolution in the child's capacity for relationships with others, which progresses from narcissism to social relationships within the family and then within the group, has been described by Anna Freud and Dorothy Burlingham in two books, *War and Children* (1943) and *Infants Without Families* (1944). Other writers have described the early stages in the relationship with the need-satisfying object and object constancy, which begins when the infant is 6 months old and which under normal circumstances undergoes progressive development from then on. This process may be disturbed by retarded development, regression, or, conceivably, by inherent—that is, genetic—defects or limitations in the capacity to develop object relationships. The development of object relationships is closely related to the concomitant evolution of drive components and the phase-appropriate defenses that accompany them.

Synthetic function of the ego. The synthetic function of the ego, which was described by Herman Nunberg in 1931, refers to the ego's integrative capacities; to its tendency to bind, unite, coordinate, and create; and to its tendency to simplify or generalize. In brief, the synthetic function is concerned with the overall organization and functioning of the ego, and it must enlist the cooperation of other ego functions in the course of its operation.

Primary autonomous ego functions. Although Freud referred to "primal, congenital ego variations" as early as 1937, this concept has been greatly expanded and clarified by Heinz Hartmann. As stated earlier, primary autonomous ego functions are based on rudimentary apparatuses that are present at birth; they develop outside of conflict with the id, in what Hartmann has called the "average expectable environment." Hartmann has included perception, intuition, comprehension, thinking, language, certain phases of motor development, learning, and intelligence among the functions in this conflict-free sphere. However, each of these functions might become involved in conflict secondarily in the course of development. For example, if aggressive, competitive impulses intrude upon the impetus to learn, this may evoke inhibitory reactions on the part of the ego.

Defense functions of the ego. It was pointed out earlier in this chapter that in his initial psychoanalytic theoretical formulations and, in fact, for a long time thereafter Freud considered repression to be virtually synonymous with defense. Repression was directed primarily against the impulses, drives, or drive representations, particularly against direct expressions of the sexual instinct, to conform with the demands of external reality. With the development of the structural view of the mind as comprising three provinces—id, ego, and superego—the function of defense was ascribed to the ego. However, only after Freud had formulated his final theory of anxiety, as described below, was it possible to study the operation of the various defense mechanisms—that is, their mobilization in response to danger signals. A systematic and comprehensive study of the defenses employed by the ego was presented for the first time by Anna Freud. In her classic contribution on *The Ego and the Mechanisms of Defense,* Miss Freud maintained that everyone, normal as well as neurotic, employs a characteristic repertoire of defense mechanisms, albeit to varying degrees. On the basis of her extensive clinical studies of children, she described their essential inability to tolerate excessive instinctual stimulation and discussed the processes whereby the primacy of such drives at various developmental stages evokes anxiety in the ego, which, in turn, produces a variety of defenses. With regard to adults, Miss Freud's psychoanalytic investigations led her to conclude that, although resistance is an obstacle to progress in treatment inasmuch as it impedes the emergence of unconscious material, it also constitutes a useful source of information concerning the ego's defense operations.

GENESIS OF DEFENSE MECHANISMS. In the early stages of development, defenses emerge as a result of the ego's struggles to mediate between the pressures of the id and the requirements and strictures of outside reality. At each phase of libidinal development, associated drive components evoke characteristic ego defenses. For example, introjection, denial, and projection are defense mechanisms associated with oral incorporative or oral sadistic impulses, whereas reaction formations, such as shame and disgust, develop in relation to anal impulses and pleasures. Defense mechanisms from earlier phases of development persist side by side with those of later periods. When defenses associated with pregenital phases of development tend to become predominant in adult life over more mature mechanisms, such as sublimation and repression, the personality retains an infantile cast.

The repertoire of defenses that an individual characteristically employs to deal with stress-evoking situations makes an important contribution to character. Character traits, such as excessive orderliness, are closely related to defenses but are distinguished from them by their greater role both in the overall functioning of the personality and in situations that are not associated with specific conflicts.

Abnormalities in the development of the functioning of ego defenses or defense mechanisms may have a fundamental relationship to the etiology of various kinds of psychopathology, but defenses are not, in themselves, pathological. On the contrary, they serve an essential function in maintaining normal psychological well-being.

Nevertheless, psychopathology may arise as the result of one of various possible alterations of normal defensive functioning. For example, in hysteria, the defense of repression is temporarily overwhelmed due to excessive sexual stimulation. This revival of previously repressed wishes calls for more desperate piecemeal efforts at renewed repression, which result in the formation of conversion or phobic symptoms. On the other hand, the individual may show an exaggerated development and overuse of certain defenses, as if the danger posed by infantile sexual and aggressive impulses were as great in adult life as it was perceived to be in childhood. This kind of hypervigilance is characteristic of obsessional personalities and obsessive-compulsive neurotics. Or the development of the ego and its defenses may itself be faulty, with excessive reliance placed on the denial-projection-distortion modes characteristic of the early oral or narcissistic phases of development. In that event, the defense mechanisms—although they permit limited functioning, particularly in the original family setting that may share these defensive patterns—cannot adequately equip the adult to meet the challenges of the external world—that is, to form object attachments, engage in heterosexual relationships, or cope with vocational competition. When the defenses fail, there may be a breakthrough of direct instinctual expressions and a regression in the ego's capacity to control motility, as exemplified in the schizophrenias.

CLASSIFICATION OF DEFENSES. It is possible to list the defenses employed by the ego according to a variety of classifications, none of which is all-inclusive or can take into account all the factors involved. For example, defenses may be classified developmentally—that is, in terms of the libidinal phase in which they arise. Denial, projection, and reality distortion would then be assigned to the oral phase of development and to the narcissistic stage of object relationships. However, certain defenses, such as magical thinking and regression, cannot be pinpointed in this way. Moreover, certain basic developmental processes, such as introjection and identification, may serve a defensive function as well under certain conditions.

The defenses have also been classified on the basis of the particular form of psychopathology with which they are commonly associated. Within this frame of reference, the obsessional defenses would include denial and distortion. But, as pointed out above, defensive operations are not limited to pathological conditions.

The defenses have also been classified according to whether they are simple—basic—mechanisms or complex, in which event a single defense would involve a combination or composite of simple mechanisms.

A brief description of several basic and complex defenses that are employed most frequently and have been investigated most thoroughly by psychoanalysts is presented below.

REPRESSION. Repression retains the central position it was accorded by Freud in relation to the defenses of the ego and in the formation of neurotic symptoms. It results in not being able to remember in those instances when what is forgotten is truly unconscious. Repression is directed at id material—wishes, impulses, and affects—and is particularly prominent in the inhibition of unacceptable sexual impulses at a phallic or genital level. Thus, repression is characteristic of hysteria, although it is used widely in other disorders as well. Repression may also be present in other defense mechanisms. For example, in sublimation, the original sexual drive may be repressed.

DISPLACEMENT. Displacement refers to the shifting of emotion or drive cathexis from one idea or object to another that resembles the original in some aspect or quality. As a defense, displacement permits the symbolic representation of the original idea or object by another idea or object that is less highly cathected or evokes less pain. However, as mentioned above in connection with Freud's theory of dreams, the unconscious aim of the associated impulse remains the same.

REACTION FORMATION. The basic defense of reaction formation enables the individual to express an unacceptable impulse by transforming it into its opposite. For example, hatred of a crucial person will be transformed into overt expressions of affection. Reaction formation is characteristic of obsessional neurosis, but it occurs in other forms of neuroses as well, and if it is employed with sufficient frequency at an early stage in ego development, it may be manifested as a character trait.

ISOLATION. As opposed to social isolation, which refers to the absence of object relationship, isolation as a mechanism of defense refers to the splitting or separation of an idea that is remembered from the affect that accompanied it and is repressed.

UNDOING. Undoing is an attempt to cancel out or nullify an act previously committed (in reality or fantasy) by certain counteractions. This mechanism is characteristic, in particular, of obsessive-compulsives, whose expiatory acts, rituals, and ceremonials often represent unconscious efforts to undo some forbidden act or to cancel the effects of a wish to which they have attributed the magical power of action.

RATIONALIZATION. The individual may advance rational explanations, which may or may not be valid, in an attempt to hide from himself and others the actual, usually instinctually determined, motives for his behavior.

INTELLECTUALIZATION. This defense, which is closely related to rationalization, refers to the excessive use of intellectual processes to avoid affective experience and expression. Borderline schizophrenics, who are emotionally unstable, frequently relate to others and themselves on an intellectual basis in an effort to maintain their hold on reality.

DENIAL. The basic defense of denial is used widely in normal as well as pathological states. Its use may vary considerably, however. It may refer only to the affect associated with a particular idea or event. Or there may be a massive denial of the experience itself or its memory. In any event, this defense cannot relegate an idea or affect to the unconscious. Consequently, it is maintained at considerable cost to the efficient operation of those ego functions related to conscious perception and the relation to reality. Consistent impairment of these functions through the excessive use of denial may be a precipitating factor in psychosis.

PROJECTION. This mechanism is characteristic of psychotic states, especially paranoid syndromes, but it is also used widely under normal conditions. In projection, the individual attributes his own feelings and wishes to another person because his ego is unable to assume the responsibility for these feelings or tolerate the painful affects they evoke. Projection is, therefore, associated with ego immaturity or vulnerability.

REGRESSION. Through this mechanism the ego attempts to return to an earlier libidinal phase or stage of functioning when gratification was assured in order to avoid the tension and conflict evoked at the present level of development. However, regression is a normal phenomenon as well. A certain amount of regression is essential for sleep and for orgasm in sexual intercourse. In addition, Ernst Kris postulated "regression in the service of the ego" as an essential concomitant of the creative process.

COUNTERPHOBIC MECHANISMS. The ego attempts to alleviate phobic anxieties by excessive and sometimes precipitous activity in specific relation to the area of concern.

WITHDRAWAL, AVOIDANCE, RESTRICTION OF THE EGO. Anna Freud considered these mechanisms, which differ only slightly, preliminary to defense. Specifically, they attempt to deal with tension- or conflict-producing situations by enabling the ego to remove itself from these sources of anxiety instead of erecting psychological defenses to deal with them.

INTROJECTION. As noted above, the process of introjection, whereby qualities of the loved object are internalized and become part of the subject's ego, plays a fundamental role in the early development of the ego. Introjection serves as a defense when it is used to obliterate the distinction between the subject and the loved object. Through introjection the painful awareness of separateness or the threat of loss that this implies is avoided.

IDENTIFICATION. Identification, which plays an equally crucial role in ego development, may also be used as a defense under certain circumstances. Identification with the loved object may serve as a defense against the anxiety or pain that accompanies separation from or loss of the object, whether real or threatened. Identification may occur out of guilt as well as love, in which event the subject identifies with a quality or symptom of the person who is the source of his guilt feelings for self-punitive purposes. The mechanism of identification with the aggressor described earlier may also be enlisted as a defense.

ACTING OUT. In the psychoanalytic treatment setting acting out refers to the discharge or gratification of some aspect of an unconscious conflict through action, without conscious awareness of the original elements of the conflict. Thus, acting out was perceived initially as a form of resistance to the treatment process. Its scope is sometimes broadened to include any substitution of action or direct gratification, including impulsive or destructive action, for remembering or talking about warded-off feelings and thoughts. However, to avoid possible confusion, its use should be restricted to the living out in action of warded-off memories when the links between the action and the memory are obscure to the patient.

SUBLIMATION. The function of sublimation extends well beyond that of a defense mechanism. It is, in addition, a fundamental outcome of the struggles among the various agencies of the mind and plays a major role in the individual's healthy psychological functioning in society. Essentially, sublimation refers to the process whereby the energy invested in a sexual aim is deflected to another aim, which is nonsexual and of greater social value. It is a defense insofar as direct sexual gratification is renounced in favor of the other aim. Sublimation differs from other defenses, however, in that a true resolution of the conflict between the ego and the id may occur concomitantly with respect to the libidinal aim in question. In that event, sublimations may become secondary autonomous ego functions insofar as they are independent of the drive or conflict.

CREATIVE ELABORATION. The specific instinctual conflicts that arouse anxiety may be elaborated and disguised in dreams, stories, and fantasies that represent the id-ego protagonists in new relationships to each other. The drive energy is thus deflected from its original objects, and the gratification provided by the imaginative processes may be substituted for satisfaction of the original instinctual aim. This mechanism differs from sublimation in that it is not related to social values. Creative elaboration may involve symbolism, identification, and other defense mechanisms.

CONCEPT OF THE SUPEREGO

Historical development. The concept of the superego, like the ego, has its historical origins in Freud's writings; the steps leading up to its formulation as a special agency of the mind can be traced to a paper written in 1896, entitled "Further Remarks on the Defense Neuro-Psychoses," in which he described obsessional ideas as "self-reproaches which have re-emerged in transmuted form and . . . relate to some sexual act that was performed with pleasure in childhood." The activity of a self-criticizing agency is also implicit in Freud's early discussions of dreams, which postulate the existence of a censor that does not permit unacceptable ideas to enter consciousness on moral grounds. He first discussed the concept of a special self-critical agency in 1914, when he published his exposition of narcissism. In "On Narcissism" Freud suggested that a hypothetical state of narcissistic perfection existed in early childhood; at this stage, the child was his own ideal. But as he grew up, the admonitions of others and his own self-criticism combined to destroy this perfect image of himself. In order to compensate for this lost narcissism when he had been his own ideal or in order to recover it, the child projects before him a new ideal or ego-ideal. It was at this point that Freud suggested that the psychic apparatus might have still another structural component, a special agency whose task it was to watch over the ego, to make sure it was measuring up to the ego-ideal. The concept of the superego evolved from these formulations of an ego-ideal and a second monitoring agency to ensure its preservation.

In the following year, 1915, in *Mourning and Melancholia*, Freud speaks again of "one part of the ego" that "judges it critically and, as it were, takes it as its object." He suggests that this agency, which is split off from the rest of the ego, is what we commonly call conscience. He further states that this self-evaluating agency can act independently, can become diseased on its own account, and should be regarded as a major institution of the ego. In 1921 Freud referred to this self-critical agency as the ego-ideal and held it responsible for the sense of guilt and for the self-reproaches that are typical in melancholia and depression. He had dropped his earlier distinction between an ego-ideal, or ideal self, and a self-critical agency, or conscience.

In 1923, in *The Ego and the Id*, Freud's concept of the superego included both these functions—that is, the superego represented the ego-ideal as well as conscience. He also demonstrated that the operations of the superego were mainly unconscious; thus, patients who were dominated by a deep sense of guilt lacerated themselves far more harshly on an unconscious level than they did consciously. The fact that guilt engendered by the superego might be eased by suffering or punishment was apparent in the case of neurotics who demonstrated an unconscious need for punishment. In later works, he elaborated on the relationship between the ego and the superego. Guilt feelings were ascribed to tension between these two agencies, and the need for punishment was an expression of this tension.

In one of his last discussions of the superego, in *Civilization and Its Discontents* in 1930, Freud expanded on its relationship to his evolving conception of the aggressive instinct. When an instinct undergoes repression, its libidinal aspects may be transformed into symptoms, whereas its aggressive components are transformed into a sense of guilt.

On another level, Freud related the development of the superego to the evolution of culture and to the relation of human beings to one another in society. In such moral precepts as "Love thy neighbor," which are aimed at controlling aggression, the cultural superego makes demands upon the individual from without, much as his personal superego dictates to him from within. Freud believed that the cultural superego, which represents the ideals of civilization, evolved from the impressions left by the personalities of great leaders—"men of overwhelming force of mind or men in which one of the human impulses has found its strongest and purest, and therefore often its most one-sided, expression." While Freud recognized that some limits on individual satisfaction were necessarily imposed by the demands of civilization, he lamented deeply the degree to which the individual must renounce instinctual gratification in order to conform to the social requirements of the larger group. These ideas, which Freud posed very tentatively, recognizing that his application of individual psychology to society was merely by analogy, have been adopted and greatly extended, often on a rather superficial level, in various discussions of the neurotic culture of our time.

Origins of the superego. The superego comes into being with the resolution of the Oedipus complex. During the oedipal period, the little boy wishes to possess his mother; the little girl wishes to possess her father. However, each must contend with a substantial rival, the parent of the same sex. The frustration of the child's positive oedipal wishes by this parent evokes intense hostility, which finds expression not only in overt antagonistic behavior but also in thoughts of killing the parent who stands in the way (along with any brothers or sisters who may also compete for the love of the desired parent).

Quite understandably, this hostility on the part of the child is unacceptable to the parents and, in fact, eventually becomes unacceptable to the child himself. In addition, the boy's sexual explorations and masturbatory activities may themselves meet with parental disfavor, which may even be underscored by real or implied threats of castration. These threats and, above all, the boy's observations that women and girls lack a penis convince him of the reality of castration. Consequently, he turns away from the Oedipus situation and enters the latency period of psychosexual development. He renounces the sexual expressions of the infantile phase.

Girls, when they become aware of the fact that they lack a penis, that they have come off badly, seek to redeem the loss by obtaining a penis or a baby from the father. Thus, as mentioned earlier, Freud pointed out that, although the anxiety surrounding castration brings the Oedipus complex to an end in boys, in girls it is the major precipitating factor. Girls renounce their oedipal strivings, first, because they fear the loss of the mother's love and, second, because of their disappointment over the father's failure to gratify their wish. However, the latency phase is not so well defined in girls as it is in boys. And their persistent interest in family relations is expressed in their play. Throughout grade school, for example, girls act out the roles of wife and mother in games that boys scrupulously avoid.

Evolution of the superego. But what is the fate of the object attachments that are given up with the resolution of the Oedipus complex? Freud's formulation of the mechanism of identification is relevant here. During the oral phase, the child is entirely dependent on his parents. When he advances beyond this stage and must abandon his earliest symbiotic ties with his parents, he forms initial identifications with them, which, however, follow the anaclitic model—that is, they are characterized by dependence on another. The dissolution of the Oedipus complex and the concomitant abandonment of object ties lead to a rapid acceleration of the identification process.

One might think, following the model proposed above, that the child would identify with the parent of the opposite sex after he has been forced to renounce his oedipal object ties, and to some degree this may, in fact, occur. However, under normal conditions, the striving toward masculinity in the boy and femininity in the girl leads to a stronger identification with the parent of the same sex. The problem is not simple; because of the bisexual potential of boys and girls, a child may emerge from the Oedipus complex with various admixtures of masculine and feminine identifications. Obviously, these identifications will have a great deal to do with his ultimate character formation and later object choices.

With specific reference to superego formation, these identifications with both parents become united and form a kind of precipitate within the ego, which then confronts the other contents of the ego as a superego. This identification with the parents is based on the child's struggles to repress the instinctual aims that were directed toward them, and it is this effort of renunciation that gives the superego its prohibiting character. It is for this reason, too, that the superego results to such a great extent from an identification with the parents' own superegos. Yet, because the superego evolves as a result of repression of the instincts, it has a closer relation to the id than does the ego itself. Its origins are more internal; the ego originates to a greater extent in the external world and is its representative.

Throughout the latency period and thereafter, the child (and later the adult) continues to build upon these early identifications through contact with teachers, heroic figures, and admired persons, who form his moral standards, his values, and his ultimate aspirations and ideals.

The child moves into the latency period endowed with a superego that is, as Freud put it, "the heir of the Oedipus complex." Its strictness at first may be compared to the imperative nature of the demands of the id before it developed. The child's conflicts with his parents continue, of course, but now they are largely internal, between the ego and the superego. In other words, the standards, restrictions, commands, and punishments that were imposed previously by the parents from without are internalized in the child's superego, which now judges and guides his behavior from within, even in the absence of his parents.

Clearly, this initially punitive superego must be modified and softened so that eventually it can permit adult sexual object choice and fulfillment. Adolescence poses a unique developmental hurdle in this regard. With the heightening of sexual and aggressive drives that is characteristic during this period, there is a threatened revival of the abandoned incestuous ties to the parents and the undermining of the efforts of the superego. Often, the rebellious acting out behavior of teenagers can be understood in terms of instinctual release that the superego has failed to curb. However, their behavior may be deflected from the more threatening attachment to the parents to their representatives in the external world. In contrast, the superego of the ascetic, oversubmissive, or intellectual adolescent has responded to the threat posed by these heightened drives with renewed vigilance and intensified instinctual renunciation. The task of adolescence is to modify the oedipal identifications with the parents. Ideally, such modification will enable the choice of a love object that is not motivated entirely by the need for a parent substitute or based exclusively on the need to rebel against their internalized images.

Current investigations of the superego. The exploration of the superego and its functions did not end with Freud, and such studies remain of active interest. Obviously, it is beyond the scope of this chapter to discuss this work in detail. However, reference should be made in particular to the fact that recent interest has focused on the difference between the super-ego and the ego-ideal, a distinction that Freud periodically revived and abandoned. At present, the term superego refers primarily to a self-critical, prohibiting agency that bears a close relationship to aggression and aggressive identifications. The ego-ideal, on the other hand, is a kinder agency, based, as pointed out above, on a transformation of the abandoned perfect state of narcissism, or self-love, that existed in early childhood and has been integrated with positive elements of identifications with the parents. In addition, the concept of an ideal object, the idealized object choice, has been advanced, as distinct from the ideal self.

A second focus of recent interest has been the contribution of the drives and object attachments formed in the pre-oedipal period to the development of the superego. These pregenital, especially anal, precursors of the superego are generally thought to provide the very rigid, strict, and aggressive qualities of the superego. These stem from the child's projection of his own sadistic drives and his primitive concept of justice based on retaliation, which he attributes to his parents during this period. The harsh emphasis on absolute cleanliness and propriety that is sometimes found in very rigid individuals and in obsessional neurotics is based to some extent on this sphincter morality of the anal period. Parenthetically, it should be noted that Melanie Klein's contention that the Oedipus complex, along with the superego, is well established within the first year of life derives from another theoretical framework and is not to be confused with the concept of pregenital precursors of the superego as postulated by classical psychoanalytic theory.

REFORMULATION OF THE THEORY OF ANXIETY

It was pointed out earlier that for many years Freud regarded neurotic anxiety as transformed libido and distinguished between such morbid distress and realistic fear of external danger. In contrast to this theory, which approached anxiety from the standpoint of the drives, the new theory, first described in 1926, attacked the problem from the standpoint of the ego. It set aside the biological approach to anxiety, which is now a subject of research chiefly in disciplines outside of psychoanalysis proper, and studied the function of this affect in relation to a variety of threats to the organism from within or without. Both real anxiety and neurotic anxiety were now viewed as occurring in response to a danger to the organism. In real anxiety the threat emanates from a known danger outside the individual; neurotic anxiety is precipitated by an unknown danger, not necessarily external.

Danger situations.   Freud distinguished two kinds of anxiety-provoking situations. In the first, for which the phenomenon of birth was the prototype, anxiety occurs as a result of excessive instinctual stimulation that the organism does not have the capacity to bind or handle. In this type of situation, which arises because of the helpless state of the individual, the excessive accumulation of instinctual energy overruns the protective barriers of the ego, and a panicky state or trauma results. These traumatic states are most likely to occur in infancy or childhood, when the ego is immature; however, they may also occur in adult life, notably in psychotic turmoil or panic states, when the ego organization is overwhelmed.

However, in the more common situation, which occurs after the defensive system has matured, anxiety arises in anticipation of danger rather than as its result, although the affect may be experienced subjectively as if the danger had already occurred. In these situations the emotion of anxiety serves a protective function, signaling the approach of danger, and may arise because the individual has learned to recognize at a preconscious or unconscious level aspects of a situation that were once traumatic. Thus, signal anxiety serves to mobilize protective measures that are then directed toward averting the danger and preventing a traumatic situation from arising. The individual may employ avoidance mechanisms to escape from a real or imagined danger from without or bring to bear psychological defenses on the part of the ego from within to guard against or reduce the quantity of instinctual excitation. According to this theory, neurotic symptoms—phobias, for example—indicate an imperfection in the psychic apparatus; the defensive activity of the ego has not succeeded in coping adequately with the unwelcome drive. As a result, mental conflict persists, and the danger that actually arose from within is now treated as though it had its origins in the external world, at least in part. Thus, neurosis is the result of a failure in the defensive function of the ego and results in a distortion of the ego's relationship to some aspect of the outside world. In psychosis, this failure of defensive function is more complete, and greater portions of external reality are perceived as dangerous; greater distortions of the ego become necessary in order to accommodate concomitant distortions in the view of the outside world.

CHARACTERISTIC DANGER SITUATIONS. Each stage of the child's development is accompanied by characteristic danger situations appropriate to the issues that are pertinent to that particular phase. Thus, the earliest danger situation, which occurs when the child is most immature and helpless psychologically and physiologically, is the loss of the primary object, the person on whom he is entirely dependent. Later, when the value of the object itself is perceived, the fear of losing the object's love exceeds the fear of losing the object itself. In the phallic phase, the fear of bodily injury or castration is most prominent. And this, too, may be thought of as fear of a loss—in this instance, of a narcissistically treasured part of the body. In the latency period, the characteristic fear is that the parental representatives, in the form of the superego, will be angry with, punish, or cease to love the child. In each of these phases, anxiety arises in the ego. Freud also noted that, although each of these determinants of anxiety was appropriate to a particular period, they could exist side by side. Furthermore, the individual's anxiety reaction to a particular danger situation might occur after he had emerged from the developmental phase with which that situation was associated. The persistence in later years of anxiety reactions that were appropriate to various pregenital phases of development has important implications for our understanding of psychopathology.

Implications of the new theory of anxiety. The new theory of anxiety is of great potential value in that it may help to further our understanding of a variety of psychological phenomena. At the same time, however, several fundamental questions remain unanswered. For example, we need to acquire further understanding regarding the conditions or circumstances under which the ego becomes overwhelmed by anxiety, beyond its precipitation by the anticipation of danger. Similarly, little is known about the normal psychology of anxiety; more knowledge is needed about the quantitative and qualitative factors that determine whether a given amount of anxiety of a particular nature will spur ego development through mobilization and stimulation of the individual's ego potential or whether the same quantity of anxiety with the same quality will impede ego development by drawing the existing ego defenses into excessive conflict formation.

It was in relation to his new theory of anxiety that Freud returned to the concept of defense, a term he had once before abandoned in favor of repression. And it was his insight into the nature of anxiety that led to the formulation of the defense mechanisms cited above. Thus, he now saw repression as one, albeit the cardinal one, of a variety of possible defenses employed by the ego, which now also included reaction formation, isolation, undoing, etc. With the development of the new theory of anxiety, the ego was no longer a passive agency helpless in the face of the demands of the id and the outside world. Now it was credited not only with serving as a kind of advance guard that could signal danger ahead of time but also with having at its disposal a variety of possible responses to danger from without or within that enabled the organism to meet the demands and threats of the drives and the outside world.

PSYCHOANALYTIC CONCEPT OF CHARACTER

HISTORICAL DEVELOPMENT

The concept of character may vary widely in meaning, depending on whether it is used in a moralistic, literary, sociological, or general sense. The application of the concept in psychoanalysis has remained restricted, despite the fact that the theoretical propositions that have been advanced concerning the meaning of character have undergone an evolution that parallels the development of psychoanalytic thought. Thus, during the period when Freud was developing his theories regarding the erotogenic zones, he noted the relationship between certain character traits and particular bodily sensations or sexual components. For example, he recognized that obstinacy, orderliness, and parsimoniousness were associated with anality and with the pleasures derived from withholding or expelling feces; that ambition was related to urethral erotism; generosity to orality, etc. And he concluded, in his paper on "Character and Anal Erotism," that permanent character traits represented "unchanged prolongations of the original instincts, or sublimations of those instincts, or reaction formations against them."

In 1913 Freud made an important distinction between neurotic symptoms and character traits: Neurotic symptoms come into being as a result of the failure of repression and the return of the repressed; character traits owe their existence to the success of repression or, more accurately, the defense system, which has achieved its aim through reaction formation and sublimation. Later, in 1923, with increased understanding of the phenomenon of identification and the designation of the ego as a coherent system of functions, the relationship of character to ego development came into sharper focus. At this point Freud observed that the replacement of object attachments by identification, which set up the lost object inside the ego, also contributed to character formation. And in 1932 Freud emphasized the particular importance of identification with the parents for the construction of character as well as superego formation.

Several of Freud's disciples made important contributions to the concept of character during this period. A major share of Karl Abraham's efforts was devoted to the investigation and elucidation of the relationship between oral, anal, and genital erotism and various character traits. Wilhelm Reich made an important contribution to the psychoanalytic understanding of character in the 1920's when he described the intimate relationship between resistance in treatment and the character traits of the patient. Reich's observation that resistance typically appeared in the form of these specific traits anticipated Anna Freud's later formulations concerning the relationship between resistance and typical ego defenses.

CURRENT CONCEPTS OF CHARACTER

The development of psychoanalytic ego psychology has led to an increasing tendency to include character and character traits among the properties of the ego, superego, and ego-ideal, although they are not synonymous with any of these. The emphasis has been extended from an interest in specific character traits to a consideration of character and its formation in general. Thus, psychoanalysis has come to regard character as the pattern of adaptation to instinctual and environmental forces that is typical or habitual for a given individual. The character of a person is distinguished from the ego by virtue of the fact that it refers largely to directly observable behavior and styles of defense and of acting, thinking, and feeling. The clinical value of the concept of character has been recognized by psychiatrists as well as psychoanalysts and, in fact, has become a meeting ground for the two disciplines.

EVOLUTION OF CHARACTER

The formation of character and character traits results from the interplay of multiple factors. Innate biological predisposition plays a role in character formation in both its instinctual and ego anlage. The interaction of id forces with early ego defenses and environmental influences, most notably the parents, constitutes a major determinant in the development of character. And various early identifications and imitations of other human beings leave their lasting stamp upon character. The degree to which the ego has developed a capacity to tolerate delay in drive discharge and to neutralize instinctual energy as a result of early identifications and defense formations determines, for example, the later emergence of such character traits as impulsiveness. A number of authors have stressed the particularly close association between character traits and the development of the ego-ideal. In this respect the psychoanalytic concept of character parallels society's use of the term "character" in a moral sense.

The exaggerated development of certain character traits at the expense of others may lead to character disorders in later life; at other times, such distortions in the development of character traits produce a vulnerability or predisposition to the psychoses. These concepts are expanded in the following part of the chapter in relation to specific forms of psychopathology.

PSYCHOPATHOLOGY: THE PSYCHOANALYTIC THEORY OF NEUROSIS

Psychoanalytic theories concerning mental disorder have undergone extensive expansion and modification since Freud discovered the free association method of investigation. However, these theories have retained their emphasis on the elucidation of etiological factors rather than the mere description of symptoms. By 1906 Freud had succeeded in understanding the psychological processes underlying many mental disorders to a degree sufficient to permit him to classify them on the basis of psychopathology. At that point in his investigations, Freud's theories contained all the major elements of present-day psychoanalytic concepts of psychopathology. He had advanced initial hypotheses concerning the psychological mechanisms of neuroses, character disorders, perversions, and psychoses. Indeed, the investigations of Freud and his followers thereafter yielded only additions and minor revisions in his earlier theories on psychopathology.

HISTORICAL EVOLUTION

Early concepts. Cases of hysteria treated by the cathartic method, a modified form of hypnotherapy, led Freud to conclude that hysterical symptoms were caused by unconscious memories of events. These memories were accompanied by the strong emotions that had been elicited originally, at the time these events actually occurred, and that had not been expressed or discharged adequately. On the basis of this conclusion, Freud hypothesized that hysterical symptoms were the result of psychic traumata in individuals congenitally or genetically predisposed to the development of such phenomena. Although this theory differed from his earlier biological concept of neurasthenia in that it provided a purely psychological explanation, it too proved to be an oversimplification.

At first, Freud believed that excessive masturbation or nocturnal emissions gave rise to the symptoms typical of neurasthenia—fatigue, listlessness, flatulence, constipation, headache, and dyspepsia. He distinguished anxiety neurosis, which was characterized principally by anxiety attacks, from the syndrome of neurasthenia. Anxiety neurosis was related etiologically to states of activity that produced sexual stimulation or excitement but did not provide an adequate outlet for discharge. He cited coitus interruptus or lovemaking without sexual gratification as examples. Thus, as late as 1906, Freud believed that the symptoms of neurasthenia and anxiety neurosis represented the somatic effect of disturbances in sexual metabolism that, most likely, were biochemical in nature, and referred to these as actual neuroses as opposed to hysteria and obsessions, which he described as psychoneuroses. Of particular interest is the fact that these classifications stressed the etiology of these disorders rather than symptomatology. Freud assumed that drive energies that should have been discharged in a sexual climax created a state of psychic tension too great for the ego to master, thus producing anxiety.

RELEVANCE OF CLINICAL DATA FOR THEORY FORMATION

As the free association method continued to provide new insights into the origins of psychopathology, Freud revised and expanded his theories. Psychic conflict was now recognized as an element in the production of psychoneurotic symptoms. This required that he extend his earlier theory of hysterical and obsessional symptoms as caused by a forgotten event of the past with concomitant emotions that had not been adequately discharged. Originally, Freud maintained that a psychic event or experience could be considered pathogenic if it was repugnant to the individual's conscious self—if, for example, it violated his ethical and moral standards to the degree that it must be consciously repudiated. Hysteria, most obsessions, and many phobias were understood in this way, although some phobias (such as agoraphobia) and some obsessions (such as doubting mania) were described as actual neuroses.

Theory of infantile sexuality. The fact that almost invariably in the course of treatment his patients recalled a previously forgotten sexual experience that had occurred in childhood led Freud to hypothesize that mental illness was the psychic consequence of a sexual seduction by a child or an adult at an early stage in the patient's development. His assumption that sexual seduction had actually occurred proved incorrect. But the basic proposition that the roots of psychoneurosis lie in a disturbance in early sexual development remains unshaken and is the cornerstone of the psychoanalytic theory of neurotic disorder.

Further clinical study led to the conclusion that these memories of sexual seduction in childhood were actually fantasies, although the patients themselves believed in their reality. Re-examination of the data elicited through free association in this connection enabled Freud to formulate the theory of infantile sexuality, which stated that sexual interests and activities were a normal part of human psychic life from earliest infancy and were not limited to traumatic events. Nevertheless, despite these psychological findings, Freud continued to stress the importance of the patient's sexual constitution and heredity in the etiology of the psychoneuroses.

Progress in elucidating the precise nature of such constitutional factors has been very slow. In contrast, our knowledge of experiential etiological factors has increased. The discovery that infantile sexuality is a normal phenomenon narrowed the gap between the normal and the psychoneurotic and enabled Freud to elucidate the origins of the sexual perversions and their relationship to both normal and psychoneurotic functioning. The abnormal persistence in adult sexual life of some component of infantile sexuality might lead to perversion. However, in the normal course of events, some components of infantile sexuality were repressed and others were integrated into adult sexuality at puberty, with genital primacy. Other insights followed. Excessive repression creates instability, so that in later life there is a greater likelihood that precipitating events will cause a failure of repression. In that event, infantile sexual impulses will emerge from the unconscious, at least to some degree, in the form of psychoneurotic symptoms.

Psychology of dreams. Freud's study of dreams showed that the dream the sleeper remembered, the manifest dream, represented a compromise between one or more repressed impulses and those psychic forces that opposed the entrance of such impulses into conscious thought and behavior. Neurotic symptoms represented a similar compromise with one exception: The latent, instinctual wish that underlay the manifest dream might or might not be a sexual one, but the repressed impulses that produced neurotic symptoms were always sexual. On the other hand, the meaning of neurotic symptoms, like the elements of a manifest dream, lies in their latent or unconscious content. They are disguised and distorted expressions of unconscious sexual fantasies. Part or all of the sexual conflict of the psychoneurotic patient is expressed in his symptoms.

CURRENT CONCEPTS OF NEUROSIS

The theory of neurosis (used in the traditional sense to refer to hysteria, obsessional neuroses, and the phobias) is central to psychoanalytic concepts of psychopathology. Neuroses develop under the following conditions: (1) There is an inner conflict between drives and fears that prevents drive discharge. (2) Sexual drives are involved in this conflict. (3) The conflict has not been worked through to a realistic solution. Instead, the drives that seek discharge have been expelled from consciousness through repression or another defense mechanism. (4) The repression merely succeeded in rendering the drives unconscious; it did not deprive them of their power and make them innocuous. Consequently, the repressed tendencies have fought their way back into consciousness, disguised as neurotic symptoms. (5) Finally, an inner conflict will lead to neurosis in adolescence or adulthood only if a neurosis, or a rudimentary neurosis based on the same type of conflict, existed in early childhood.

DEVELOPMENT SCHEMA OF THE ETIOLOGY OF NEUROSIS

Early childhood. In the course of development, many vicissitudes may contribute to the future malfunctioning or malformation of the psychic apparatus. Maternal deprivation in the first few months of life may impair ego development in a manner that is particularly devastating to its integrative capacities. Failure to make the necessary identifications, either because of overindulgence or because of excessive frustration, interferes with the ego's task of mediating between the instincts and the environment, with consequent limitations of drive discharge and restriction of the ego's capacity to obtain pleasure and assert itself usefully. Lack of capacity for equitable expression of drives, especially aggressive ones, may lead the individual to turn them onto himself and to become overtly self-destructive. Inconsistency, excessive harshness, and/or undue permissiveness on the part of the parents may result in the disordered functioning of the superego. Instinctual conflict may impair the ego's capacity for sublimation, resulting in excessive inhibition of its autonomous functions. Severe conflict that cannot be dealt with through symptom formation may lead to severe restrictions in ego functioning and the impairment of the capacity to learn and to develop new skills.

Puberty and adult love. When the ego has been weakened, a shock or traumatic event in later life that threatens survival or appears to— especially when combined with external factors that further weaken ego resiliency, such as toxic conditions or exhaustion—may break through the ego defenses. A large amount of libido is then required to master the resultant excitation. But the libido thus mobilized has been withdrawn from the supply normally applied to external objects and from the ego itself, and this further diminishes the strength of the ego and produces a sense of inadequacy.

In summary, precipitating factors in neuroses are experiences that disturb the balance between warded-off impulses and warding-off forces. Increase in the warded-off drive may be absolute, as at puberty or the climacteric, due to the physiological intensification of sexual drives at these times. Or there may be a relative increase in a specific warded-off drive at the expense of other instinctual demands, as in the case of conscious or unconscious temptation or stimulation of a particular wish.

Disappointments or frustrations of adult strivings can revive infantile longings that may be dealt with through symptom formation or further regression. Decrease in the warding-off forces due to fatigue, intoxication, sickness, or overexacting tasks may loosen previously effective defenses against drive derivatives and precipitate a neurotic or even a psychotic illness. As long as the warded-off instincts cannot be tolerated in consciousness, the ego has no choice but to form symptoms or to modify its aims so that the unfulfilled strivings become less urgent.

SECONDARY GAINS OF NEUROSIS

The reduction of tension and conflict through neurotic illness is the primary purpose or gain of the disorder. The ego, however, in making the best of it, may try to gain advantages from the external world via the illness—by provoking pity in order to get attention and sympathy, by manipulating others, or even by receiving monetary compensation. Similarly, the patient may imply to others that his suffering entitles him to a compensatory reward of pleasure. These are the secondary gains of the illness.

Each form of neurosis has its characteristic and predominant form of secondary gain. In phobias (anxiety hysteria) there is a regression to childhood, when one was still protected. Gaining attention through dramatic acting out and, at times, deriving material advantages are characteristic of conversion hysteria. Frequently, in compulsive neurosis there is a narcissistic gain through pride in illness. In the organ neuroses (psychosomatic states), psychic conflicts are denied by projecting them onto the physical sphere. In the psychoses, the warding-off of a painful idea, experience, or frustration in the outside world leads to severe regression, which requires that the patient be taken care of, thus satisfying his extreme dependency needs.

Brenner has summarized the contemporary psychoanalytic concept of mental disorder as follows:

> In terms of modern psychoanalytic theory, what we refer to clinically as mental disorders can best be understood and formulated as evidences of malfunction of the psychic apparatus to various degrees and in various ways. As usual, we can best orient ourselves if we adopt a genetic, or developmental approach.

NOSOLOGY

Conversion hysteria. Conversion hysteria provides a defense against overintense libidinal stimulation by means of a transformation or conversion of psychical excitation into physical innervation. As a result, various alterations of motor function or sensation may occur. The innervation is not haphazard; it represents a genitalization of the particular part of the body associated with repressed unconscious wishes directed toward a love object. Fixation of the phallic stage of psychosexual development, a tendency to libidinize thoughts and images, and frustration in external life in relation to strong unconscious fantasies are etiological factors.

The change in physical function that occurs gives expression, in distorted form, to instinctual impulses that had been repressed previously. However, conversion symptoms are not simply somatic expressions of affects but very specific representations of thoughts that can be retranslated, through the free association method, from their somatic language into words. The syndromes of conversion are unique in every individual; and in each instance the specific type of distortion is determined by the historical events that created the repression. The distortion mechanisms employed in dreams are employed in conversion hysteria as well—condensation, symbolism, displacement, etc.

PATHOGENESIS AND SYMPTOMATOLOGY. Usually, hysterical spells or attacks, which are rarely encountered in current clinical practice, are pantomimic expressions of rather complicated fantasies relating to the child's concept of his parents' sexual relations during the oedipal period. However, the hysterical seizure may also express pregenital actions that are regressive substitutes for the original oedipal fantasies. Some attacks are less specifically sexual and occur in the form of convulsions; as emotional outbursts or moods that appear to be entirely unmotivated; or as screaming, crying, or laughing spells. Related to the seizures are various bizarre symptoms, including the sudden appearance or disappearance of normal physical needs, attacks of hunger or thirst, an urgent need to defecate or urinate, and difficulties in breathing.

In monosymptomatic conversions the somatic innervation expresses the memory of an event that took place in the forgotten situation. For example, Breuer's patient, Anna O., had a paralysis of her arm whenever she was unconsciously reminded of her feelings for her father. (At the time her father died, she had been sitting at his bedside with her arm pressed against the chair at the side of the bed.) The motor disturbance represents a defense against an action, specifically an action associated with an objectionable infantile impulse. Hysterical pain may represent a signal or warning not to yield to the pleasant sensations associated with the memory of a painful episode. Pain originally experienced by the patient himself recurs in the conversion symptoms as a substitute for the pleasant excitement once connected with it. At times, the hysterical pains, imitated in the conversion symptoms, have been experienced not by the patient but by another person with whom the patient identifies in producing his symptom. Freud's patient Dora illustrated hysterical identification with a rival by developing a cough like that of Frau K., with whom she unconsciously competed for Herr K. A female patient whose hysteria is due to her unresolved Oedipus complex may make an identification not with her rival, her mother, but with her beloved father. In this way the girl struggles to free herself of the frustrating love for the father; she may then seek to satisfy negative oedipal wishes by taking her mother as a love object. The most frequent form of hysterical identification takes place with an object with whom the patient has no genuine object relationship. It is formed on the basis of identical ideological needs. Freud used an hysterical epidemic in a girls' school to illustrate this phenomenon: A girl reacts with a fainting spell to a love letter, and the other girls in the school get fainting spells as well. The unconscious meaning is, "We would like to get love letters too." There may also be multiple identifications by a single patient, as exemplified by cases of multiple personality described in the literature.

Hysterical dream states are closely related to seizures. The day dreams, which represent derivatives of the repressed oedipal fantasies, involuntarily take possession of the personality, thereby removing the patient from reality. A mixture of hysterical spells and hysterical dream states is represented by the conversion symptom of sleepwalking. The typical aim is the wish to participate in adults' sexual night life. Other alterations in states of consciousness, such as amnesic or dissociative states, also result from the repression or warding-off of an intolerable aspect of infantile sexual life that has been revived by current sexual stimuli. Hysterical disturbances of the senses represent an attempt to reject upsetting sexual perceptions.

CHOICE OF NEUROSIS. Somatic compliance symptoms described above illustrate that the entire cathexis of the objectionable impulses appears to be condensed into a definitive physical function. The choice of the afflicted region may be determined by the unconscious sexual fantasies and the corresponding erogenicity of the afflicted part, by physical injury or a change in a part of the body that increases its susceptibility, by the nature of the situation in which the decisive repression occurred, and by the ability of the organ to express symbolically the unconscious drive in question. As is well known, hysteria may imitate a wide variety of diseases, which complicates the clinical picture considerably.

Phobia. Phobia, which is often referred to as anxiety hysteria, is an abnormal fear reaction caused by a paralyzing conflict due to an increase of sexual excitation attached to an unconscious object. The fear is avoided by displacing the conflict onto an object or situation outside the ego system. After this displacement has occurred, the readiness to develop anxiety is bound to the specific situation that precipitated the first anxiety attack. If situations occur that duplicate or represent the original event symbolically, it will become manifest. The ego fights off the anxiety through states of inhibition, such as impotence and frigidity, or through avoidance of objects that have become connected with unconscious conflicts either through historical associations or through their symbolic significance.

PATHOGENESIS. The manifestations of phobias are protean. As the degree of displacement increases, the connection between the fear situation and the original instinctual conflict becomes more concealed. The feared situations or persons have a specific unconscious signficance and in a distorted way symbolize either a forbidden gratification or a punishment for an unconscious impulse or a combination of both. The advantage of the displacement is that the original offensive idea does not become conscious. In Freud's famous case history of "little Hans," the boy's fear of a horse instead of his father helped him to avoid hating his father, by whom he was threatened and whom he also loved. Projection from an internal danger onto an external one, such as a wolf, that exists chiefly in the imagination has another advantage: Wolves are seen only in picture books, which need not be opened, or at the zoo, where one does not have to go very often. Although the objects or situations from which the phobic individual flees represent the threatening parents primarily, he is also in flight from his own impulses; even the fear of castration, which is perceived as an external threat, arises primarily as a consequence of the child's own phallic impulses.

SYMPTOMS. The patient's history, the nature of the drives warded-off, and the mechanisms of defense employed determine the clinical symptoms. Phobias about infection and touching often express the need to avoid dirt and show that the patient has to defend himself against anal-erotic temptations. Fear of open streets and stage fright may be a defense against exhibitionistic wishes. Anxieties about high places, closed places, falling, cars, trains, and airplanes are developed to fight pleasurable sensations connected with stimulation involving the equilibrium.

As a rule, the first neurotic reactions in children have the character of anxiety hysteria. With regard to adults, the onset of phobic reactions typically occurs at a time of crisis in the sexual life. Fixation at the phallic stage, sexual frustrations, the presence of an external factor that may weaken the ego, increases in libidinal excitement, and a particular susceptibility to anxiety reactions are the most common etiological factors.

Obsessional neurosis. The obsessional or obsessive-compulsive neurosis is characterized by persisting or urgently recurring thoughts and repetitively performed behavior that bear little relation to the patient's realistic requirements and are experienced by him as foreign or intrusive.

PATHOGENESIS. The obsessional neurosis comes about as a result of the separation of affects from ideas or behavior by the defense mechanisms of undoing and isolation, by regression to the anal-sadistic level, or by turning the impulses against the self. As a defense against a painful idea in the unconscious, the affect is displaced onto some other, indirectly

associated idea, one more tolerable, which in turn becomes invested with
an inordinate quantity of affect. As mentioned earlier, Freud described
obsessional ideas as self-reproaches that have re-emerged from repression
in a transmuted form. He also suggested that they relate to some sexual
act that was performed with pleasure in childhood. Nevertheless, in early
childhood there are few indications of the development of obsessional
tendencies. Moreover, usually at the time such trends develop in latency,
no self-reproach is attached to the memory of earlier pleasurable activities.
However, a primary defense system, the superego, develops at approximately this point; it consists of general conscientiousness, a sense of
shame, and self-distrust, now referred to as character defenses. A period of
apparent health or successful defense functioning may occur before the
onset of the illness. The period of illness proper is distinguished by the
return of repressed memories in the form of obsessive-compulsive symptoms—that is, by the failure of the character defenses. The obsessional
ideas that emerge are derivatives that express the warded-off drives. Sometimes they preserve their character as impulses. Sometimes the original
drive cannot be readily discerned, and the patient is aware only of ideas
that must be thought about, which indicates that the energy associated
with the original impulse has been diverted to a more neutral idea.

In other words, compulsions and obsessive symptoms are a condensation of both instinctual and anti-instinctual forces. In some instances—in
obsessions related to incestuous or murderous ideas, for example—the
manifest clinical picture reveals the direct instinctual aspect more clearly.
In other instances, as when symptoms obviously express the defensive or
punishing commands of the superego, the anti-instinctual forces are predominant. Actually, the individual tries to protect himself from the
threatened loss of his self-respect, which is precipitated by the guilt feelings occasioned by the disapproval of the superego rather than the loss of
love or castration. As mentioned above, the onset of obsessive-compulsive
neurosis occurs relatively late in childhood because it depends on the formation of the superego. The introjection of the parents into the superego
explains the relative predominance of punitive and expiatory symptoms
that affect the total personality of the patient.

A phobia may be transformed into an obsession. Certain situations
must be avoided by the phobic person, and he exerts great effort to ensure
this avoidance, to the degree that in time these efforts assume an obsessive-
compulsive character. Other obsessions may then develop so remote from
the situation that was the original source of fear that the avoidance is
assured. For example, touching rituals may replace taboos; washing compulsions take the place of the fear of dirt; social rituals supersede social
fears; sleeping ceremonials replace fears of falling asleep.

It has already been stated that, in the obsessive-compulsive neurosis,
fixation of libido at the anal-sadistic stage has occurred. Concomitantly,
ego development has been arrested at the accompanying stage of omnipo-

tence of thought. Factors that result in frustration of post-anal-sadistic impulses, usually of a phallic nature, or that impede more mature ego functioning will lead to the precipitation of overt symptomatology. Defenses are first directed against the phallic-oedipal drives, but, as regression occurs, they are directed against the anal-sadistic impulses themselves. External circumstances that remobilize the repressed infantile sexual conflicts and disturb the hitherto effective equilibrium between the repressing and repressed forces may precipitate acute cases of the neurosis. The more frequent chronic type continues more or less without interruption from adolescence. However, particular external circumstances may precipitate exacerbations from time to time if the defenses become less effective or the impulses defended against more unbearable. Freud's most important clinical study of this syndrome was his case history of the "Rat Man" in "Notes on a Case of Obsessional Neurosis."

Organ neuroses (psychophysiologic disorders). Between the realm of organic disorders from known physical causes and the group of conversion disorders, there exists a large group of syndromes characterized by functional and even anatomical alterations. Originally, these were called "organ neuroses"; they were then referred to as "psychosomatic disorders." They are now called "psychophysiologic disorders." Peptic ulcer, asthma, and ulcerative colitis have been regarded as typical examples of these disorders.

GENESIS OF PSYCHOPHYSIOLOGIC DISORDERS. Many theories have been advanced to explain the origins of these phenomena. For one, psychophysiologic symptoms have been described as affect equivalents, which represent dammed up emotions or their symbolic representation that cannot be discharged through behavior or speech and that find expression instead along somatic pathways in the form of a structural or functional alteration in an organ or organ system. According to this theory, anger or sexual excitement as well as anxiety may be supplanted by sensations and other changes in the intestinal, respiratory, or circulatory apparatus. For example, cardiac neurosis is considered to be an anxiety equivalent. Although it has some validity, the theory of affect equivalents is generally regarded as an oversimplified explanation of the multitude of complex interrelationships between psychological and somatic processes that obtain in these disorders and that, as yet, are not completely understood. Furthermore, although all affects are carried out by motor or secretory means, the physical manifestations of any given disease may occur without a clearly established etiological relationship to specific mental or emotional experiences. The difficulties are compounded by the fact that the psychophysiologic disorders themselves may bring about various pathological adaptive responses in the individual, the pathoneuroses described by Ferenczi, in which event it is difficult to determine whether the emotional disorder preceded the physical or vice versa.

CURRENT ISSUES. The normal interrelationship between hormonal physiology and instinctual phenomena is a subject of much current study and interest. Unfortunately, space limitations preclude a detailed discussion of the rationale underlying this research. Briefly, those workers who are involved in such investigations maintain that, given a predisposition or susceptibility to psychophysiologic disorders in a particular individual, the inhibition of specific affects may lead to certain hormonal secretions, to change in physical functions, and eventually to alteration in the tissues themselves. Different unconscious affects, as they occur in specific disorders, probably cause quantitative and qualitative differences in hormone secretion and thereby bring about in the vegetative nervous system a complex combination of stimulatory (sympathetic) and inhibitory (parasympathetic) responses.

Character (personality) disorders. It was stated earlier that, in its psychoanalytic sense, character refers to the ego's habitual mode of bringing into harmony the tasks presented by internal demands and the external world. When and how the ego acquires the qualities that enable it to adjust first to the demands of the instinctual drives and of external reality and later to the demands of the superego could be the subject of a separate treatise. The description of pathological character types may be complex and rather confusing in that discrete types without overlap rarely exist.

DEFINITION. A particular character pattern or type becomes pathological when its manifestations are exaggerated to the point that behavior destructive to the individual or to others results or the functioning of the person becomes distorted or restricted, so that it becomes a source of distress to himself or others. Those character types of particular clinical interest are described briefly below. Character disorders are also known as personality disorders.

PHOBIC CHARACTERS. These individuals limit their reactive behavior to the avoidance of the situations they yearned for originally. Thus, certain external situations are avoided, as is true of neurotic phobic behavior. In addition, however, internal reactions, such as rage or love or all intense feelings, may be subjected to phobic avoidance.

COMPULSIVE CHARACTERS. Reaction formations are characteristic of these individuals. Typically, they attempt to overcome sadism by kindness and politeness, to conceal pleasure in dirt by rigorous cleanliness. As the result of isolation, there is a lack of adequate affective response and a restriction in the number of available modes of feeling. Object relationships are of an anal-sadistic nature.

HYSTERICAL CHARACTERS. Hysterical characters have been described as persons who are inclined to sexualize all relationships and who tend toward suggestibility, irrational emotional outbreaks, chaotic behavior, dramatization, and histrionic activity.

CYCLIC CHARACTERS. These persons exhibit periodic mood swings from depression to varying degrees of elation. Cyclic characters are particularly concerned with unresolved oral needs and conflicts.

SCHIZOID CHARACTERS. The schizoid character evidences a heightened narcissism and the withdrawal of libido from outside persons into his own thoughts and feelings. He may manifest an intense need for approval or an omnipotent narcissism that is independent of the opinions of other people and is associated with limitations and distortions in the reality-testing function of the ego.

IMPULSE-RIDDEN CHARACTERS. The impulse-ridden character, who is frequently encountered in psychiatric practice, habitually discharges tension or avoids inner conflict by urgent activity, which is sometimes of a destructive or self-destructive nature.

Perversions. Perversions are manifestly sexual in character. When the pathological impulses are released, orgasm is achieved. As we have noted, the sexual aims in adult perversions correspond to components of the sexual drives of children. But the genesis of perversion cannot be attributed solely to the hypertrophy of an infantile, partial instinct. Factors of anxiety at phallic and pregenital levels, bisexuality, identifications, structural considerations, and external circumstances—all play a part in determining the genesis of perversion. These factors are described briefly below.

HOMOSEXUALITY. Homosexuality may be considered a vicissitude of the Oedipus complex in that the resolution of the oedipal conflict is based on the negative oedipal constellation. The child has identified with the parent of the opposite sex and chosen the parent of the same sex as a love object. Narcissistic factors also play an important role in homosexuality. The choice of an object is based, in part, on its sexual resemblance to the individual himself.

FETISHISM. Fetishism refers to the veneration of inanimate objects that symbolize parts of the body of an ambivalently loved person.

TRANSVESTISM. The transvestite finds dressing in garments characteristic of the opposite sex a source of sexual excitement.

EXHIBITIONISM. Exhibitionism is the deliberate exposure, usually compulsive, of sex organs under inappropriate conditions.

VOYEURISM. The voyeur achieves sexual gratification by watching the sexual activities of others.

In their extreme form, sexual submissiveness, sadism, and masochism represent perversions. These phenomena are discussed at length in the psychoanalytic literature.

Impulse neuroses. The impulse neuroses, which are related to perversions, involve impulsive actions that, though not necessarily overtly sexual, serve the purpose of avoiding or mastering some type of pregenital anxiety that is intolerable to the ego. Thus, the strivings for security and for instinctual gratification are characteristically combined in the impulsive action. Running away, kleptomania, pyromania, gambling, drug addiction, and alcoholism are well known examples of irresistible impulsive activities.

PSYCHOANALYTIC THEORY OF PSYCHOSIS

Early concepts (1893–1923). The most important finding to emerge from the psychoanalytic clinical investigations of the neuroses was the existence of an unconscious mental life and the description of its effects on conscious thought, symptoms, and behavior. On the basis of these data, Freud was able to demonstrate that the biological concept of adaptation was valid for all mental disorders. This concept led, in turn, to Freud's insight into the purposefulness of a psychosis. He suggested that psychosis might best be understood as the patient's mode of adapting to his emotional and realistic needs, to his physical health and intelligence, and to the environmental stresses with which he is confronted. Freud offered clinical evidence in support of this hypothesis by demonstrating that a definite psychotic symptom, hallucination, served a useful purpose.

In a broader frame of reference, Freud's greatest contribution to the psychology of psychosis came from his study of dreams. He pointed out that both the dream and psychotic thought were representative of a primitive type of thinking characteristic of infancy and of the animistic stage of development that antedates mental differentiation of autistic and objective experiences. This application of the investigation of dreams to schizophrenic thought was elaborated on in detail by Carl Jung, and his formulations enabled other workers to demonstrate the validity of this basic concept that delusions and hallucinations, like dreams, are prelogical forms of thinking. For example, in his paper "The Influencing Machine," Viktor Tausk described a schizophrenic patient's delusion that he was magically influenced by a machine, and he showed that it derived from genital sensations.

Studies of paranoia. Understanding of the mental symptoms of paranoia was greatly facilitated by discovery of the existence of unconscious homosexuality and the mechanism of projection. Freud's theoretical formulations concerning this form of psychopathology were, of course, based on his clinical experience. In addition, however, he acquired considerable insight into its genesis as a result of his careful analysis of the autobiography of a patient (Schreber) who had recently recovered from a severe attack of paranoia and whom Freud had never seen.

Freud postulated that in paranoia the need to project coincided with an unconscious need for homosexual love that, though of overwhelming intensity, was consciously denied by the patient. He also suggested that paranoid delusions represented sexual conflicts concerning persons of the same sex that had been projected onto some other person or force, which were then perceived as persecuting.

Other workers emphasized the close relationship of paranoid symptoms to infantile fantasies in which feces are personalized and considered animistically as dangerous beings that threaten the individual. In this connection, the relationship between paranoia and a stage of development at which the emotions are centered on a particular part of the object's body rather than the total person was demonstrated by Abraham. Abraham also noted that paranoid psychosis resembles certain phases of melancholia in that the patient's fantasies indicate a desire to incorporate the object. However, paranoid psychosis differs from melancholia in that in paranoia the hostility is directed against a part of the object rather than the whole and also in the prominence of fantasies that this incorporated part object can be destroyed and eliminated by defecation. The concurrent demonstration of the relationship of very primitive fantasies of aggression to overwhelming anxiety and the need to project has facilitated further understanding of this clinical entity. One question remained open, however: The reason why the homosexuality of paranoid patients had become so intense and was so intolerable was not investigated by Freud or his coworkers.

Role of narcissism in psychosis. In his paper "On Narcissism," Freud stated that psychosis was characterized by the patient's incapacity for normal emotional interest in other people and things. He did not agree that the psychotic process represents a total depletion of libido; rather, it involves a redistribution of those proportions of libido normally devoted to object love and self-love. The energy withdrawn from impoverished love relationships produces an abnormally excessive interest in the bodily functions and psychic attributes of the self. The psychotic patient's use of language indicates an emotional interest in the verbal symbol rather than the object the word represents. Many of the more obvious symptoms of psychosis are secondary to this primary loss of the capacity to love others; indeed, they are rudimentary and primitive efforts to re-establish an interest in others.

Regression to functioning at an earlier stage of mental development is manifested not only in prelogical ways of thinking but also in the fact that psychotic patients extract pleasurable experience chiefly from their own sensory experience without requiring a reciprocal relationship between themselves and another person.

In summary, the conspicuous elements of the clinical picture in most psychotic states consist of fragments of the intact personality, incomplete phases of psychotic regressions, and efforts at restitution. Freud concluded that delusions, hallucinations, and certain forms of disorganized behavior were secondary phenomena that represented rudimentary efforts on the part of the patient to restore his lost feelings for objects.

CURRENT CONCEPTS

Subsequent investigations have followed Freud's suggestion that the conflicts that result in psychotic adaptations occur primarily between the individual and his environment. In contrast, in neurosis the conflicts are primarily within the personality, between unconscious infantile wishes and adult attitudes. Recent work has focused on the detailed analysis of the disturbances and disorganizations in ego functioning that have impaired the patient's relationship with reality. Psychoses are seen as resulting from defects in the ego's integrative capacities, from the ineffectiveness of those functions essential to the capacity for establishing real relations with people for both pleasurable and egoistic reasons, and from the impairment of those functions essential to the control of intense infantile wishes by normal or neurotic mechanisms. Investigations of the ego's adaptive capacities have shown that the psychotic, like the neurotic, needs to adapt in a way that will enable him to avoid anxiety. However, the psychotic person's adjustment depends on the more primitive types of defense, which normally predominate before a high degree of personality organization is attained. The most important among these primitive defenses are flight, shown in social withdrawal, and the simple inhibition of impulses, which is very apparent in many psychotic delusions. Obviously, these defense mechanisms are much less highly organized than repression or reaction formation, for example. Again, in contrast to the neurotic, the fear of detection by others rather than the guilt of later childhood and maturity is also more conspicuous in the social reactions of the psychotic. Identifications, the adoption and organization of patterns with elements that were originally perceived as details of other people's behavior, also play a very important role in psychosis. These derive from emotional relations and early reactions to other people that have played a conspicuous role in the development of the psychotic patient's ego capacities.

The development of greater understanding and perhaps therapeutic techniques that bear a more specific relationship to etiological factors awaits the accumulation of further knowledge regarding the primitive ego of the child and the phases and mechanisms of its development. Recent studies of the development of the ego's capacity to transform primitive drives into socially useful functions—that is, sublimation, and of factors that interfere with the development of this crucial ego function have enhanced our understanding of the pathogenesis of psychosis. With respect to treatment, modifications in the free association method have made possible an approach, not hitherto possible, to a variety of psychotic states and to the problem of vulnerability and predisposition to psychosis. It must be pointed out, however, that many of these concepts are still in a state of transition.

NOSOLOGY

Hypochondriasis. The actual neuroses, the term Freud used to describe neurasthenia and anxiety neurosis, have ceased to be a significant part of psychoanalytic nosology. In fact, these clinical syndromes can be recognized as phases of ego regression or phases in the return to optimum ego functioning, yet they are referred to only rarely in the literature.

Hypochondriasis which Freud included among the actual neuroses originally, and the pathoneuroses may well be indicative, at least in certain instances, of phases of disorganization and reorganization of integrated ego functioning; the consensus of psychoanalytic opinion on this issue has not been determined. It is recognized, however, that hypochondriasis is an organ neurosis, although the physiological factor involved is still unknown. It may be assumed that certain psychogenic factors, such as a state of dammed-up libido or anxiety to which the individual responds with narcissistic withdrawal, create organic changes that, in turn, give rise to hypochondriacal sensations. Hypochondriasis rarely appears as an isolated neurosis; more frequently, it appears to complicate the picture of some other psychopathological condition, such as compulsion neurosis or depression, or it appears as a stage in the development of or recovery from psychosis. Sadistic and hostile impulses withdrawn from objects and represented in the form of organic complaints may play a particularly pronounced role in hypochondriacal syndromes. The typical hypochondriac is a conspicuously narcissistic, seclusive, monomaniacal person, often in a transitional state between reactions of a hysterical character and those that are delusional and clearly psychotic. It is hoped that further psychoanalytic study of infantile development will contribute to our understanding of these frequently encountered clinical states.

Melancholia.   Initial insights into the internal origins of various forms of affective regressive states were advanced by Freud as early as 1915. In his paper "Mourning and Melancholia," Freud emphasized the topographical regions and systems of the psychic apparatus that were involved in melancholic states, the regression of the libido, and the abandonment of the unconscious cathexis of objects. Freud's views differed in this respect from those of Abraham, who also stressed the importance of anal-sadism and maintained that its role in melancholia was comparable to that of anal erotism in obsessional neurosis. Abraham also pointed out, however, that anal-sadistic impulses contribute to many other clincial syndromes as well. Freud, in turn, emphasized the fact that the pain in mourning was limited to loss of an external object. In contrast, in melancholia the ego itself is impoverished because it has experienced an internal loss. Thus, melancholic depressions may or may not be precipitated by an actual loss. As a concomitant of loss, the melancholic suffers a shattering fall in self-esteem. The ego itself seems poor and empty; as such, it is deserving of reproach by the superego. The early formulations of both Freud and Abraham concerning melancholia and depression emphasized the precipitating frustration in object love, accompanied by flows to narcissistic libido, which reinforced early oedipal disappointment, and early introjection of an ambivalently loved parental image. These concepts are still considered valid.

Depression.   Abraham's continued investigations of his own and Freud's propositions within the framework of infantile libidinal development, particularly in regard to the oral phase, led to further understanding of the mechanisms involved in depression. He suggested that the conflicts of depressed persons centered around oral and anal-sadistic impulses and pointed out that persons who were prone to depression often had a markedly obsessional underlying character.

PATHOGENESIS. On the basis of these hypotheses, Abraham formulated the concept of primal depression to designate severe narcissistic injury that had occurred in early childhood through disappointments in "love." Later, Rado studied the effect of various vicissitudes of the nursing situation on the infantile ego and postulated a relationship between the etiology of depression and oral frustration on the one hand and aggression, particularly at the oral level, on the other. More recently, Edith Jacobson has discussed the impact on the young child's ego formation of early disillusion about parental omnipotence and subsequent devaluation of the parental images. Disillusion and devaluation of the parental images leads to destruction of the infantile self-esteem and gives rise to a primary depression that is repeated whenever the adult is similarly disillusioned. Thus, early ambivalent relationships with the parent figures may play a decisive role in the etiology of depression.

Other authors have expanded on this concept. Fenichel ascribed the general predisposition to depression to an "oral fixation, which determines the later reaction to narcissistic shocks" and added that "the narcissistic injury may create a depressive disposition because it occurs early enough to be met by an orally oriented ego"—that is, an ego that depends on external oral-narcissistic supplies. Fenichel also discussed the possibility that shocks to the self-esteem in early childhood may secondarily create the decisive oral fixation in the sense that the ego may become fixated to oral defense mechanisms. Much of the evidence cited by these authors in support of their hypotheses seems to confirm Melanie Klein's theory that the achievement of a whole object relationship is regularly accompanied by anxiety, together with a definite and specific vulnerability to depression in the event of object loss. Zetzel, however, has argued that this view implies a greater incidence of infantile psychosis than actually exists.

MECHANISM OF DEPRESSION. All persons experience periods of depression in the face of real or fantasied disappointments. However, the orally dependent person, who requires constant narcissistic supplies from outside, is most likely to manifest this reaction in its most severe form. The prototype of depression is the deprivation, suffered by the infantile ego, of vital narcissistic supplies. The availability of such supplies in the form of love, affection, and care is most significant, in terms of future development, at the oral stage.

Later, with the internalization of the parental images, which signifies the passing of the Oedipus complex, the struggle to secure love from the need-satisfying object on an intrapsychic level takes place—that is, the ego now seeks the approval of the superego. However, the child experienced this subsequently internalized need-satisfying object as frustrating and strict initially, and his attitude toward the object displayed a corresponding hostility. The quality of this early and most crucial object relationship gives the superego a critical and aggressive cast. The severe self-reproaches of depressed persons are another concomitant of the infant's hostility toward the internalized object and also represent the ego's efforts to win the favor of the superego through devaluation of the self. In summary, when early object relationships were defective, early intrapsychic conflicts may be revived. Once the mechanisms described above are set into operation by frustration and loss in adult life, they give rise to depression.

SYMPTOMATOLOGY. The symptom of depression is as ubiquitous as life itself, for it is a natural reaction to events that must be counted among the normal vicissitudes of life. Consequently, it is the excessive duration and domination of the organism by depressive affect rather than its occurrence that is pathological. Both depression and melancholia are characterized by a decrease in self-esteem, a sense of helplessness, the inhibition of ego functions to varying degrees, and a subjective feeling of sadness or loss of varying intensity. It has also been described as a basic affective state in which the ego feels incapable of fulfilling its aims or aspirations, although these aims persist as desired but hopeless goals. Persons prone to depression often display a pseudoindependence and self-assurance that, in fact, is a reaction to early severe deprivation and is intended to serve as a defense against future deprivation.

Manic-depressive psychosis. The manic-depression person manifests a particular kind of infantile narcissistic dependency on his love object. To offset his feelings of unworthiness, he requires a constant supply of love and moral support from a highly valued love object, which may be an individual or an organization or cause that he feels he belongs to. As long as this object lasts, he is able to function with enthusiasm and high efficiency. However, because of his strong self-punitive tendencies, the manic-depressive's object choice is masochistically determined and is bound to disappoint him. Thus, he himself sets the stage for his illness. All the ambitions and pursuits of the manic-depressive individual evolve from representations of the overvalued parental love objects, which extend, as it were, to the whole world. Consequently, when he is disappointed by the love object, ego functioning is impaired at every level.

THE DEPRESSIVE PHASE. Often, the depressive phase of manic-depressive psychosis closely resembles paranoia insofar as the patient's fantasies show a similar desire to incorporate the object. However, paranoia differs from depression in that hostility in the former condition is directed against a part of the object—breasts, penis, buttocks, hair, feces—rather than the whole and also in the prominence in paranoia of fantasies that this incorporated part object can be symbolically destroyed and eliminated by defecation.

The depressive phase subsides and gives way to temporary elation, mania, (1) when the narcissistically important goals and objects appear to be within reach once again, (2) when they have become sufficiently modified or reduced to be realistically attainable, (3) when they are renounced completely, or (4) when the ego recovers from its narcissistic shock and regains its self-esteem with the help of various recuperative agencies and with or without a change in object and goal.

THE MANIC PHASE. Theoretical efforts to grapple with the problem of mania in psychoanalysis have passed through various stages. Initially, mania was approached from the libidinal standpoint; however, more recent studies have stressed the role of the structural components of the psychic apparatus and the importance of object relationships and their inner representations. Since the purpose of manic flight is to avoid introspection, mania does not lend itself to fruitful psychoanalytic study. It is generally agreed, however, that mania represents a way of avoiding awareness of inner depression and includes denial of painful, inner reality and flight into external reality; in other words, it is a denial of the sensations of depression by proclaiming specific opposites. Since the manic person does not want to become aware of his own feelings, he cannot permit himself to empathize with others; thus, he is emotionally isolated.

Lewin's work on elation focuses on the oral-libidinal and oral-aggressive elements in mania, which he expands into an oral triad of wishes to eat, to be eaten, and to sleep—all of which are linked up with the infant's experience at the breast. He describes in structural terms the fusion of ego and superego (ego-ideal) in elation and the prominent use of projection, denial, and identification as major defenses. Lewin has also emphasized ego regression as a concomitant of elation insofar as there is a return to the pleasure principle. And he compares mania to a waking dream; in terms of the economics of elation, the abundance of energy characteristic of this phenomenon represents a concomitant depletion in the energy available for reality-testing or coping with superego demands.

The schizophrenias. Psychoanalytic concepts regarding the schizophrenias continue to undergo modification and revision. Originally, Freud postulated that the onset of schizophrenia signified a withdrawal of libido from the outside world; this libido was subsequently absorbed into the ego (megalomania) or returned to the outside world in the form of delusions.

Recent clinical interest in schizophrenia has centered on the intense ambivalence characteristic of these patients, their retaliation anxiety, and the infantile ego mechanisms they typically employ in their relationships with objects and the ultimate failure of which has resulted in the patient's decompensated or regressed state. Two stages are particularly conspicuous in the clinical picture of schizophrenic regression, as emphasized by Freud and Fenichel: first, the break with reality; second, the attempts to reestablish contact with reality.

CLINICAL CONCEPTS. Object relationships in schizophrenia are based on the wish to possess the parental objects or their substitutes through fusion. Primitive introjective mechanisms, fixation at the early oral stage of libidinal development, and multiple impairment of ego functions have been demonstrated repeatedly. Frustration of basic libidinal needs or factors that weaken ego resiliency, such as physical illness or increased demands on the patient's love or work capacity, may precipitate the acute psychosis.

Poorly warded-off homosexual and other pregenital impulses, particularly those of a sadistic and destructive nature, play an important role in schizophrenic regression. With the onset of the psychosis, these early sources of libidinal excitation cannot be mastered, and they flood the ego apparatus. If the libido returns to the ego, a megalomanic picture results. If, on the other hand, the sadistic impulses are projected onto the external world, as is the case in paranoid schizophrenic states, the once ambivalently loved person or his representative is perceived as the persecutor.

PSYCHOPHYSIOLOGICAL CONCEPTS. Several workers have approached severe regressive states from the standpoint of a unified concept of psychophysiological functioning. Such an attempt to conceptualize schizophrenia as a psychophysiological entity has been made by Mann and Semrad. These authors, extending the work of Felix Deutsch, conceive of the conversion process as the pathway that may illuminate the dynamic interrelationship between mind and body. They attribute schizophrenia to a defect in ego development that, in turn, is the consequence of the early failure of the conversion process to bind excessive instinctual excitation. Individuals vary in the face of severe psychophysiological distress in their capacity to manage or absorb affect through somatic conversion processes. If the capacity of an individual in this regard is exceeded, the need for further defenses arises, and these are then regressively invoked. Thus, the more immature or narcissistic ego defenses that are employed in schizophrenic psychoses are much more body-oriented than the more mature defenses. In the narcissistic defenses affect is concentrated on the self to the marked exclusion of external objects. It is reasonable to assume, then, that the need for these defenses arises in inverse proportion to the success with which the conversion process can absorb affect.

PATHOGENESIS. Identifications, following the mechanism of identification with the aggressor, are prominent in schizophrenic psychoses, and such identifications result in character traits related to the unconscious perception of the aggressor. In schizophrenia, the aggressor may well be experienced primarily as a foreign body in the patient's ego. The defenses available to the ego at this point in its development, the narcissistic defenses, may also be affected in that they become intensified and specialized so that they emerge as a prominent executant series of patterns in the form of denial, projection, and distortion. Such prominence seriously compromises the functioning ego in its interpersonal negotiations and eventually assures the frustration of its object needs.

Although the object with which the ego identifies is experienced as an aggressor and perceived as a foreign body, there is some ambivalence in this relationship. In this intense, symbiotic relationship, the object becomes a positive, pleasure-giving source as well. Indeed, these positive pleasurable aspects become the source of narcissistic supply and the major factor in balancing aggression, making it possible for the ego to remain intact. However, this stability is extremely vulnerable; it can be maintained only until such time as the individual loses, realistically or in fantasy, primary satisfying objects and/or, to a lesser extent, secondary substitutes for these objects.

Once this kind of loss has occurred, the previously balanced poison of the aggressor is liberated; now the ego is confronted anew with the problem of containing and controlling aggression, and libidinal problems assume a secondary position. We might say that at this point the conversion process has failed; the individual is thrown once more into a disorganizing and exhausting state of exquisite psychophysiological pain and must soon reach toward another solution. The total process may be acute and overwhelming, or it may be slowly regressive. This explains the fact that, invariably, schizophrenic reactions include distortions of the external world in the form of a series of frightening, confusing, and distorted body perceptions.

Thus, one may describe the predisposition to psychosis as due to the tenuous and delicate balance between identification with the ego-ideal and identification with the aggressor. This balance is maintained by special ego defenses, by character disorder, or by disorders in psychophysiological functioning that enable symbolic expression of conflict, although the psychophysiological relationships are poorly understood. The special narcissistic defenses used by schizophrenic patients are molded into organized patterns of denial, projection, and distortion. The ego is altered so that it operates in a self-consoling manner; to do so, it must either deny the presence of sensation, deny responsibility for sensation, or lose the ability to distinguish between sensations that emanate from internal or external stimuli. Denial, projection, and distortion are themselves methods for altering sensory perceptions so that they may become ego-syntonic. Specialization of the narcissistic defenses becomes necessary because of the inadequacy of ego-ideal identification, which impairs the ego's capacity for repression and other, more mature defenses to varying degrees.

In summary, most frequently schizophrenic regression is precipitated by loss and frustration of object needs. Dynamically, the effect of loss results too readily in the supremacy of negative affect, thus dislocating the delicate balance between ego-ideal identification and identification with the aggressor. This inundation with negative feeling necessitates regression to the point of deepest fixation, the narcissistic position, where the patient not only is a potential victim but also operates for self-consolidation, for only in this position can he achieve tension relief. The path of regression will vary according to whether the losses are acute and overwhelming or slow and cumulative. It will depend, too, on the individual's structural organization. When the illness is correctly diagnosed, its course can be plotted accurately, and it is possible to demonstrate conclusively, especially in situations of chronic loss, an orderly progression or relinquishing of the more mature defense mechanisms.

Admittedly, the preschizophrenic ego is weak in terms of the development of more mature defense mechanisms. However, with the onset of psychosis, elements of more mature mechanisms that have become established become admixed with infantile patterns. This may account for the clinical confusion surrounding schizophrenias, which demonstrate not only many different kinds of mechanisms but also various shadings of these mechanisms, giving rise to a confusion of terms, such as schizo-affective component, hysterical component, hypochondriacal component, and neurasthenic component.

In general, clinical evidence has shown that the acute onset of schizophrenia is related to increased intensity of the paranoid anxiety, the patient's feelings of omnipotence, and intolerable depressive anxieties—all of which had been previously warded off by narcissistic ego patterns of behavior. In addition, the patient typically demonstrates perceptual distortion, self-hatred, and reliance upon infantile and highly dependent patterns of object relationships.

CLASSICAL PSYCHOANALYTIC TREATMENT

The therapeutic technique that Freud elaborated and that was later expanded by his followers is summarized briefly herein because of its crucial relationship to the evolution of psychoanalytic theory.

Evolution

In essence, modern psychoanalytic treatment procedures differ from those that Freud developed originally in just one fundamental respect. At first, Freud anticipated that recognition by the physician of the patient's unconscious motivations, his communication of this knowledge to the patient, and its comprehension by the patient would, in itself, effect a cure. But further clinical experience demonstrated the fallacy of these expectations. He found that his discovery of the patient's unconscious wishes and his ability to impart his findings to the patient so that they were accepted and understood were not sufficient. Although this might permit clarification of the patient's intellectual appraisal of his problems, the emotional tensions for which he sought treatment were not alleviated. This led to a significant breakthrough. Freud realized that the success of treatment depended on the patient's ability to understand the emotional significance of an experience on an emotional level and to retain that insight. In that event, if the experience recurred, it would elicit another reaction; it would no longer be repressed. And the patient would have undergone a change in his psychic economy.

Freud continually refined his technique on the basis of his theoretical advances, so that psychoanalysis is now recognized as a specific method for reaching and modifying unconscious phenomena that give rise to conflict. In order for a conflict to be considered a neurotic conflict, at least one aspect must be repressed. Psychoanalysis attacks repression and tries to bring repressed material back to consciousness so that the patient, on the basis of his greater understanding of his needs and motives, may find a realistic solution to his conflict. Freud elaborated a treatment method that attaches minimum importance to the immediate relief of symptoms, moral support from the therapist, or guidance counseling. The goal of psychoanalysis is to pull the neurosis up by its roots rather than prune off the top. In order to accomplish this, the therapist must break down the deep pregenital crystallization of id, ego, and superego and bring the material of conflict near enough to the surface of consciousness so that it can be modified and re-evaluated in terms of adult reality. This, above all, distinguishes the classical psychoanalytic treatment from psychotherapy.

The repression of the forces of conflict is accomplished by design, and the patient is unaware of the psychic mechanisms he has employed. By means of this isolation of his basic problem, the patient has protected himself from what seems to him to be unbearable suffering. No matter how it may impair his functioning, the neurosis is preferable to the emergence of unacceptable wishes and ideas. All the forces that permitted the original repression are mobilized once again in the analysis as a resistance to this threatened encroachment on dangerous territory. No matter how much the patient may cooperate consciously and no matter how painful his neurosis may be, he automatically defends himself against the reopening of old wounds with every subtle resource available to him.

TREATMENT TECHNIQUES

Free association. The cornerstone of psychoanalytic technique is free association. The patient is taught this method and instructed to use it to the best of his ability throughout the treatment. Occasionally, it is suspended for a rational review of the material elicited, and, indeed, these intellectual discussions are indispensable interruptions. However, by psychoanalytic standards, their function in effecting therapeutic change is quite secondary.

Resistance. The most conscientious efforts on the part of the patient to say everything that comes to mind are never completely successful. Signs of resistance are apparent throughout the course of every analysis. The patient pauses abruptly, corrects himself, makes a slip of the tongue, stammers, remains silent, fidgets with some part of his clothing, asks irrelevant questions, intellectualizes, arrives late for appointments or finds excuses for not keeping them, offers critical evaluations of the rationale underlying the treatment method, cannot think of anything to say, or censors the thoughts that do occur to him and decides they are banal or irrelevant and not worth mentioning.

The development of resistance in analysis is quite as automatic and independent of the patient's will as the development of the transference, and the sources are equally unconscious. However, the emotional forces that give rise to resistance are opposed to those that produce the transference. As a result, the analysis becomes a recurring conflict between transference and resistance, manifested by involuntary inhibition of the patient's efforts to freely associate that may last for moments or days. The significance of this conflict for analytic therapy is obvious. It is a repetition of the very same sexuality-guilt conflict that originally produced the neurosis. The transference may itself serve as a form of resistance in that the wish for immediate pleasure in the analysis can circumvent the essential goals of treatment. Thus, the analysis of resistance constitutes the prime function of the analyst; it also accounts for the extended period of time required for psychoanalytic treatment. No matter how skillful the analyst, resistance is never absent except perhaps in those patients who are seriously ill and would not be eligible for classical psychoanalytic treatment in any event.

Role of the analyst. Interpretation is the chief tool available to the analyst in his efforts to reduce unconscious resistance. As mentioned earlier, in the early stages in the development of psychoanalytic therapeutic techniques, the sole purpose of interpretation was to inform the patient of his unconscious wishes. Later, it was designed to help the patient understand his resistance to spontaneous and helpful self-awareness. In other words, in current psychoanalytic practice the analyst's function as interpreter is not limited to paraphrasing the patient's verbal reports but includes indicating, at appropriate moments, what he is *not* reporting. Consequently, as a general rule, analytic interpretation does not produce immediate symptomatic relief beyond the usual honeymoon period. On the contrary, there may be a heightening of anxiety and the emergence of further resistance.

The procedures unique to psychoanalysis help to circumvent resistance. The first of these is the patient's use of free association. The second is the passive role assigned to the analyst in the treatment setting. As described above, free association refers to the spontaneous expression of uncensored thoughts that supplement the patient's efforts to fathom his own mind by direct and logical intellectual thought. Free association is the path to the unconscious. As such, it is central to the classical psychoanalytic method, and the patient's eligibility for treatment depends on his willingness and ability to comply with this basic rule of treatment. The patient is obligated thereby to express verbally everything that comes to his mind, without selection or reservation. Ordinary rules of conversation—such as adherence to the topic under discussion, orderly presentation, or regard to the social conventions and amenities—are abrogated.

The passive role of the analyst implies his avoidance of permissive as well as authoritative expressions and allows him to limit himself to interpretations offered at the proper time of the patient's mental dynamics as these emerge in his free associations and to clarification of the way the patient's ego defense mechanisms operate to preclude free association and thereby to preclude insight into his unconscious wishes and impulses. In this respect, the passive role of the analyst reduces the realistic features of the patient-physician relationship to a minimum.

If a correct interpretation is given at the proper time, the patient may react either immediately or after a period of emotional struggle, during which he offers new associations. These new associations often confirm the validity of the previous interpretation and add significant additional data, disclosing motivations and experiences of the patient that the analyst could not previously have been aware of. Generally speaking, however, it is not so much the analyst's insight into the patient's psychodynamics that produces progress in the analysis. Rather, it is his ability to help the patient gain this insight for himself by reducing unconscious resistance to such self-awareness through appropriate, carefully timed interpretation. Psychoanalysis has shown that, at best, the therapeutic benefits produced by the pressure of the analyst's exhortations are only temporary. The only pressure of lasting therapeutic value derives from the patient's awareness of his own instincts.

DYNAMICS OF THE THERAPEUTIC PROCESS

In the course of his analysis, the patient undergoes two processes, remembering and reliving, which constitute the dynamics of the treatment procedure.

Remembering refers to the gradual extension of consciousness back to early childhood, at which time the core of the neurosis was formed, for this stage of development marked the onset of the interference and distortion of the patient's instinctual life. Consequently, making the unconscious conscious is accomplished, in part, by the recovery of important childhood experiences through the patient's actual memory of these events but more often in other ways, such as fantasy, inference, and analogy. In patients who have been analyzed successfully, this means more than a mere verbal autobiographical reconstruction. Inevitably, inner convictions and values, which were formed early in life, will be re-evaluated and altered so that they will contribute to rather than hinder the patient's optimal functioning.

Reliving refers to the actual re-experiencing of these events in the analysis itself in the context of the patient's relationship with the analyst.

Transference. Through free association, hidden patterns of the patient's mental organization, fixated at immature levels, are brought to light, comparatively free from disguise. These free associations refer to events or fantasies that are part of the patient's private face. When they are shared in the analytic setting, the listener (analyst) is gradually invested with some of the emotion that accompanies them. That is, the patient displaces the feelings he originally directed toward the participants in these early events onto the analyst, who becomes, alternately, a friend or an enemy, one who is nice to him or frustrates his needs and punishes him, one who is loved or hated. Moreover, this tendency persists, so that to an increasing extent the patient's feelings toward the analyst replicate his feelings toward the specific people he is talking about or, more accurately, those his unconscious is "talking about." The special type of object displacement that is an inevitable concomitant of psychoanalytic treatment is called "transference."

As unresolved childhood attitudes emerge and function as fantasy projections toward the analyst, he becomes, for the patient, a phantom, composite figure who represents various important persons in the patient's early environment. Those earlier relationships that remained unresolved are reactivated with some of their original vigor. Gradually, the patient sees himself as he really is, with all his unfulfilled and contradictory needs spread before him. The conscious, scientific use of transference as a dynamic therapeutic force through the analysis of its unconscious sources is unique to classical psychoanalysis.

The combination of these two processes—remembering and reliving—enables the patient to gain deeper insight into the defects in his psychological functioning in spite of himself.

Transference neurosis.   Psychoanalytic treatment may be divided into specific phases. During the introductory phase, the patient becomes familiar with the free association method and the routine aspects of treatment, the ideas and feelings characteristic of the individual begin to emerge, and there is an increasing mutual understanding of the patient's assets and the life difficulties that have brought him to treatment.

The transference neurosis usually develops during the second phase of analysis. A patient who, at first, was eager for better mental health no longer consistently displays such motivation during treatment hours. Rather, he is engaged in a continuing battle with the analyst, and it becomes apparent that his most compelling reason for continuing his analysis is his desire to attain some kind of emotional satisfaction from the analyst. In other words, at this point in treatment, the transference emotions are more important to the patient than the permanent health he was seeking. It is at this point that the major unresolved, unconscious problems of childhood begin to dominate the patient's behavior. They are now reproduced in the transference with all their pent-up emotion. The patient is striving unconsciously to recapture what he was actually deprived of in childhood.

The analytic situation is governed by the three outstanding characteristics of the instinctual life of early childhood: the pleasure principle (prior to effective reality-testing), ambivalence, and repetition compulsion. The full comprehension and management of the transference neurosis is a test of skill that sharply differentiates those analysts who have received adequate training in classical psychoanalytic theory and technique from those who have not. One situation after another in the life of the patient is analyzed until the original infantile conflict is revealed. Only then does the transference neurosis begin to subside. Termination of the analysis dates from this time; but, again, it is a gradual process and is never complete with the last visit to the analyst. However, if exposure of the unconscious source of the patient's major problems was fairly thorough, thereafter, at times of emotional crisis, the patient can resolve, through association and without assistance, those areas of conflict that were not entirely worked through with the analyst. After a variable period, the temporarily accentuated awareness of the unconscious diminishes, useful repressions are partially re-established, the former patient has less need of introspection, and he is able to deal with life on a more mature and satisfactory basis than was possible previously.

MODIFICATION IN TECHNIQUE

There is no short-cut; psychoanalytic treatment typically extends over a period of years and requires interminable patience on the part of both the physician and the patient. The classical analytic method, which, on the one hand, best serves the aims of therapy also constitutes the best experimental situation yet devised for studying the more complex features of human nature. However, rigid adherence at all times to the fundamental mechanistic principles of psychoanalytic technique is impossible. For example, the immediate environmental situation may be so serious that the analyst must pay common sense attention to its practical implications. Those patients whose early childhood was extraordinarily deficient in love and affection must be given more praise and encouragement than is advocated by strict analytic technique. Very narcissistic patients and borderline psychotics must establish strong personal feeling for the analyst before they can develop sufficient interest and motivation for treatment. At the same time, however, clinical evidence has demonstrated conclusively that every deviation from strict technique that such special conditions compel prolongs the length of treatment and increases its difficulties considerably.

RESULTS OF TREATMENT

The therapeutic effectiveness of psychoanalysis presents problems of demonstration. Impartial and objective critics are handicapped in their appraisals by the fact that so many patients state that they have been analyzed when no such procedure was undertaken or when it was undertaken by someone who exploited the use of the title "analyst" and who, in fact, had no understanding of the science and technique of analysis. Other patients remained in analysis only a very short time and then discontinued treatment themselves or were advised that they were not suitable candidates for such treatment. Except for psychoanalysts themselves, professionals as well as laymen demonstrate varying degrees of confusion as to what psychoanalysis is and what it is not.

No analyst can ever eliminate all the personality defects and neurotic factors in a single patient, no matter how thorough the treatment. On the other hand, mitigation of the rigors of a punitive superego is an essential criterion of the effectiveness of treatment. Psychoanalysts do not usually regard alleviation of symptoms as the most significant datum in evaluating therapeutic change. The absence of recurrence of the illness or of further need for psychotherapy is a more important index of the value of analysis. However, the chief basis of evaluation remains the patient's general adjustment to life—his capacity for attaining reasonable happiness, for contributing to the happiness of others, and his ability to deal adequately with the normal vicissitudes of life. More specific criteria of the effectiveness of treatment include reduction of the patient's unconscious neurotic need for suffering, of neurotic inhibition, and of infantile dependency needs and, on the other hand, an increased capacity for responsibility; for success in marriage, social friendships, and work; and for pleasurable sublimation and recreation relative to his potentialities. The most important criterion of the success of treatment is the release of the patient's normal potentiality, which had been blocked by the basic neurosis, for further development and maturation.

INDICATIONS AND CONTRAINDICATIONS

Psychoanalysis is not the treatment of choice for all forms of mental disorder. It has proved to be most effective in the common psychoneuroses, in which definite symptoms predominate and motivate the patient to seek medical or psychiatric help. These include cases of conversion hysteria (including classic hysteria), phobias without psychosis (anxiety hysteria), obsessive and compulsive neuroses, and neurotic depression.

Conversion hysteria. Conversion hysteria, which usually occurs in women, is characterized by bodily symptoms that resemble those of physical disease—such as paralysis, anesthesia, blindness, convulsions, pathological blushing, fainting, headaches, and other types of pain—but that have no somatic basis. Unless these symptoms occur in very mild form in an otherwise well-adjusted personality, they are positive indications for analysis. The typical course of treatment in such cases is the early alleviation of symptoms and the recognition of basic conflicts produced by genital wishes. Analysis of these conflicts usually leads to fundamental changes in personality in addition to permanent symptomatic relief. But a minority of cases of hysteria are very difficult to analyze or may even be unanalyzable. This applies particularly to cases of hysteria in women whose personalities are exceptionally infantile and to some chronic cases in which the pleasure derived over a period of years from secondary gains is too great to be renounced.

Phobias. Phobias (anxiety hysteria) produced a variety of symptoms in people whose personalities and conflicts are very like those of patients with conversion hysterias. Indications for the treatment of both these clinical entities are similar.

Obsessive-compulsive neuroses. This form of neurosis is more common in men. Treatment is usually much more difficult and protracted than treatment of other neuroses, and, not infrequently, such patients do not derive full benefits from analysis. However, these patients present serious disturbances in total adjustment, so that extended treatment is usually justified, even though the cure would not be considered complete by psychoanalytic standards.

Neurotic depression. This syndrome is well understood and often much helped by analytic treatment.

Other symptomatic neuroses. Overt sexual symptoms, such as impotence based on psychic factors or impaired capacity for mature sexual love, usually represent the repression of fundamental conflicts in early object relationships and are usually permanently relieved through analysis. However, other symptomatic psychoneuroses—such as adult enuresis, tics, and stammering—may be much more resistant to modification. Yet such symptoms are usually definite indications for psychoanalytic treatment; and treatment generally produces important alterations in basic personality problems, even though the chronically established abnormal muscle habits are not entirely cured.

Homosexuality. Sexual perversions often tend to be quite intractable, and the results achieved in the psychoanalytic treatment of overt homosexuality have been equally disappointing on the whole. Thus, the indications for psychoanalytic treatment of patients whose homosexuality is accompanied by psychoneurotic difficulties are much the same as they would be for neurotics who are heterosexual, and the results of treatment with respect to the neurotic symptoms of the homosexual patient are quite similar. Alteration of an erotic preference for one's own sex is by no means assured. The more indications there are, either conscious or repressed, of some heterosexual interest in the past history of the individual and the less completely he has adopted the psychological traits and habits of the other sex, the better is the patient's prognosis.

Psychoneurotic character problems. These clinical phenomena are closely allied to hysteria and the obsessive-compulsive neurosis in etiology and prognosis. Both hysterical and obsessive-compulsive characters display a variety of traits of definitely neurotic origin. When these are a conspicuous and persistent source of tribulation for the patient and the people in his environment, they constitute positive indications for psychoanalysis. A few of the more common of these traits are uncontrollable temper, chronic nagging and constant complaints about others or oneself, excessive diffidence or feelings of inferiority, an inclination to change one's occupation constantly, repeated unsolved work problems, a succession of unhappy love affairs, an inability to concentrate at work or to finish a job, an inability to derive pleasure from recreation or avocation, and an inability to form friendships. Particularly common in such cases are complaints of marital discord, which is either the result of a neurotic choice of partner or a neurotic reaction to a maturely selected spouse.

Today, neurotic character disorders are far more common than clear-cut symptomatic neuroses, and these patients make up a large portion of the population for whom analysis is recommended. Narcissistic characters are helped greatly and even transformed by analysis, but the therapeutic prognosis is extremely variable. The more evidence there is of the presence of problems that are definitely psychoneurotic, in combination with narcissistic traits, the more favorable the prognosis for such patients. On the other hand, the prognosis is especially poor for anaclitic personalities who are very unassertive and readily accept entirely dependent and passive relationships. Mild schizoid characters may be helped by analysis, but they should never be treated by analysts who lack general psychiatric experience; this applies to paranoid characters as well. More serious psychological disturbances—such as alcoholism, drug addiction, psychopathic personality, and criminality—have been helped occasionally by analysis. But, too often, the benefits from therapy are limited because the infantile demands of these patients are almost unbelievably excessive. In fact, their ego functions are seriously impaired in that their sense of reality is defective; they lack the capacity to tolerate frustration and other tensions.

Classical psychoanalysis is a completely appropriate treatment method for the neuroses. Moreover, it can produce a far more complete and fundamental reorganization of the neurotic personality than any other psychotherapeutic technique currently in existence. On the other hand, this unqualified endorsement pertains only to the neuroses. In other forms of psychopathology, the usefulness of psychoanalysis as a treatment method is limited, depending on the extent and strategic location of neurotic elements in these conditions.

Psychophysiologic illness. Certain organic illnesses, reversible somatic symptoms, are so common an accompaniment of psychoneurosis that cures incidental to the major problems of a neurosis are a common experience of practicing analysts. Chronic and intermittent constipation, anorexia, and other minor ailments of the digestive tract are regularly relieved as a secondary consequence of the analysis of personality problems. The alleviation of a variety of menstrual disorders and sometimes of sterility of long duration as a concomitant of the resolution of emotional conflicts surrounding female sexuality is common. Analysis frequently has a therapeutic effect on a variety of other common complaints as well, such as constant colds, headaches, insomnia, pseudopregnancy, frequency of urination, and skin eruptions. The effect of psychoanalysis on asthma, thyroid disease, disturbances of stomach and intestine, and some skin diseases varies considerably from case to case. Possible reversibility of psychophysiologic disease is a major consideration. If the disease process is irreversible, psychoanalysis may still be recommended with the aim of trying to slow the destructive process. However, the somatic process may be not only irreversible but also impossible to halt. In such cases, the misery produced by the somatic disease and the social incapacitation have become the major problems, and the original neurosis is of secondary significance.

Psychoanalytic treatment of psychosis. The effectiveness of analytic treatment of psychosis must be discussed with still less certainty. Classical psychoanalysis is clearly contraindicated. However, there is no question that skillful and prolonged psychotherapy can ameliorate or even permanently remove the more morbid features in some cases. But the question is still open as to whether psychoanalytic technique is as specifically indicated for the treatment of schizophrenia as it is for the psychoneuroses. Moreover, in general, paranoid psychosis is even less amenable to analytic therapy than many cases of schizophrenia, although, in those cases where the paranoid process absorbs only a limited portion of the patient's intellectual and emotional life, the prognosis is considerably better.

Eligibility for treatment. The capacity for mature adjustment may be very limited in some individuals, even though they may not have a particularly severe neurosis. Evaluation of their personalities indicates that no aspect of their functioning is really adult. Nor is there evidence of a strong drive to combat these infantile aspects.

Analysis is contraindicated in extreme cases of this kind, for no element of the personality will strive to utilize the treatment for eventual maturity; the patient will continue to regard the analytic session as an enjoyable hour during which he has someone's exclusive attention just as long as the analyst will put up with it. The psychoanalyst does not regard the secondary gain as the primary rationale for classical psychoanalytic treatment but as an important obstacle to be circumvented in his work. Not infrequently, however, the secondary gain is so great as to seriously impede or entirely preclude successful analysis; in such instances, the patient has learned to derive so much satisfaction from these secondary gains that the advantages of illness outweigh his suffering.

During treatment the patient must continue to derive some gratification from life, even though these gratifications may perpetuate his neurotic patterns. Sometimes, relationships that were conspicuous consequences of the neurosis cannot be renounced, even after the patient no longer requires the infantile gratification and the suffering they afford. No individual is a self-sufficient unit; his repressed impulses as well as his mature emotions constantly mingle with, stimulate, and respond to those of others. The infantile sadism of one partner responds to the infantile masochism of the other and demands it of him, despite the fact that, after analysis, the masochist desires a more mature relationship, unconsciously as well as consciously. In other instances, however, analytic results have a favorable effect on the neurotic problems of the patient's spouse as well as on those of the patient, and there is a mutual improvement in marital adjustment.

SPECIFIC CRITERIA. Several factors must be kept in mind in judging an individual's eligibility for psychoanalysis. Apart from the capacity for logical thought and a certain degree of ego strength, fundamental vigor of personality is a prerequisite. The analytic patient undergoes a difficult experience. From time to time, he must be able to accept a temporary increase in unhappiness in the expectation of eventual benefits. The capacity to undergo such stress is an excellent indication of a person's capacity to face the real vicissitudes of life after analysis. When there is some question as to the patient's qualification in this regard, a short period of trial analysis in order to appraise the problems and potentialities of the patient more completely may be recommended. A youthful mind, in terms of either actual years or a certain elasticity of functioning, is essential. Chronologic age is a rough measure of total life experience; the more mature a person's experience is, the more apt he will be to utilize the analysis. In general, however, treatment will proceed more quickly to an effective result when patients are in their twenties and thirties. But it is also recommended in adolescence and middle age. The capacity to fight the neurosis is as great an asset in psychoanalysis as it is in life crises, and it varies greatly among individuals, as does the degree of neurosis itself.

Honest skepticism concerning analysis is usually a good prognostic sign if it is not so extreme as to prevent the patient from making a determined effort to utilize the unique advantages this method offers. On the other hand, a naive, exuberant conviction at the beginning of treatment that the omnipotent analyst will point the way to an existence that will remain untroubled forever after, that analysis offers a magic formula that will automatically and painlessly make everything right, forebodes special difficulties after treatment is underway.

REFERENCES

Abraham, K. *Selected Papers on Psychoanalysis.* Basic Books, New York, 1953.

Brenner, C. *An Elementary Textbook of Psychoanalysis.* International Universities Press, New York, 1955.

Breuer, J., and Freud, S. Studies on hysteria. In *Standard Edition of the Complete Psychological Works of Sigmund Freud,* vol. 2, p. 3. Hogarth Press, London, 1955.

Deutsch, H. *The Psychology of Women,* 2 vols. Grune & Stratton, New York, 1944.

Erikson, E. H. *Childhood and Society,* ed. 2. W. W. Norton, New York, 1963.

Fenichel, O. *The Psychoanalytic Theory of Neurosis.* W. W. Norton, New York, 1945.

Freud, A. *The Ego and the Mechanisms of Defense.* International Universities Press, New York, 1953.

Freud, S. *An Outline of Psychoanalysis.* W. W. Norton, New York, 1949.

Freud, S. The interpretation of dreams. In *Standard Edition of the Complete Psychological Works of Sigmund Freud*, vols. 4 and 5. Hogarth Press, London, 1953.

Freud, S. Three essays on the theory of sexuality. In *Standard Edition of the Complete Psychological Works of Sigmund Freud*, vol. 7, p. 135. Hogarth Press, London, 1953.

Freud, S. *The Origin of Psychoanalysis: Letters to Wilhelm Fliess, Drafts and Notes*, M. Bonaparte, A. Freud, and E. Kris, editors. Basic Books, New York, 1954.

Freud, S. Analysis of a phobia in a five-year-old boy. In *Standard Edition of the Complete Psychological Works of Sigmund Freud*, vol. 10, p. 5. Hogarth Press, London, 1955.

Freud, S. The interpretation of dreams. In *Standard Edition of the Complete Psychological Works of Sigmund Freud*, vol. 18, p. 7. Hogarth Press, London, 1955.

Freud, S. On narcissism: an introduction. In *Standard Edition of the Complete Psychological Works of Sigmund Freud*, vol. 18, p. 7. Hogarth Press, London, 1957.

Freud, S. Mourning and melancholia. In *Standard Edition of the Complete Psychological Works of Sigmund Freud*, vol. 14, p. 243. Hogarth Press, London, 1957.

Freud, S. The case of Schreber. In *Standard Edition of the Complete Psychological Works of Sigmund Freud*, vol. 12, p. 3. Hogarth Press, London, 1958.

Freud, S. Inhibitions, symptoms and anxiety. In *Standard Edition of the Complete Psychological Works of Sigmund Freud*, vol. 20, p. 87. Hogarth Press, London, 1959.

Freud, S. The ego and the id. In *Standard Edition of the Complete Psychological Works of Sigmund Freud*, vol. 19, p. 12. Hogarth Press, London, 1961.

Freud, S. Further remarks on the neuropsychoses of defense. In *Standard Edition of the Complete Psychological Works of Sigmund Freud*, vol. 3, p. 45. Hogarth Press, London, 1962.

Freud, S. New introductory lectures on psychoanalysis. Lecture 33; femininity. In *Standard Edition of the Complete Psychological Works of Sigmund Freud*, vol. 22, p. 112. Hogarth Press, London, 1964.

Hartmann, H. Comments on the psychoanalytic theory of the ego. In *Psychoanalytic Study of the Child*, vol. 5, p. 74. International Universities Press, New York, 1950.

Hartmann, H. *Essays on Ego Psychology.* International Universities Press, New York, 1964.

Hendrick, I. *Facts and Theories of Psychoanalysis*, ed. 3. Alfred A. Knopf, New York, 1958.

Jones, E. *The Life and Work of Sigmund Freud*, 3 vols. Basic Books, New York, 1953–1957.

Lewin, B. D. *Psychoanalysis of Elation.* Psychoanalytic Quarterly, New York, 1961.

Mann, J., and Semrad, E. Conversion as process and conversion as symptom in psychosis. In *On the Mysterious Leap from the Mind to the Body*, F. Deutsch, editor, p. 131. International Universities Press, New York, 1959.

Rapaport, D. A historical survey of psychoanalytic ego psychology. (Introduction to Erikson, E. H. Identity and the life cycle.) Psychol. Issues, 1: 1, 1957.

Waelder, R. *Basic Theory of Psychoanalysis.* International Universities Press, New York, 1960.

CHAPTER TWO

Erik H. Erikson

ALFRED M. FREEDMAN, M.D., &
HAROLD I. KAPLAN, M.D.

INTRODUCTION

ERIK H. ERIKSON knew Freud when the founder of psychoanalysis was in his seventies, aging and famous. In his late twenties, Erikson was undergoing psychoanalysis with Freud's daughter Anna, teaching the children of psychoanalytic patients, and occasionally encountering Freud in such informal situations as family outings.

Erikson had reached Vienna by a roundabout route. At 18 he had eschewed the university to walk through the Black Forest and ponder life on the shores of Lake Constance. After a year of roaming, he returned to his comfortable family home in the industrial city of Karlsruhe, Germany, where he spent a year in art school before restlessness sent him on for two more years of art in the larger city of Munich. From Munich he moved to Florence and gave up woodcuts and etchings; instead he walked about, piecing together what he would later call an identity during that period between adolescence and adulthood he would style a "moratorium."

The question of identity for Erikson involved three factors, to start: his being a Dane living in Germany, a country that resented Denmark for its designs on Schleswig-Holstein; his being the son of an absent Danish father and a Danish mother with both a rabbi and a minister in her ancestry, and his being stepson of a German Jew, a pediatrician who wanted Erikson to become one too. Erikson would later describe himself as a man of the borders. Much of what he was to study involved the question of how group values are implanted by culture-bearing mothers in the very young; of how youth grasps onto group identity in the period of delay and hesitancy before adulthood; and of how a few, like Ghandi, outgrow their local, national, and even temporal identities by influencing a group of men with wider sympathies who, in time, span the ages.

From Florence, the 25-year-old Erikson decided to return to Karlsruhe and settle down to the study and teaching of art and to drawing portraits of children. He was so engaged when Peter Blos, a high school friend, wrote him from Vienna. Blos, not yet a psychoanalyst, had met Dorothy Burlingham, a New Yorker who had come to Vienna to be psychoanalyzed; she had brought her four children with her and had hired Blos to tutor them. Blos was looking for a fellow teacher in his new school for the children of English and American patients and students of the new discipline of psychoanalysis. Erikson accepted his offer.

While teaching in an informal style that brought students toward equality with their teacher, he was quietly marked as one of the few to undergo analysis, in the hope that he would carry forward in the field. He talked daily to Anna Freud, who was involved in practicing psychoanalysis. At the same time she was trying to turn some attention from the adult's corrective backward look at childhood to a study of childhood that sought to achieve neurosis prevention. Still undecided about his future, Erikson took on a few children as patients under the guidance of August Aichhorn. He also studied to become an accredited Montessori teacher. He married Joan Serson, an American, and was hastily made a full rather than an associate member of the Vienna Psychoanalytic Society—unorthodoxy that allowed him to leave a Vienna threatened by Fascism and to go to the United States immediately after his graduation in 1933.

That same year he became Boston's only child analyst, holding a position at the Harvard Medical School and at Massachusetts General Hospital. After three years he moved to Yale University's Institute of Human Relations, where he furthered an interest sparked at Harvard in the work of American anthropologists. He left for study among the Sioux Indians of Pine Ridge, South Dakota, and in 1939 moved to a post at Berkeley, from which he studied the Yurok Indians, a group of salmon fishers. He left Berkeley in 1950 after refusing to sign what he called a "vague, fearful" addition to the loyalty oath. He resettled at the Austen Riggs Center in Stockbridge, Massachusetts, working with young people. In 1960 he was appointed to a professorship at Harvard. He is now retired but engaged with his wife in studies of American children, predominantly from minority groups.

THEORY OF PERSONALITY

THE HEALTHY PERSONALITY

Erikson added to Freud's theory of infantile sexuality by extending the study of the developing child beyond puberty, thus emphasizing his own belief that the ego continues to acquire new characteristics as it meets new situations throughout life. He brought Freud's psychoanalytic theory out of the bounds of the family home, looking beyond the molding power of the family romance to the wider matrix of the social world, where children meet peers, teachers, national ethics, and expectations. Freud himself had been working in a more social direction late in life. Erikson also took the focus of psychoanalysis from pathology to health, providing a picture of how the ego can usually develop healthily, given the right environment. Erikson brought Freud's theories out of the past, the home, and the hospital.

"We have a name for the pressure of excessive wishes (the 'id')," wrote Erikson, "and for the oppressive force of conscience (the 'superego')," he continued, bringing the labels of early psychoanalysis down to the ground of common language from which they had earlier been transmuted. But the emphasis, he argued, should be on the ego. This emphasis had not been the case because of the historical evolution of psychoanalysis out of psychopathology.

In considering the healthy personality, Erikson selected the ego as the tool by which a person organizes outside information, tests perception, selects memories, governs action adaptively, and integrates the capacities of orientation and planning. This is the positive ego, whose functioning produces a sense of self in a state of heightened well-being—an Indian "just calmly being an Indian," as Erikson put it. This state of well-being is how one feels when what one is and does is pretty much what one wishes and feels he ought to be and do.

The wishing and the "oughtness" form polarities in Erikson's scheme. Excessive and barbaric wishes pull from one end of the horizontal axis, and the internalized restrictions of parents and society pull at the other end. Erikson's superego is as barbaric as the id, being that which turns the screw on the rack or punishes with mutilation. The image of Freud's superego, on the other hand, "the internalized sum of all the restrictions to which ego must bow," brings forth a vertical picture, with a wild id at the bottom, a defensive ego mediating in the middle height, and a judging superego high above.

With good functioning of the ego, the person is not neurotically crippled, wasting energy, or suffering. How does one come by this ego? The strong ego acquires its strength gradually through the expansive process of living, in a course that does not simply plow forward, picking up a permanent trust here and a never-to-be-lost industry there, but in stages during which the person meets a new situation with his accumulated make-up and, once again dealing in polarities, emerges from conflict having established a certain ratio of so much identity, for example, versus so much role confusion. This ratio is not stable; beneficent occurrences in the social milieu or corrective measures at home can change the ratio. Even a strong ego at 40 or 45 or 50 can face critical situations that thrust it back on the negative balance within and stir up infantile rages and anxieties that never entirely vanish.

Oral-sensory stage: trust versus mistrust. The fetus develops sequentially, Erikson points out, each organ having its own time of origin and all of them bound together temporally in a standard sequence. After birth the infant continues to develop sequentially, mastering parts of his muscular and nervous systems at different times.

During the first months the mouth is the most sensitive zone of the body, and the first year or so is termed the oral stage of life. But every infant has an individual nervous system; his own oral sensitivities are not necessarily like those of the baby in the neighboring bassinet. Furthermore, the oral stage is not something to be grown out of or left behind, since eating, drinking, and making noise continue to be vital throughout life. It is not, therefore, neurotic to be oral.

The mother welcomes the infant and reduces by food and care the discomfort of homeostasis with which he is born. She smiles and he smiles; mutual warmth takes hold and develops. The infant comes to trust that his wants will continue to be satisfied, at least within the spectrum of his minimal needs and maximum tolerance for denial. Somewhere within this spectrum lie the expectations that the society has for the child. Although the mother adds her own opinions about satisfying the oral needs of infants, she also transmits the reality orientation of the society. This involves such things as the existence of plenitude or scarcity, of peace or war, of limitation or fulfillment, of totalitarianism or democracy. The infant learns how to get his mother to give something; building on this base, he will later allow himself to be a giver.

The main action the infant performs with his mouth is termed "incorporating"—that is, taking in food, a nipple, a finger, or such. There is hunger for nourishment and for stimulation of the sense organs and the whole surface of the skin.

The infant learns to coordinate his vision and to attach meanings to specific sounds. His eyes pick objects from the general background, and he learns to control arms, fingers, and legs. He begins to sit or lean, giving his hands more freedom. The baby who stared longingly at a colorful toy is able to pick it up himself, although sometimes he drops it and sometimes finds it removed by his mother. He is living with an environment where he will sometimes get what he wants and sometimes not. Depending on what happens between the baby and the mother or "other," who is also a bearer of the values of the society, the baby develops a basic feeling of trust that his wants will be frequently satisfied or a sense that he is going to lose most of what he wants.

During the second six months of life, that ability to reach out and take the toy develops toward mastery of the taking gesture. At the same time, the teeth erupt painfully, filling the mouth, formerly a zone of pleasure, with a pain relieved only by biting. The teeth can bite on, through, and off, just as the eyes have begun to isolate individual items and the ears to attach significance to sound. The dominant social mode moves from the getting of the first half-year to the taking of the second, and taking manifests itself orally in biting. However, the nursing child finds the nipple removed if he bites. Weaning begins. Sorrow or nostalgia begins too; it was with a bite, Erikson points out, that Eden was lost. The infant survives the rages of teething and weaning with "a residue of primary sense of evil and doom and of a universal nostalgia for a lost paradise." But if his basic trust is strong, he has an in-built and lifelong spring of hope instead of a well of doom.

Muscular-anal stage: autonomy versus shame and doubt. In the second and third years of life, the child learns to walk by himself, to feed himself, and to talk. Although the hour-old infant can suck and swallow, it is two years or so before he can control the anal sphincter muscles to the point where he can release waste material at will. He then has a choice of social modes—to keep or to let go.

Whether or not this choice becomes fraught with anxiety in the area of bowel and bladder retention or elimination depends on where, within the spectrum of indoor hygienic intolerance and outdoor informality, the society is placed. Other meanings are, of course, involved in the idea of keeping or letting go; implications about the inside and outside of the body—where the body ends and where the outside becomes the inside—and the difference between native and foreign become entwined. The two properly dominant modes must be mastered in alteration.

It is not only in anality that the struggle over keeping or letting go occurs. The walking child struggles for mastery of his whole self in contradiction to such restraining forces as gravity and parental wishes. It is the age that Americans refer to as the terrible twos.

If parents encourage a child to rely on his own abilities to control himself and provide for him a framework that is not arbitrary, whimsical, or too difficult, he gains a certain confidence in his autonomy by age 3. He feels a balance of love over hate, of cooperation over willfulness, of self-expression over suppression. He feels that he is good inside; he walks with confidence, uses his hands and eyes in a coordinated manner, and talks. He runs about independently and vigorously. Pride in an independence that Erikson calls autonomy must be based on a trust that the world will support his rage for a choice. But if his feces are called bad, if he is over-restrained, he feels enraged at his impotence, foolish, and shamed. Once shamed, he mistrusts his own rightness and comes to doubt himself.

Locomotor-genital stage: initiative versus guilt. At 3, children become very interested in the differences between the bodies of boys and girls, children and adults, men and women, as Freud innocently stated, alarming most of Europe. As Erikson notes, the child now moves among peers and into infantile politics of nursery school, street, and yard—out to the world itself, where his learning becomes intrusive, something he goes after and grabs with eagerness and curiosity. In his desire to experience the world, however, the child takes his first initiative at home, where he expresses passionate interest in his parent of the opposite sex. Of course he is disappointed. The boy is refused intimacies with his mother; once refused, he has to deal with the sense that his not being welcomed implies a wrong attempt on his part. If he did something wrong, he is bad. He feels guilt. He also knows that he is too small to rival his father effectively.

He may simultaneously be trying to wrest a place for himself, rather than just protect his autonomy, in the affection of parents against siblings. As he casts himself about, he develops a division between what he wants and what he is told he should do. The division increases until a gap grows between the infant's set of expanded desires, his exuberance at unlimited growth, and his parent's set of restrictions. He gradually turns these parental values into "self-obedience, self-guidance, and self-punishment." Gradually, he lessens his pregenital attachment to his parents and begins to think of the possibilities of becoming a parent and culture-bearer himself.

Usually, the child extracts more initiative than guilt from the conflict and turns happily outward from the home, where he knows he cannot act out sexual desires. Beyond getting, taking, peeking, and letting go, there is the excitement of being on the make, of attack and conquest for the boy, who becomes dominant in the intrusive mode, and of catching for the girl, who returns to the receptive mode of orality. All this takes place in a world that is gradually opening its mysteries to them.

Stage of latency: industry versus inferiority. Learning to use the tools that adults use—language, deduction, the written word, machines, implements, objects of all sorts, bodies of knowledge—presents the child with another polarity. He can become confident of his ability to use adult materials during this period of latency, when he, as a rudimentary parent, is waiting, learning, and practicing to be a provider. Or he can forsake the attempt, forsake industry itself, and come to the conclusion that he is inferior and cannot operate the things of the world.

In school the child encounters teachers who may or may not encourage his industriousness and sense of worth. Through play, alone or with other children, he tries to make sense of the world and bring some part of it under control. He makes models of experience and experiments with them, planning out of his memory and then producing the future he has chosen for his model. He learns to play and later work side by side with peers. He adjusts himself to the inorganic laws that govern the physical world. A sense of valuable industry results from achievement that has real meaning in the culture, not from artificial praise. The child of 8 or 10 must lay a groundwork of worthwhile achievement on which he can later base his sense of value.

Stage of puberty and adolescence: ego identity versus role confusion. The teenage years bring the question of whether a child will opt for the future and the career his parents want him to choose or whether he will choose another. If another, what? Indecision and confusion often cause young people to cling to each other in a clannish manner; when individual identity is unknown, group identity becomes much more necessary. A group shares the awareness of a past and of a future that follows logically from it; it shares tradition, place, frontiers. A youth may sense a lack of connection between his own individual past and future. He is in suspension between "the morality learned by the child and the ethics to be developed by the adult." This suspension Erikson calls a moratorium.

Ego identity is harder for certain groups of people to attain than for others. Girls must confront traditions of reduced status; those whose lives have already seen rapid change between childhood and adolescence have trouble with the new change; minority group members see possibilities narrowing in a limiting manner.

The youth cares a great deal how he looks, since exterior presence helps commit him to a self. In the search for identity, the youth falls in love with heroes, ideologies, and girls. He talks a lot in his love affairs, his image reflecting off others to get a clearer picture of himself. Eventually, the adult emerges, tests his identity on others, and finds it recognized.

Stage of young adulthood: intimacy versus isolation.   Once identity is secured, the healthy person wants to share it. He can now care about another without losing his own identity. The intimacy of sexual relations, of friendships, of all deep affiliations do not frighten him as they do the person who reaches his adult years in a state of continued role confusion. Accordingly, a young adult either shares himself in intense and long-term relationships or becomes self-interested and self-indulgent. The family of origin may have contributed to failures here by its contribution to earlier failures in nuclear family conflicts, but this is an adult crisis. Without a partner in marriage or a friend, a sense of isolation grows to dangerous proportions.

In true intimacy, there is mutuality. The word is reminiscent of the first stage of life. If a child achieves initiative in genitality, if the sensual pleasure of childhood merges with the idea of genital orgasm rather than becoming enemy to it, if love and sex become united rather than separated, the young adult is able to make love that can be shared with another person. It is not only a love that is a sphere of isolated mutuality but one that goes back to the world through the children produced by love.

Mutuality in heterosexual orgasm is harder to come by in societies that do not devote a lot of leisure to its pursuit. Erikson's definition of ultimate genitality includes orgasm with a partner of the opposite sex who is loved, trusted, and able and willing to regulate the life's work, play, and procreation and to look to the healthy development of the offspring. This genitality must, of course, be mutual on all counts.

Stage of adulthood: generativity versus stagnation.   In the all-important decades that span the middle years of life, the polarity offered is that of generativity versus stagnation. Generativity does not mean an individual couple's bearing of children but a vital interest outside the home in establishing and guiding the oncoming generation or in bettering society.

The childless can be generative; it is the adults living only to satisfy personal needs and to acquire comforts and entertainment for themselves who are engaged in the self-absorption that is stagnation. The new generation depends on the adults and the adults on the young.

Stage of maturity: ego integrity versus despair. In the later years, when death has come within the range of daily thought, the mature adult develops a set of feelings whose stem is despair. He may be able to admit that despair, or triumph over it, by ego integrity—that is, a strong sense of self and of the value of life, his own and every other life. As one aging scientist professed, "I can go on cheerfully so long as I remain convinced that cell division will continue indefinitely."

In old age there is, for the first time, little future. Strength comes from looking back to a life that has produced satisfaction. There is no contented backward look, however, Erikson says, unless one has lived beyond narcissism, into intimacy and generativity. Without generativity, there is no sense of world order and, without world order, no conviction of the calming idea that one's single, accidental life has come at a time and in a segment of history when one developed exactly as one did. Without that conviction, there is a fear of death, a despair, and its mask, disgust.

ABNORMAL DEVELOPMENT AND FUNCTIONING

Veerings off a normal course can originate in the three spheres that Erikson usually considers simultaneously and attempts to unify: within the body of the organism, within the interpersonal relationships of the individual, and within the society to which the human being attempts to adapt himself. The focus here is on interpersonal relationships.

To be human is to undergo a long childhood, and to be civilized and highly technological requires further extension of that learning period. As long as the child is a controlled member of a partnership, he is unequal, and mutuality is lost. It is frightening just to be small in body or in capability. He lives a long time with infantile fears and finds them erupting at critical times during adult life.

A certain amount of anxiety is natural to the state of humanness. The infant is born helpless and uncomfortable; he has no knowledge of what is real and outer and what is imagined and inner, and so he cannot distinguish between fear and anxiety. The anxiety-fears of an infant that persist into adulthood can become neurotic anxieties. Erikson's theory of zones and modes forms the skeleton by which certain forms of malfunctioning can be understood. The social modes of getting, taking, holding, letting go, and being on the make or making have already been mentioned. The physical modes underlying these are the physical actions by which the zone under question is capable of performing. The oral zone, for instance, can get by simply opening to receive. Or the jaws can clamp down and the teeth bite in a form of taking. Then the lips can close and refuse to open, retaining what is inside the mouth. Or things can be let go or spit out from the mouth. Or the lips can become aggressive against the nipple, the head pushing in an attempt to press against the breast. Thus passive and active incorporation, retention, elimination, and intrusion are Erikson's five physical modes of action.

The zones of the body come into prominence in a sequence from mouth-skin-sensory to muscular and anal to locomotor and genital. The modes also have a sequence. The matching should be correct; otherwise, the wrong mode will take predominance at the wrong time and start a pattern that is neurotic. In a chart, Erikson organizes the zones along a vertical axis and the modes along a horizontal axis. The child begins life in the lower left-hand corner with an oral stage in which all modes are used but simple incorporation should be dominant. If any other mode is dominant, trouble ensues. In the second part of the oral stage, once the teeth develop, the dominant mode should be biting. In the muscular-anal stage, the dominant modes should be an alternating retention and elimination. In the locomotor-genital stage, the dominant mode for boys should be intrusive and for girls a return to the two incorporative modes. Later, the boy works toward an image of masculinity that does not have intrusion as its dominant mode but a new behavior that is procreative and takes into account the fact that the boy will become the carrier of sperm and the provider for offspring. The girl works toward an image of femininity in which she will carry and bear the young and care for them.

A zone can become too prominent, causing an adult to be aware of the oral or the anal, for instance, in a way that is out of proportion to his stage of life. Or a mode can become too habitual; elimination, for example, can start with spitting, move on to uncontrolled bowels, and then to many but incomplete orgasms in women or to premature ejaculation in men.

Lying and sitting stage. If during the first months the mother does not supply the newborn with food when he wants it—withdrawing the nipple for fear of being nipped, for instance—the child may try to hang on even harder, causing the nipple to be even more forcibly removed. The infant may develop a biting reflex too soon and a frustrating sense that he will lose what he wants.

The newborn fears being manipulated, especially being interrupted while engaged in a pleasurable activity, such as nursing. Stereotypic behavior represents one attempt to complete an action on one's own. The infant lives in a world where there is much more outer than inner control; his resentment at being manipulated can make him compulsive and obsessive as he later turns his willfulness toward the manipulation of others.

If trust does not develop and mistrust does, fertile ground for schizophrenia exists. Trust involves mutuality. The mother enters the room, touches the infant, the infant smiles, his mother smiles, the infant reaches out, his mother strokes his hand. If, however, the infant's sending power is weak, and he doesn't smile or touch in answer to his mother's overtures, she may cease to provide so many smiles and touches. In other cases, she may not have provided overtures of great affect. If either partner is withdrawn, the gap widens, and the infant may begin a flight into a schizophrenic withdrawal. He cannot, after all, distinguish what is inside himself from what is outside, and so he tries to push all the pain outside and live happily within, where there is pleasure.

The infant fears not being fed. He may feel empty, as does the addict who yearns to incorporate through mouth or skin something to give him a sense of satiation. Manic-depressives can feel empty, as if there were nothing inside of them. The infant may feel starved not just for food but for sensual or visual stimulation. He may become, in a manic expression, a seeker after stimulating thrills that do not involve intimacy.

At the weaning or biting stage, an evil dividedness can begin. The infant is enraged with his painful teeth, with his mother when she withdraws, and with himself for his powerlessness, developing a sadistic and masochistic confusion. A drastic, sudden weaning and loss of mother without a close substitute can lead to infantile and lifelong depression.

The infant's fear of manipulation becomes the baby's fear of loss of autonomy. At the time of bowel and bladder control, this fear becomes a fear of being robbed by outsiders or by inner saboteurs. A paranoid fear that evil lurks nearby or even within the body can originate at this time. If the baby cannot resist being manipulated, he may develop such a rage against manipulation that he tries to control everyone and every event in a compulsion neurosis. There is a concurrent fear of being closed up, without outlet.

The crawling baby fears not only too much restraint but also too little; he is apprehensive of losing boundaries. Without boundaries, he has trouble delineating autonomy.

Standing stage.   In becoming upright, the child experiences his sense of smallness in a new way. He is now vertically measurable and smaller than anyone else. Will he grow? The boy looks down and sees his genitals exposed from a new angle. Will they grow? Will he lose them? His fears may expand into anxieties about castration. He lets go of the chair and wavers, losing his balance. Will he fall? On standing, the girl, according to Erikson, "learns to hate him who so smugly has what it takes—and can take it with him." Yet she is already aware of a "valuable inside" and returns to fears of an earlier stage with the new idea of inside value—she is afraid of being left empty or of being robbed. She may also develop a fear of being eaten into or of being raped. The future female hysteric may here find the receptive role undesirable and become obsessed with it.

He who stands upright experiences front and back as never before. He looks forward to see the eyes of others examining him. Feeling small, he may not be ready for that exposure. If he cannot force the other to cease examining him, he may want to become invisible. If shaming is practiced and continues, he can ultimately develop extreme and sustained defiance after realizing that he cannot be all bad. Erikson considers the backside to be the area connected with doubt. The child cannot see his own buttocks, but others can. A feeling develops that others can dominate the backside, even invade and lay low one's autonomy. Paranoid fears of unseen and hostile people can come into being. Others can condemn the feces that seemed acceptable when leaving the body, and a doubt begins that what one produces and leaves behind is inadequate, bad. Paranoid fears of threats from within are based on this sense.

When the child finally walks, he fears losing that ability or becoming imprisoned or immobile. He also fears having no guidance. He fears meeting no borders, as he did when he can crawling. Without being told when familiar ground ends, the child does not know against whom he must arm himself or when he can relax.

As sexual fantasies are accepted as unrealizable, a child may punish himself for those fantasies by fearing harm to his genitals. Under the brutal assault of the developing superego, he may repress his wishes to the extent that he cannot accept even having had them and begins to hysterically deny them. If this pattern is carried forward, paralysis, inhibition, or impotence can result. Or, in fear of not being able to live up to what he or others expect, the child may turn to psychosomatic disease.

The dominant physical mode for boys at this time is intrusiveness, but by the time of true sexuality that aggressive intrusiveness has given way in the normal person to mutuality. If it has not, a phallic-aggressive pattern results. Other neurotic boys may eschew the intrusive and prefer the physical modes of incorporaton, retention, or elimination. A dominance of the physical modes of biting rather than of phallic intrusiveness at this period could indicate a tendency toward a form of male homosexuality in which the man who wants to be receptive to the penis does so in order to take male power. The dominance of an eliminative mode may later involve incomplete or premature ejaculation.

In girls, continued dominance of incorporation that does not give way to mutuality can lead to forms of frigidity, expressed with the passivity of simple incorporativeness or with the greed of the biting mode. Retentive dominance can produce such tightness of vaginal muscles as to refuse male entry or an inability to relax vaginal muscles once the penis has been enclosed. The dominant eliminative mode can produce many small orgastic spasms that do not produce a satisfactory orgasm.

School stage. Erikson talks of two dangers during the elementary school years. One is that of considering oneself less of a workman and provider than the next person. A child who acquired trust, autonomy, and initiative at home can come to school and find himself discriminated against or told that he is inferior. This can cause him to draw away from identification with peers and go back to the personal scene in the home, where he will always remain small. The other danger is that of making work the whole of life. Especially in technological societies, a child can narrow his values down to the point where what is good is only what works.

Adulthood. If a young man or woman has unresolved feelings about his or her sexual identity or role, the pressures of choosing a career and planning a life can more easily overcome the adult and lead to psychic or delinquent episodes.

If adult identity is not secure, a man or woman may so fear the loss of what fragile ego identity there is that he or she shuns the process of sharing friendship, orgasm, or affiliation of any kind. This individual avoids intimacy and retreats into self-absorption or isolation.

The adult who has no interest in guiding or establishing the oncoming generation is likely to look obsessively for intimacy that is not truly intimate. Such people may marry and even produce children but all within a cocoon of self-concern and isolation. These persons pamper themselves as if they were the children, becoming prey to psychosomatic invalidism. Often their narcissism results from severe struggles to acquire self-made personalities. Others may lack a belief in the species. Indeed, parents who do not truly believe life in the given society to be worthwhile may find their feelings come home to roost in the lack of grandchildren.

If, looking back on his life, a man feels he never acquired the things he wanted, did not do anything meaningful, never found a sense that his life was integrated into a world order, he is open to a panic at seeing his time run out, his chances used up.

TREATMENT

Since the infant normally develops trust as the cornerstone on which all other ego characteristics depend, the neurotic or psychotic person who lacks it must be given his second chance for building that trust by the therapist. Beginning as an analyst for children, Erikson tried to provide that mutuality and trust while he observed children structuring dolls, blocks, vehicles, and miniature furniture into the dramatic situations that were bothering them. Then he correlated what he had observed with statements by the children and other family members. He began treatment of a child only after eating an evening meal with the entire family. After each regressive episode in the treatment of a schizophrenic child, he spoke with every member of the family to ascertain what had been going on with them before the episode. When he had thoroughly satisfied himself that he had identified the problem, he might provide corrective information to the child—telling one boy, for instance, that food is not an unborn infant. Or he might turn to play.

Play is not work, Erikson points out. It has no product, no confines of time, no goal or fate. It is outside the realm of true causality and beyond social realities. In play a child can feel at one with his ego. He can manipulate the environment and develop the sense of control that the ego needs. Play itself is curative.

Mutuality, so important in Erikson's system of health, is also vital to the cure. Erikson applauds Freud for the moral choice of abandoning hypnosis, since hypnosis heightened the demarcation between the healer and the sick, an inequality that Erikson mentions in an analogy to the inequality of child and adult. He urges that the relationship of the healer to the sick person be more one of equals "in which the observer who has learned to observe himself teaches the observed to become self-observant."

In talk of cures, the familiar axis images are evident as Erikson discusses four dimensions of the job of the psychoanalyst. The patient's desire to be cured and the analyst's desire to cure him run along an axis of cure-research. It is a common research; there is mutuality in that patient and therapist are motivated by cure, and there is a division of labor in the guidance of how to observe oneself and in the actual self-observation.

The second dimension Erikson calls objectivity-participation. The therapist must keep his mind open. "Neuroses change," says Erikson, and the knowledge of the therapist must stay plastic, his mind fresh and able to deal with new information in a new way. New generalizations must be made and arranged in new configurations that must be abstracted into new models.

The third dimension runs along the axis of knowledge-participation. Combining these two, the therapist "applies selected insights to more strictly experimental approaches."

The fourth dimension is tolerance-indignation. "Identities based on Talmudic argument, on messianic zeal, on punitive orthodoxy, on faddist sensationalism, on professional and social ambition," which were early involved in the new analyst identity and profession, lent themselves, Erikson says, to a control of patients without dedication to the enlightenment being produced. The expression of indignation by a controlling therapist is harmful. It widens the gap of inequality that makes more difficult the realization of that recurrent Eriksonian idea, mutuality.

REFERENCES

Coles, R. *Erik H. Erikson: The Growth of His Work*. Little, Brown, Boston, 1970.

Erikson, E. Identity and the psychosocial development of the child. In *Discussion on Child Development*, vol. 30. International Universities Press, New York, 1958.

Erikson, E. *Young Man Luther: A Study in Psychoanalysis and History*. W. W. Norton, New York, 1958.

Erikson, E. *Childhood and Society*, rev. ed. W. W. Norton, New York, 1964.

Erikson, E. *Insight and Responsibility*. W. W. Norton, New York, 1964.

Erikson, E. *Identity: Youth and Crisis*. W. W. Norton, New York, 1968.

Erikson, E. *Gandhi's Truth*. W. W. Norton, New York, 1969.

AREA B

Cultural and Interpersonal Psychoanalytic Theories

CHAPTER THREE

Alfred Adler

HELENE PAPANEK, M.D.

INTRODUCTION

In Alfred Adler's first publication, a pamphlet issued when he was 28, on the health hazards of tailors, he described two concepts that remained basic to all his later teachings. The first of these concerned the relationship of the individual to his social environment. The second focused on the interrelatedness of body and mind, the holistic approach. The expression of these two key ideas indicated Adler's awareness of the existence and importance of psychological components in all physical disease.

RELATIONSHIP WITH FREUD

Areas of agreement. Adler read Freud's *The Interpretation of Dreams* with great interest and was invited to join Freud's weekly discussion circle in 1902. For a period of nine years thereafter, Adler was Freud's co-worker, but his role was that of critic rather than disciple. In 1907 he published his *Study of Organ Inferiority*, which received Freud's enthusiastic endorsement, and in 1910 Adler became president of the Vienna Psychoanalytic Society and co-editor of the *Zentralblatt für Psychoanalyse*. It is quite fascinating to observe how the thinking of Freud and Adler developed, based on their common interest in neurosis and psychosis. They were in agreement that the meaning of neurotic and psychotic symptoms must be understood by the physician, that the physician's knowledge of the patient's experiences in early childhood and his dreams might help to clarify the hidden meaning of these symptoms, and that the patient's understanding of the connection between these early experiences on the one hand and current dream content and symptomatology on the other could result in significant improvement or cure of his mental illness.

Dissension. Fundamental differences in the thinking of Adler and Freud began to emerge in 1908. Initially, these differences stemmed from Freud's focus on the pathogenesis of neurotic symptoms as opposed to Adler's interest in their final goal, their purpose. In other words, in contrast to Freud's emphasis on causal explanation, Adler's basic orientation was finalistic and teleological. In a series of heated debates, each man tried to win the other over to his point of view, but the breach grew wider. The final break occurred in 1911, when Adler developed his own theory of personality, in which he redefined the unconscious and challenged the validity of Freud's concepts of basic drives and the phenomenon of repression as an essential prerequisite for the development of neurotic symptoms. Shortly thereafter, he left Freud's circle, together with eight colleagues, to establish the Society for Free Psychoanalytic Research. In 1912 Adler coined the term "individual psychology" to describe his school of thought, and in the same year he published *The Nervous Character*, which summarized his main concepts.

BASIC ORIENTATION

The Ansbachers have organized and presented Adler's main contributions and theoretical hypotheses in several books and articles. Heinz Ansbacher, in his introduction to the recent edition of Adler's *Problems of Neurosis*, has evaluated the significance of Adler's work as follows:

> Freud was revolutionary for his day in that he listened to every word of his patients, knowing that this would be valuable basic information for solving the puzzle of mental disorder. But he was scientifically conservative in that he firmly believed that the patient's inner psychological world was ultimately determined by objective causes that rested in his past. It was scientifically more revolutionary to proclaim, as did Adler, that the inner psychological world of the individual, which had such far-reaching consequences, was not objectively caused, but was ultimately the individual's own creation, and that the individual's course of life received its direction not from relatively objective drives, but from his highly subjective goals and values. And it was more difficult to accept [the fact] that the individual could be quite unaware of the goals and values which he himself had created or accepted than that he was the pawn of an unconscious which supposedly controlled his conscious self.

THEORY OF PERSONALITY

Adler's basic concepts concerning personality development may be summarized as follows.

UNITY OF THE INDIVIDUAL

Adler was the first theoretician to describe man as an organic purposeful system with the goal of self-realization and social survival. Thus, the unity of personality is emphasized from both an objective and a subjective viewpoint. Theories that try to explain psychological processes objectively, as independent entities, or in the form of dichotomized categories may be satisfying in their orderliness. In fact, however, they are limiting and artificial and do an injustice to the complexities and interrelatedness of life. The individual (*in-dividuum* = indivisible) and his behavior must be understood as the result of interwoven, dynamic, somatic, psychological, and social processes. We have a need to perceive ourselves as a unit subjectively as well. This sense of unity and continuity is the basis for our sense of identity, for self-esteem and self-acceptance. This theory of the unity of self was developed further in Adler's concepts of life style and life goal, described below.

Adler's concepts in relation to compensation are part and parcel of this holistic approach, which stresses the unity of mind and body and their mutual influence on each other. Useful illustrations of these formulations can be found in Kurt Goldstein's descriptions of the compensatory devices employed by brain-injured patients. For example, Goldstein observed that certain patients, after they have sustained an injury to the brain, never regain adequate functions to any appreciable degree. Yet other patients with brain lesions that are similar or even more extensive are able to achieve an amazingly good adjustment to society. In brief, the patient's progress depends on his premorbid personality and on his desire to recover.

UNIFIED CONCEPT OF MOTIVATION

The helplessness of the infant gives rise to universal feelings of inferiority that supply the motivation for a compensatory striving for superiority. The term "inferiority complex" describing real or imagined social, physical, or psychological inadequacies stems from this concept. Consequently, the dynamic force behind all human activity is the striving toward superiority, perfection, and totality. The child wants to overcome his smallness and dependency in his desire for security, mastery, and self-esteem. This striving for self-realization is an integral aspect of life, just as is physical maturation.

SELF-DETERMINATION AND LIFE GOAL

The striving for superiority and success is subjective in that it is based on man's awareness of himself, on his ability to remember past experiences and to project himself into the future. The individual's life goal is determined by his inventive and creative power; it is an expression of his uniqueness. Each individual develops his concept of self and of the people and things that surround him in his own unique, personal way. And his perception of objective realities influences the formation of his future subjective goals.

The specific kind of superiority the individual wants to attain and the methods he adopts toward its achievement derive from the particular circumstances of his own life, particularly his biological endowment and his early environment. Out of these biological and environmental factors, the adult has created the fiction of a self-ideal. He is only dimly aware of what he is striving for in an effort to preserve his identity and maintain his self-esteem.

Adler's theory has been criticized for oversimplification or reductionism on the grounds that he reduces all sources of motivation to feelings of inferiority and the striving for superiority. But these terms were used by Adler in a very broad sense. As can be seen from a study of his original writings, the concept of inferiority includes insecurity and anxiety. The striving for superiority implies the adult's search for meaningfulness, for the significance of life; it is the striving for perfection and completion. Striving for superiority as the goal of life is specific and different for each individual. His subjective interpretation of the past and present determines his ideas of the future; or, expressed differently, traces of the subjective past, present, and future are present in the individual's phenomenological field.

LIFE STYLE

Adler's phenomenological explanation of personality development centers on the concept of life style. Life style is defined as the individual's active adaptation to the social milieu, which develops as a unique, personal product of his need for integration into that social milieu and for differentiation from it. The growing child selects from among his experiences, especially from his own interactions within his family and his observations of their social relations with others, events can fit into a consistent, coherent pattern. If he is to function effectively in life, order must emerge from confusion. Events that do not fit into a coherent pattern are considered unimportant and are forgotten. He is unaware of thoughts and feelings that would painfully contradict his self-concept. Thus, Adler was convinced that conscious and unconscious processes are not in conflict but represent dual aspects of a unified relational system.

Recent research on early infantile development has confirmed Adler's ideas on the earliest phases of development of the self in the infant's social interaction with his first immediate human environment, his mother. Charlotte Bühler has detected the "rudimentary beginnings of self-awareness" in the infant at the age of about 10 months, and she believes that identity as a self-perception occurs simultaneously with the perception of the other person, the mother, as a person.

The life style develops in a step-by-step maturational process. Children concentrate on and seem singularly preoccupied with the behavior of the adults who surround them. The nonverbal and verbal responses of these significant adults are observed, interpreted, integrated, and remembered—digested and assimilated might be an appropriate analogy. Escalona, in her detailed observations of infantile behavior, has said that a milestone in the course of personality development is the realization by the infant that his behavior, directed toward a person or object in the outer world, has elicited a response. These myriad, repeated, primary experiences constitute the minute pieces of the mosaic created by the child in the first five years of his life to form a relatively stable scheme of apperceptions. This individual, creative, goal-directed structuring of memory, perception, and cognition is the basis for the person's life style. The creative interpretation given to his experiences in childhood, the meaning he finds in them, makes for mature freedom of choice and self-determination in later life.

SOCIAL CONTEXT AND SOCIAL FEELING

Just as the partial functions of the individual must be understood within the context of the unity of personality, so the total person must be considered within the broader context of society. Adler's distrust of fixed and separate categories, of artificial entities, of dichotomized thinking, is again illustrated by the apparent contradiction between the name he chose for his theory, individual psychology, and his emphasis on the importance of the social milieu in which man functions. Both components, the individual (a lower system, less open, an indivisible entity) and society (a higher, more open system), are of equal importance in Adler's theory. Adler repeatedly emphasized the fact that individual psychology views and examines the individual within the framework of his social milieu, as a member of society, that the individual cannot be considered in isolation.

In fact, even the child sees himself as dependent on and embedded in a social situation or milieu. The infant develops his innate potentiality for social feeling as a by-product of the relationship between mother and child and their need for each other. And the educability of the child derives from growing social interest. Reason and intelligence develop with and through human interaction. If the child grows up under favorable circumstances, his early self-interest will be transformed into the desire for a socially meaningful life, and this goal will be attained in accordance with social reality. Adler conceptualized social feeling as a criterion for mental health. Since man's greatest fears concern social isolation and vulnerability of the self through loss of self-esteem, a healthy life style is directed toward achieving competence and social success by working toward the goal of social usefulness. Perhaps Jules Masserman was expressing a similar idea when he spoke of man's ur-defenses against anxiety and disintegration, when he described feelings of mastery, of invulnerability of the self, and the conviction of man's kindness to man as "faiths necessary to mankind." Adler also pointed out that increased social feeling enhances man's intelligence, heightens his self-esteem, and enables him to adjust to unexpected misfortunes. When the individual experiences himself not in helpless and frightening isolation but as a useful and contributing member of the community, he shares with others common ethical and esthetic standards and ideals.

THEORY OF PSYCHOPATHOLOGY

Whether Adlerian theory is explaining normal or abnormal personality development, its concepts blend to form an integrated whole, and each concept can best be described in terms of its relation to all the others. Accordingly, the following brief account of Adler's theory of the etiology of neurosis and psychosis, their manifestations and dynamics, is presented within the framework of the basic assumptions of individual psychology concerning normal development. These include the concept of a unique, self-consistent, active, and creative self (style of life); an open, dynamic system of motivation (the striving for a subjectively conceived goal); and an innate potentiality for social living (social interest).

ETIOLOGY OF NEUROSIS

A neurotic disposition stems from childhood experiences characterized by either overprotection or neglect or by a confusing, alternating mixture of both. Out of these experiences, the growing child creates a negative self-image of helplessness, a conviction of his inability to develop mastery or to cope with the tasks of life. This distorted image of the helpless self is supplemented by his apperception of a social environment that is overtly hostile, punishing, and depriving, or subtly demanding and frustrating.

Thus, these early experiences provide misleading cues, which prevent the child from constructing an apperceptive scheme, a cognitive map, adapted to the tasks of social life. Instead of providing encouragement to engage in further efforts toward mastery and achievement, these experiences leave the child fearful and discouraged. Instead of experiencing the pleasures of trusting and loving relationships, the child becomes distrustful or manipulative. He develops a neurotic striving for superiority to compensate for his exaggerated feelings of insecurity and anxiety. And his vulnerable self-esteem is buttressed by various forms of behavior. In brief, self-protection becomes his primary objective. Moreover, his self-centeredness and his uncooperative struggle for personal superiority to compensate for his exaggerated feelings of insecurity are substituted for the socially directed goal of a meaningful and useful life. Accordingly, problems are solved in a self-centered private sense rather than a task-centered common sense fashion.

DYNAMICS OF NEUROSIS

The neurotic individual cannot cope with problems or enjoy social life because, as a child, he interpreted and integrated his experiences so that they might serve a protective function rather than provide adequate building stones for orientation and identity. Once his cognitive organization, private map, or inner psychological world has developed, it is difficult for such an individual to give up even the smallest segment of his distorted subjective creation. All the pieces fit together, and any change would disrupt the only adaptive pattern the individual has been able to construct from what appeared to be the crucial cues in his early environment.

In contrast, a life goal shaped positively by the child's healthy experience of growing mastery and achievement by the development of his potential capacities for learning, for creativity, and, above all, for the pleasures of social relatedness and love will result in a flexible life style in which there is no fear of trial and error or of new experiences. Integration of these, correction of previous cognitive errors, and the learning of new patterns continue throughout the individual's lifetime. If, in essence, the life goal is shaped negatively by fear and anxieties, by the need for protection and safety, then the individual's subjectivity becomes distorted, and his lack of awareness of objective reality serves to maintain a shaky and constantly threatened self-image. Lack of awareness is pathological if and when the individual develops perceptual and conceptual constancies or opinions about himself and the world based on previous experiences that he wrongly assumes to have general validity. These faulty assumptions remain uncorrected, first, because he is afraid of facing new, corrective experiences. Second, he lacks common sense; that is, he avoids human contact that mighty clarify these distortions.

In many case histories and clinical examples, Adler elaborated on the private logic of such individuals as the neurotic, the psychotic, the criminal, and the addict. Private logic lacks reason or common sense. It is the basis for the formulation of a personal goal, as a product of the individual's misguided conflict with society, "on the useless side of life." Common sense, on the other hand, is the basis for an essentially cooperative harmony between individual and society, and an innate potentiality for social living.

DIAGNOSTIC CLASSIFICATION

Adlerian theory has always stressed the idiographic aspects of clinical observation on the premise that rules and generalizations may become an obstacle to the understanding of the patient's creative potential. Observation and description of the unique individual are, therefore, considered more important than diagnostic categories and classifications. For teaching purposes, however, Adler described four personality types. The first three—the ruling, the getting, and the avoiding—all lack social feeling and are unprepared to solve life's problems. They differ only in the degree to which these characteristics are manifested. In contrast, the fourth type, the healthy and socially useful person, is actively cooperative with and contributes meaningfully to society. From his cooperation and contribution, he derives feelings of usefulness and fulfillment.

Adler considered compulsion neurosis to be the prototype of all neuroses. In many case histories he described the indecision and doubt, the striving for god-likeness, the depreciation of others, and the pedantic striving for accuracy as safeguarding or protective devices that are used by the neurotic individual in his attempt to attain a goal of personal superiority. Although normal psychic life always involves movement—from one problem to another, from indecision to choice and decision, from conflict to solution in a variety of significant and useful styles—neurotic conflict is perpetuated by an evasion of these tasks.

THEORY OF PSYCHOSIS

From Adler's viewpoint, psychosis, whether schizophrenic or manic-depressive, was due to a combination of somatic and psychological etiological factors. Importance is placed on understanding the psychotic's private logic and recognizing its coherence in either grandiose or depressing fantasies, despite a lack of reason or common sense.

Adler also pointed out that—although the neurotic may suffer from a sense of failure, whether real or imagined—the psychotic does not accept the ultimate criterion of social validity, and his fantasies compensate for his sense of utter hopelessness and despair of ever achieving significance in the real world.

TREATMENT

CHILD GUIDANCE

As mentioned earlier, Adler was convinced that the experiences in early life are the first training and testing ground in social behavior. The mother-child relationship is of crucial importance, and emotional closeness during infancy and early childhood provide the most intensive and immediate experience of love and fellowship that the child will ever have. Ideally, this love and dependency will pave the way for the child's optimistic, trusting, and responsible attitude toward people and society. Nursery school, kindergarten, and elementary school, with their opportunities for companionship and friendship, continue his training in social feeling and provide a testing ground for self-assertion and interaction.

Although he was aware of the multiple factors that contribute to the ultimate personality, Adler also emphasized the influence of the family constellation—that is, the totality of interactions among all the members of the family—in particular, the significance of the child's ordinal position in relation to his siblings. Adler's theoretical approach permeated every facet of the child's growing personality and, in addition, included a therapeutic concern for the problem child that focused on child guidance and education.

The ideas outlined by Adler in this connection played a crucial role in the decision to organize child guidance clinics in Vienna at the beginning of this century; in a broader sense, they also influenced the organization of the Austrian school system and its educational philosophy. Adler maintained that close cooperation between family and school was an important principle in the treatment of disturbed youngsters. Not only the child but also his family and teachers were interviewed and counseled with various professionals present. These techniques were especially helpful in alleviating the child's feeling of isolation and in clarifying for the patient, for his siblings, and for the adults in his immediate environment the interaction among all the people involved and the impact each had on the other. An atmosphere of optimism prevailed, which derived from the knowledge that others had experienced and solved similar problems, and this optimism was reinforced by attitudes of helpfulness and acceptance. All of Adler's methods—diagnostic exploration of the child's familial and educational situation by questionnaires; family interviews and family treatment; the combined efforts of a therapeutic team consisting of a counselor, parents, teachers, truant officers (if necessary), and other representatives of society —are still in use in child guidance clinics in both Europe and this country.

PSYCHOTHERAPY

Adler conceived of psychotherapy as an attempt to mobilize the patient's creative resources and help him achieve cognitive reorganization. The goal of Adlerian psychotherapy is the reorganization of the patient's life style, which is a concomitant of a diminished sense of insecurity and a strengthened social feeling. This leads, in turn, to a less rigid and more accurate appraisal of reality, to better relationships with others, and to the fulfillment of the patient's creative potentialities.

Therapeutic process. Therapeutic change is accomplished in several steps, which partly overlap and always dovetail.

INITIAL PHASE OF THERAPY. A relationship is established between therapist and patient that enables the patient to experience contact with a fellow man. The patient's mother may have failed to fulfill her duty to interpret society to the patient in childhood. In that event, the therapist must assume this responsibility as the first step in the therapeutic process, although he will be heavily handicapped in his attempt to convince the adult patient to correct a scheme of apperceptions he developed in childhood.

SECOND PHASE. The therapist and then the patient learn to understand the patient's life style and goal. The therapist's understanding of the patient is, in fact, essential if a reconstructive relationship is to develop and persist throughout therapy. On the other hand, the patient's increased insight into his motivations, intentions, and goals contributes to but is not a prerequisite for therapeutic change; his insight may follow and not necessarily precede changes in behavior.

THIRD PHASE. The patient's inferiority feelings and fears diminish; he develops a positive self-image; and, concurrently, his social feeling is strengthened.

FOURTH PHASE. The patient is encouraged to select and try out new ways of relating to people and to enjoy new methods for coping with the tasks of life.

The third and fourth steps in the therapeutic process may occur with or without insight. Adler believed that insight was not a necessary precondition for cure in all cases. He suggested that in some cases the neurotic's self-centeredness might give way to a healthy interest in others, either because of a favorable change in the patient's external situation or as a result of the therapist's encouragement and the diminished anxiety achieved in therapy. Inevitably, new social experiences will bring about slow changes in perceptual organization and concept formation even when the patient does not comprehend the dynamics of his behavior. Although this kind of perceptual reorganization is undoubtedly due to the therapeutic experience, it is similar to the noninsightful learning that takes place before the patient enters therapy.

Psychotherapeutic techniques. Encouragement was Adler's main weapon in combating the schizophrenic's life style. The patient's exaggerated sensitivity can be overcome by the therapist's kindly and consistent interest in him, despite his bizarre and contradictory behavior. As a result of this experience in human relatedness, the patient becomes more hopeful that he will achieve some of his goals; and he learns to feel less isolated and begins to feel that he is part of society.

In the one-to-one relationship or in the therapeutic milieu of a group or an institution, the therapist must combine acceptance of the patient as he is with the therapist's awareness of the kind of person the patient can become once the neurotic pattern and goals have been removed and the patient's potentialities have been freed to develop. The therapist's assumptions of the possible healthy self in the patient's future will, of course, influence his attitudes toward the individual patient. In a broader sense, however, such an awareness will also influence the establishment of desirable social norms in a given therapeutic group or milieu. If both therapist and patient understand and accept what Adler termed the "logic of man's communal life," and what Erikson has called the "societal meaning in frustrations," then even a delinquent or psychopath can be re-educated in a proper therapeutic environment. This would imply an environment in which he feels accepted as a full member of society, fully responsible for his actions and able to learn new ways to correct his failures.

In individual psychotherapy the patient's behavior is interpreted as a unitary field of interweaving psychological forces, all of which are directed toward achievement of his life goal. The therapist must be attentive to details and sensitive to the clues offered by the patient's verbal and nonverbal communications. These must be combined into a meaningful whole, which forms the image of the patient's life style. This combining of parts or fragments to form a whole is, needless to say, a difficult and challenging task for the therapist. It may be helpful, therefore, to delineate four types of observation that are generally regarded as particularly important in the creative reweaving of the fabric that constitutes the patient's life style.

EARLY RECOLLECTIONS. Reports of conscious memories of childhood demonstrate that the child makes active choices from the multitude of experiences to which he is exposed daily and that some incidents are regarded as particularly important and memorable. The nature of these memories—whether pleasant or unpleasant, whether the child's participation in the experience was active or passive, whatever the role played by each person in his environment—will determine the child's and subsequently the adult's apperceptions and expectations. In other words, these early recollections can be used as a projective test in order to infer a great deal about the patient.

FAMILY CONSTELLATION. An understanding of the patterns of interaction and dynamic group forces and the structure of the patient's original family enables reconstruction of the matrix from which the adult has formed his picture of reality. Thus, his impressions of his environment depend, in part, on whether he is an only child; the first, middle, or youngest child; or an only boy among girl siblings or vice versa. The term "masculine protest" refers to the attitude of a boy or girl who is raised in a patriarchal culture, in which the real man is respected and admired and the feminine role connotes submissiveness and immaturity. In contrasting the biological concept of penis envy with the social construct of masculine protest, Adler anticipated some of Erikson's work on this topic.

DREAMS. In wakefulness and in sleep, all psychic activities serve to strengthen the individual's sense of self-worth and protect against damage to his self-esteem. Thus, conscious, semiconscious, and unconscious processes contribute to the unity of life style and serve a single life goal. The understanding (and interpretation) of dreams is meaningful only in this context. Sexuality and sexual strivings are part and parcel of the individual's life style. To reduce all dream content to its sexual implications precludes an understanding of the dreamer's orientation to his own future. In his dreams the patient reveals his imagined or fantasied solutions to his pressing problems and his expectations for the immediate future. His dreams also reflect the patient's self-concept and his concepts of the nature and meaning of life.

BEHAVIOR IN THE THERAPEUTIC SITUATION. The patient frequently misunderstands and makes an unconscious effort to restructure the therapeutic relationship. This may be attributed to the fact that the patient experiences the therapist's attitude and personality in accordance with his (the patient's) life style, and his response to the cues from the therapist are determined by his life goal. To illustrate, a dependent patient may try to prove his helplessness in order to manipulate or exploit the therapist. The distrusting, guarded patient continues to protect himself against the humiliation and hostility he encountered as a child. The patient who needs to feel superior to compensate for real or imagined handicaps continues to compete with and test the therapist.

Adler considered the Freudian concept of transference as misleading. He maintained that the patient's sexual involvement with the therapist was an unnecessary obstacle to therapeutic progress. On the other hand, despite his safeguarding operations, the patient expects his therapist to be trustworthy, reliable, warm, able, and interested in his welfare in the here-and-now situation. Adler was convinced that every human being, with his aptitude for social interest, needs and wants this kind of relationship.

The therapist understands the patient's resistance to change as a fear of giving up the attitudes he developed in childhood as part and parcel of his life style. An active approach, based on the therapist's empathy and expressed awareness of how much courage the neurotic patient requires to seek creatively an alternate choice for his life goal, will restore the patient's faith in himself, help him to realize his strength and ability, and foster his belief in his own dignity and worth. Without encouragement, neither insight nor change is possible.

During this process of re-education, therapeutic neutrality should be replaced by the therapist's firm insistence on his right to his own values and his respect for the patient's right to be different. The therapist may have religious values or ethical subgroup values that differ from those of the patient. His frame of reference concerning sexual morality and the structure of roles within the family setting may differ from that of the patient. He must be able, nonetheless, by thinking about these issues objectively and rationally, to recognize the patient's integrity and accept his values if these are genuinely held and are directed toward social feeling.

If the patient's uncertainty regarding ethical values arouses guilt feelings, it is particularly important for the therapist to discuss the question of right and wrong from his own viewpoint as well as from that of the patient. Once the problem of values has been resolved through such therapeutic cooperation, the next step in the progression is to encourage the patient to use his guilt feelings as a motivation for change. Neurotic guilt is destructive; active remorse is purposeful and constructive.

The therapist's rapport and empathy with the patient, his optimistic attitude with regard to the possibility of change, and his responsive and responsible actions increase the patient's belief in his own worth. Emphasis on the past may perpetuate and strengthen neurotic attitudes. An explanation of persistent neurotic symptoms that focus on the purpose they serve is a useful therapeutic aid in unlocking the static feedback mechanism of early experiences that has created a vicious circle of distorted apperceptions, leading to behavior motivated by irrational anxiety and discouraging any attempt to correct faulty expectations and concepts.

CURRENT STATUS OF ADLER'S INDIVIDUAL PSYCHOLOGY

As this chapter has attempted to indicate, Adler's basic thinking differed profoundly from Freud's. Whereas Freud created a theory in which man's psyche was divided into discrete, sharply defined entities, Adler explained human nature in terms of continuous, interweaving processes. His field approach led to the concepts of life style, implying the continuity and unity of the living organism, and of social feeling, emphasizing the embeddedness of the human organism in society. These viewpoints anticipated many later developments in psychology and psychiatry.

Harry Stack Sullivan's self-system has much in common with the Adlerian concept of life style. Sullivan's ideas concerning the importance of the patient's social environment and the effect on the individual of his social relationships and vice versa are congruent with Adler's concepts. Karen Horney acknowledged the similarities between her own system and Adler's. And Adler's concept of motivation as movement toward an unconscious, subjective goal corresponds to the notion in Gestalt psychology that the future is "part of the actually present phenomenal field." As Cantril stated more recently, "Our perception depends in large part on the assumptions we bring to any particular occasion; it is 'transaction with the environment.'" Or, phrased differently, "we seem to give meaning and order to sensory impingements in terms of our needs and purposes, and this process of selection is actively creative." In these two sentences, we find the Adlerian concepts of the style of life, the scheme of apperceptions, and goal-directedness expressed. Similarities in the concepts elaborated by Adler on the one hand and by Kurt Lewin, Gordon Allport, Kurt Goldstein, Martin Buber, and the theories of phenomenology and existential and humanist psychology on the other hand have been pointed out frequently.

The comparisons and parallels cited above are an indication that Adler's conceptual framework consists of strong, bold outlines that allow other scientists to fill in their own detailed viewpoints and preferences. Adler staked out the ground, as it were, for the development of present-day integrative approaches. Because he was intuitive, his system in no way contradicts modern thinking and has not required revision. Adler's conceptual scheme provided a useful instrument in his daily practice. As a physician and psychiatrist interested in the cure and prevention of mental disorders, his efforts were directed to the kind of social action that would be described as "community psychiatry" today. He established child guidance clinics, trained teachers in the dynamics of classroom mental hygiene, discovered methods to re-educate juvenile delinquents, and demonstrated methods of family diagnosis and treatment to workers in the helping professions.

Adler contributed to the field of psychotherapy by stressing the methods and success of short-term therapy. The techniques he advocated for this purpose were confrontation of the patient with the self-defeating and self-deceptive attitudes that made him cling to his symptoms; the purposeful use of interviews and explanations; the therapist's active engagement with the patient; and his hopeful outlook toward the possibility of cure, based on the conviction that every human being, even the psychotic and psychopathic, would prefer to be socially useful and accepted. And, because the techniques and attitudes developed and elucidated by Adler have markedly increased the impact of the therapeutic situation and have, thereby, made it possible to shorten the period of treatment, therapy has become available to many who could not afford it otherwise.

REFERENCES

Adler, Alexandra. The concept of compensation and over-compensation in Alfred Adler's and Kurt Goldstein's theories. J. Indiv. Psychol., 15: 79, 1959.

Adler, Alexandra, and Papanek, H. Erziehungsberatung und child-guidance. In *Handbuch der Neurosenlehre und Psychotherapie*, V. E. Frankl, Freiherr von Gebsattel, and J. H. Schultz, editors, vol. 4, p. 569. Urban & Schwarzenberg, Munich, 1959.

Adler, Alfred. *What Life Should Mean to You*. Capricorn, New York, 1958.

Adler, Alfred. *The Problem Child*. G. P. Putnam's Sons, New York, 1963.

Adler, Alfred. *Problems of Neurosis*. Harper & Row, New York, 1963.

Adler, Alfred. *Superiority and Social Interest*, H. L. Ansbacher and R. R. Ansbacher, editors. Northwestern University Press, Evanston, 1964.

Adler, K. A. Life style in schizophrenia. J. Indiv. Psychol., 14: 68, 1958.

Ansbacher, H. L., and Ansbacher, R. R. *The Individual Psychology of Alfred Adler*. Basic Books, New York, 1956.

Cantril, H. Perception and interpersonal relations. Amer. J. Psychiat., 114: 119, 1957.

Dreikurs, R. Adlerian psychotherapy. Progr. Psychother., 1: 111, 1956.

Landsman, R. Symposium on phenomenological conceptions of personality: discussions of the papers by Patterson, Kilpatrick, Luchens and Jessor. J. Indiv. Psychol., 17: 39, 1961.

Munroe, R. *Schools of Psychoanalytic Thought*. Dryden Press, New York, 1955.

Papanek, H. Psychotherapy without insight: group therapy as milieu therapy. J. Indiv. Psychol., 17: 184, 1961.

Salzman, L. The role of sexuality in the formation of ideas: a critique. J. Indiv. Psychol., 17: 108, 1961.

Van Dusen, W. Adler and existence analysis. J. Indiv. Psychol., 15: 100, 1959.

White, R. W. Is Alfred Adler alive today? Contemp. Psychol., 2: 1, 1957.

CHAPTER FOUR

Carl Jung

EDWARD C. WHITMONT, M.D.

INTRODUCTION

THIS DESCRIPTION of Jung's contribution to psychiatric thought, which he called "analytical psychology" to differentiate it from Freud's psychoanalysis, is limited to a definition of his main concepts and formulations—his symbolic method and his views of the collective unconscious or objective psyche, the archetype, and the complex—and a brief description of his practical methodology.

Jung differed from Freud, above all, in his concept of the unconscious as the original, a priori mold of the personality and not merely the repressed part. He viewed the unconscious as an original pattern of motivation that manifests itself gradually throughout life but that never can become completely conscious. Jung regarded the symbolic approach to unconscious phenomena—dreams and other unconscious manifestations —as the most rewarding means of comprehending the language of the psyche and of describing its dynamics. He believed that the psyche communicates with us through images rather than concepts and that these images take the form of analogies and parables that represent the meaning of a given situation. He regarded this "as if" method of communication as the spontaneous and original means of psychic expression, "the forgotten language of the soul."

In Jung's estimation, it is not possible to define the psyche with objective accuracy, for in any such attempt the psyche is both subject and object of the definition. Accordingly, he charted the territory of the psyche in the language most germane to it, symbolism. He utilized the methods of modern physics and sought symbolic descriptions or working models based on observation of the way an otherwise unknown, which defies precise description, acts in the world of matter.

However, it is important to note here that, to Jung, psychic symbols were not freely chosen, abstract designations attached to a specified object by convention, as a verbal or mathematical sign might be. Rather, they are genuine and organic forms of experiencing life; they extend beyond their obvious implications to take on a meaning that cannot be conveyed within our accustomed rational framework. Jung defined a symbol as the best possible description or formula of a relatively unknown fact, of a fact that, although it is unknown, is recognized or postulated as existing.

The generally accepted view regards rational conceptual thought as the standard of normality; dreams and fantasy are relegated to the level of the primitive, regressive, and even abnormal mental functioning. In contrast, Jung revealed the autonomous image world of the psyche, as expressed in dreams and fantasies, to be a vital and indispensable source of guidance and information that was not to be found elsewhere. His method of dream interpretation, which is different from that used in other analytic techniques, originates in this radical and unique view of what he called the objective psyche.

OBJECTIVE PSYCHE

Definition

This term replaced Jung's earlier reference to the "collective unconscious," which had given rise to serious misunderstanding and misinterpretation. Jung defined the objective psyche as nothing less than the totality of a priori psychic prefigurations and predispositions, the whole substratum of autonomous psychic functioning; and he held that this reservoir of a priori psychic existence gives birth to consciousness. In other words, he maintained that this substratum of psychic phenomena exists prior to the conscious mind and continues to function together with or despite consciousness; it is autonomous and has laws unto itself. Although the objective psyche may subsequently contain many elements that were once conscious and have become unconscious again—through repression, for instance—the unconscious as a whole cannot be considered a mere relic of consciousness, any more than the psychic functions of animals can be considered remnants of consciousness. The autonomy of the objective psyche can be observed in the peculiarly organized character of the image and emotional drive patterns that arise spontaneously from that realm. Quite frequently, these patterns take on the character of separate personalities. Jung reasoned that if each of these splinters, regardless of whether the fragment is big or small, has an independent personality, then the larger block from which they were separated must have personality autonomy to an even greater degree. He conceived of this larger segment of total personality as a concealed entity. It can be dormant or dreaming; it does not necessarily include consciousness.

In summary, then, the objective psyche is so labeled because it lives an independent, autonomous life prior to and regardless of consciousness and personal experience; it possesses a meaning and reality of its own, only one particular aspect of which is ego consciousness. The objective psyche is not a part of the subjective being that the individual calls "I"; rather, his subjective experience of himself is only a part—and, in fact, an incomplete and relatively inadequate part—of the encompassing wholeness of psychic existence. General, impersonal, and as yet undifferentiated, the objective psyche counterbalances individual ego personality with varieties of unconscious and, therefore, not yet individualized partial personalities.

THE PERSONAL UNCONSCIOUS

Jung described what is commonly referred to, by Freudian and other schools of thought, as repressed material—that is, experience that was once conscious but was subsequently rejected—as the "personal unconcious." Attitudes, urges, feelings, etc., that have been repressed as incompatible with one's ego-ideal appear in personalized form in dreams and fantasies as the shadow, the alter ego, the individual's unacceptable and repressed other personality, which is experienced through an automatic projection upon another person for as long as it remains unconscious. But, again, this personal unconscious is only a small part of the total objective psyche.

INTROVERSION AND EXTROVERSION

It follows from this view of the reality of the inner world of the psyche that the introverted life adaptation is equal in value to the extroverted one. Introversion, which is defined as that approach to life experiences in which the individual's predominant sense of reality derives from the actions and reactions of his inner world—thoughts, intuitions, emotions, and sensations—is regarded as complementary to extroversion. Extroversion, in turn, is defined as the attitude in which the individual's concern with material objects and people predominates. Just as an overemphasis on introversion may result in inadequate external adaptation, extreme extroversion, which is fostered by prevailing cultural and educational values, may lead to depersonalization, loss of a sense of identity, and submersion of the individual in conformist herd psychology.

ARCHETYPES AND COMPLEXES

The two chief elements of the objective psyche are the archetypes and the complexes that surround them. The archetypes of the objective psyche are a priori energy field configurations that express themselves in typical representational images and in typical human emotion and behavior patterns. They are analogous to the instinctual patterns observed in animal behavior. All psychic energy is channeled and directed into these basic forms of experience, behavior, and emotion. Thus, the archetypes constitute the predispositions of the psyche or the basic motivations and drives around which the conscious personality subsequently organizes itself. The representational images that express the arrangements of elemental psychic life are universal images that appear in dreams in forms similar to past and present mythologems, such as the motifs of mother, father, child, hero, death, rebirth, and the search for treasure.

Complexes may develop as a result of long-term conditioning and/or early traumatic experience. However, their structure derives from an archetypal model; that is, they are based on transpersonal and universal forms of human experiencing. To illustrate, the mother complex—one's unique and at times bizarre manner of reacting to one's mother or one's way of being motherly—is determined not only by personal experience with one's own mother but also by the universal human predisposition and reaction pattern in terms of "The Mother," by a preformed image or gestalt pattern that exists within the psyche. Jung called this preformed image the mother archetype. It corresponds to a mythological image, which is personalized in the process of being projected as an expectation onto the woman who fills this role in real life.

The mother complex develops as the result of the conflict between archetypal expectation and actual experience with the real woman or women who function in a motherly role. For example, a man may project his archetypally based expectations regarding the mother onto any eligible woman in his environment. He will then experience her as life- and love-giving and as protective, sheltering, all-understanding, and unconditionally forgiving; at the same time, he will see her as diminishing his life strength by means of her unfathomable wiles. She is both beautiful and ugly, attractive goddess and destructive witch. And, indeed, all these features are personified in the mother-goddesses of mythology. Although no human being has all these capacities and destructive powers, the human mother who is aware of the degree to which she represents this image can realistically embody its positive, life-giving female aspects and can reduce its negative archetypal elements to an equally realistic degree. However, should the man's relationship with his mother be problematic due to her possessiveness or cold remoteness, the negative aspect of the mother archetype, the devouring witch or dragon, may become activated and form the core of a disruptive mother complex, which forces the ego personality to flee forever from the witch that is projected upon every woman.

In summary, complexes operate as larger or smaller splintered personalities and represent autonomous affect-motivated patterns that are endowed with an organized structure and will of their own. Complexes and the archetypes on which they are based can disrupt and even submerge consciousness by replacing the rationality of the ego with their own weird images, emotion, and action patterns. If the conscious ego cannot translate the archetypal expressions symbolically, their meaning will not be accessible, and the ego cannot relate to them in a way that will utilize their energy creatively. Only through the symbolic approach can the archetypes and complexes serve the needs of consciousness and personality growth; if the archetypes are denied, then compulsive, obsessive patterns will develop, which in their extreme forms become psychotic.

ARCHETYPAL CONFIGURATIONS

As mentioned above, the archetypes—mother, father, child, hero, etc.—are manifested as mythological or personalized images in dreams and fantasies; in addition, they are invariably projected onto other people. The archetypal configurations encountered most frequently are the persona, shadow, animus (in women), anima (in men), and self.

Persona. Jung used this term, which when translated from the Latin means "the actor's mask," to characterize expression of the archetypal drive toward conformity and external reality. The persona is the mask that covers the personality of the individual; it is the face he presents to the outside world, the surface that embodies his external expectations about his social role. In dreams, the persona is represented in the form of images of clothing and as problems involving dress.

Overidentification with the persona results in a pseudoego—a stereotyped, false personality based on early values and standards of performance that emphasized the need to conform. Thus, one actually becomes the professor, judge, policeman, or society matron, rather than an individual who has adopted the role or profession of professor, policeman, or matron, and gives the role its due at the necessary times. Similarly, other people are viewed not in terms of their unique individual characteristics but as personifications of the sister, the doctor, a brain, or a rich man. If the persona is pre-eminent, dream images show clothing that is too tight, rigid, or armorlike.

Conversely, an inadequate persona means an inadequate adaptation to collective and social demands; hence it can represent as much of a threat to adequate ego functioning as an overly rigid persona. In such cases, dream images may show the dreamer appearing in the street or at a party inadequately dressed or naked.

Shadow. The shadow is represented in dreams as another person of the same sex as the dreamer, and it personifies the dreamer's repressed personal unconscious qualities, his other personality. To the extent that the individual is not aware of his shadow and, consequently, identifies with it, he ascribes those qualities he rejects and cannot accept in himself to the other fellow or, collectively, to other people, such as minority groups, who then become the enemy.

Anima and animus. Anima and animus are archetypal representations not of personal qualities but of predispositions or potentials—instinctual as well as emotional and spiritual—that have not yet become personalized or entered conscious awareness. The anima and animus configurations are universal basic human drives from which both conscious and unconscious individual qualities develop. These drives do not belong to the manifest personality but represent other as yet unrealized or recessive elements. Since they include a man's undeveloped femininity and a woman's undeveloped masculinity, they appear in unconscious imagery as persons of the opposite sex, as indicated in the use of both genders of the term: anima to denote the man's feminine aspect, and animus for the woman's masculine qualities. The anima represents the man's feminine potential that is undeveloped to varying degrees and, therefore, relatively primitive and unconscious. It includes his capacity for emotionality, fantasy, imagination, receptivity, and the moodiness over which he has no control. When these attributes are projected, they form his anticipations, fears, hopes, and expectations about women. Conversely, the animus, the woman's recessive masculinity, represents her potential initiative and aggressiveness, her ability to reason, her spirituality, and her capacity for activity and organization. When they are not assimilated by consciousness and, therefore, are beyond her control, the animus aspects take hold of her as dogmatic opinionatedness, self-righteous argumentativeness, and stubborn aggressiveness. When the animus is projected, it forms her anticipations, expectations, and reactions to men.

Self. A good deal of misunderstanding has arisen concerning Jung's concept of the self. In contradistinction to Freud's use of the term "self" to refer to the empirical ego-personality, Jung used the term to hypostatize a central archetype that embraces both conscious and unconscious elements, a psychic wholeness. Since his idea of the unconscious—that is, the objective psyche—extends to future potentialities as well as to all current and past experience, the self, as the center of a personality that is both actual and potential, represents not only what we were and are but also what we are still to become.

In a broader sense, the idea of the self represents the inherent law of one's being, the archetypal drive toward individuation, toward becoming what one was meant to become in terms of one's own nature. Jung did not regard the psyche as a *tabula rasa* to be imprinted with environmental influences. In his view, individuality is preformed in the psyche of the neonate. Environmental influences serve to modify, enhance, repress, distort, or fragment the unfolding archetypal potentials as they develop into complexes. Thus, at various phases of development varying degrees of tension arise between the potential self and the actual ego. This ego-self tension is the underlying cause of one's sense of splitness and incompleteness; it provides impetus for the autonomous drive toward individuation, the urge to become whole, to bridge the split between the actual ego and the potential self, between what is conscious and what is unconscious.

THE EGO AND THE UNCONSCIOUS

The individual ego is confronted with the basic determinants of the objective psyche, the archetypes—namely, the typical predispositions of behavior, patterns of emotion or affect configurations, and representational images. It is also confronted with the complexes that result from the personalized modification or distortion of archetypes when they interact with early childhood experience, conditioning, and traumata. The archetypes and the complexes that form around them operate independently of the ego and are, to varying degrees, in conflict with the intents of the conscious personality; therefore, they are capable of causing psychic dissociation and fragmentation. The resultant threat to emotional stability can be overcome only if these archetypes and complexes are consciously confronted and understood in symbolic terms.

For example, a male patient's compulsive urge to prostrate himself and worship a woman's feet was resolved and integrated into his personality once he understood the symbolic content of his fetish. His seemingly bizarre urge had to be understood *as if* it referred to a gap in his potential wholeness; it had to be translated as symbolizing his unrealized need to worship and adore the feminine world of emotion, fantasy, and intuition as it exists in himself and in others, which his one-sided, rational outlook had previously devalued. Once he acquired such insight, his behavior was no longer governed by the primitive urge. The reorientation of conscious contents and values that occurs consequent to such symbolic understanding enlists the cooperation rather than the obstruction of the unconscious in daily life.

PROCESS OF INDIVIDUATION

Jung described the process of individuation as the growth and expansion of personality that occurs through realizing and becoming what one intrinsically is. This process defines the purpose of therapy for both the neurotic and the psychotic patient, and it delineates the goal of the healthy person who is seeking a clearer or deeper understanding of the meaning of life. Jung commented on this point as follows:

> . . . psychoneurosis must be understood . . . as the suffering of a soul which has not discovered its meaning. But all creativeness in the realm of the spirit as well as every psychic advance of man arises from the suffering of the soul, and the cause of the suffering is spiritual stagnation, or psychic sterility.
> (Psychology and Religion. *Collected Works*, vol. 11, p. 330).
> Conscious and unconscious do not make a whole when one of them is suppressed and injured by the other. If they must contend, let it at least be a fair fight with equal right on both sides. Both are aspects of life. Consciousness should defend its reason and protect itself, and the chaotic life of the unconscious [should] be given the chance of having its way too—as much of it as we can stand. This means open conflict and open collaboration at once. That, evidently, is the way human life should be. It is the old game of hammer and anvil: between them the patient iron is forged into an indestructible

whole, "an individual." This, roughly, is what I mean by the individuation process.

(The Archetypes and the Collective Unconscious. *Collected Works*, vol. 9, Part I, p. 288.)

The achievement of personality means nothing less than the optimum development of the whole individual human being.

(The Development of the Personality. *Collected Works*, vol. 17, p. 171.)

It . . . means fidelity to the law of one's own being.

(The Development of the Personality. *Collected Works*, vol. 17, p. 173.)

In so far as every individual has the law of his life inborn in him, it is theoretically possible for any man to follow this law and so become a personality; that is, to achieve wholeness.

(The Development of the Personality. *Collected Works*, vol. 17, p. 179.)

LIBIDO THEORY

Jung viewed the libido as every possible manifestation of psychic energy. It is not limited to sexuality or to the power drive but may express or include these in addition to any and every other possible expression of the psyche, including the religious or spiritual urge, the urge to find meaning in life. Jung's definition of religion is not confined to any particular creed but is derived from the original meaning of the Latin *religere*, namely:

. . . A careful consideration and observation of certain dynamic factors that are conceived as "powers," "spirits," "daemons," "gods," laws, ideas, ideals, or whatever name man has given to such factors in his world as he has found powerful, dangerous, or helpful enough to be taken into careful consideration, or grand, beautiful, and meaningful enough to be devoutly worshipped and loved.

(Psychology and Religion. *Collected Works*, vol. 11, p. 8.)

Accordingly, analytic psychology gives conscientious consideration to the nonrational archetypal factors of the psyche as they delimit, modify, and direct the conscious ego's functioning and goals. At the same time, the individual who seriously explores the products of the unconscious finds symbols and images arising within himself that have occurred again and again in the past as part of the mythological and religious experience of people of all races, both within and outside the framework of the church. Since religion and the religious attitude arise spontaneously within the unconscious in the form of mythological representations, they are not, from the Jungian point of view, to be identified with any specific belief or doctrine. Nor, for that matter, should they reflect the teachings or convictions of the analyst. They are concerned exclusively with the individual's relation to his own deepest reality. What they demand of him is not abstract consideration in philosophical terms. Rather, they serve to under-score further the need for a symbolic understanding of the images of his unconscious, a total psychic reorientation in terms of his concrete, every-day problems. The following segment from a case history may serve to illustrate.

A middle-aged man of decidedly atheistic convictions, in modest circumstances, had decided to leave his wife and children to marry a wealthy girl, many years his junior. After he made this decision, he had the following dream. The patient dreamed that he was about to set out on a trip to a rather out of the way destination. Rushing off hurriedly, he passed a group of respectable looking elderly men who shook their heads disapprovingly. He disregarded them, however, and pushed on. Suddenly, from out of the clouds, a huge hand appeared, grabbed him, and shoved him back to the place from which he had started.

This dream shows that the patient was well aware that what he set out to do was "out of the way" and contrary to generally and culturally ac-cepted moral standards (the disapproving elders = Freud's superego). It shows that it might be possible for him to disregard these considerations with relative impunity and still manage to get by. Something else, how-ever, could not be disregarded. A power or entity, visualized or symbolized *as if* it reached from heaven to earth, did not allow him to proceed. We may call this power the inner judge of conscience, the moral integrity of the personality, the self (as distinguished from the conscious ego), or the will of life, or characterize it in the symbolic terms of this dream image as the hand of God. All these phrases and symbolic representations express the same thing: They refer to an entity that is both unknown and un-knowable yet objectively real, that is transpersonal and supreme, that has appeared in the form of many symbols and under many names, and that has been instinctively acknowledged by mankind throughout the ages. The dream contains a warning that the hand of God would not permit the patient to proceed.

Of course, one is justified in asking whether dreams of this sort may not express the patient's own unadmitted and unconscious wishes rather than the requirement of an objectively real transpersonal self, an unknowable entity anthropomorphically symbolized through the images of the objec-tive psyche. Could this religious symbolism have been invented in order to furnish the dreamer with a plausible alibi for changing a plan he did not really want to go through with? Quite frequently, however, as was true in this case, the dreamer is startled, even shocked, by such material. Far from fulfilling his wishes or representing any attitude he can recognize as his own, it actually makes a demand upon him and confronts him with a point of view that is apparently unacceptable and opposed to his own desires and convictions.

Not infrequently, there are serious consequences when warnings of this sort are overlooked. The disregarded, unconscious other will then obstruct and sabotage rather than complement the conscious personality, thus producing psychopathology that stems from varying degrees of guilt and conflict. Such observable results certainly seem to justify acceptance of the objectiveness of a nonpersonal source of meaning as a working hypothesis.

ANALYTIC PRINCIPLES

The aim of psychotherapy, as Jung defined it, is to bring about an adequate adaptation to reality. But, as we have seen, he conceived of an internal as well as an external reality. That is, reality includes the demands of the unconscious and the as yet unrealized potentialities of the inner world of the objective psyche centered in the self as well as one's adaptation to society. Thus, the wholeness of the human individual requires an awareness of both inner and other demands. In general, the need for outward adaptation is well-recognized and has been stressed in clinical practice; Jung's major contribution stems from his unique view of man's inner adaptation. Jung maintained that all psychic drives are amoral and ambivalent; that is, they do not fit into positive-good or negative-bad classifications. Rather, it is our conscious attitude toward these drives and toward archetypal meaning as well that determines whether they play a constructive or destructive role in our lives.

JUNG'S CONCEPT OF PSYCHOPATHOLOGY

When drives, archetypal urges, talents, or qualities are repressed or not allowed to develop, they remain primitive, undifferentiated, unadapted, and negative. And, as such, they exert a potentially threatening or destructive influence on personality. When they interfere with reality adaptation, they manifest themselves in pathological obsessions or symptoms. However, these same elements can be integrated into the personality and transformed into positive and even creative assets. Once the conscious ego is able to confront these hitherto unconscious or repressed components, once it is able to recognize their significance and inherent positive potential applications and can find ways to accord them a constructive role in life, a deepening of personality and life experience ensues. Thus, the drives, archetypal urges, etc., which, in their repressed form, pose a threat to our stability, may serve as a force for individuation and growth when rechanneled. Anger or vindictiveness may be transformed into initiative and courage; evasive thoughtlessness may become the talent for lightness and playfulness; rigidity may express itself as firmness.

THERAPEUTIC TECHNIQUES

Jung's therapeutic approach aims not merely at discipline and sublimation but at transformation of the drives and archetypal urges themselves—that is, the transformation of one's innermost being through experiencing the objective psyche not merely in an abstract, intellectual sense but symbolically, as an autonomous other personality, thereby effecting a reconciliation of conscious and unconscious drives and goals. This is accomplished by basing the conduct of the therapeutic process on guidance from the unconscious itself. This, in turn, involves conscious observation and scrutiny of the symbolic statements of the objective psyche as they manifest themselves in dreams, fantasies, and artistic productions, such as painting and sculpting. Of these, the dream is regarded as the most authentic, most autonomous, and purest product of the unconscious. Artistic productions contain varying degrees of unconscious elements, which are contaminated by deliberate conscious formulations; and fantasies stand midway between dreams and artistic productions. The messages inherent in these phenomena must be integrated into conscious life and tested in terms of external values and adaptations.

INTERPRETATION OF DREAMS, FANTASIES, AND ARTISTIC PRODUCTIONS

Jung's analytic technique relies heavily on the interpretation of dreams, fantasies, and artistic productions and on a concern with the trend that emerges in the course of their continued observation. His radically unique method of dream and fantasy interpretation had its roots in his emphasis on the symbolic language of the objective psyche. As was evident in the preceding clinical example, Jung did not subscribe to Freud's concept of the dream as an expression of latent repressed wishes. Rather, he conceived of the dream as the involuntary expression of psychic process, which is not subject to conscious control and which, therefore, presents the patient's subjective state as it really is.

The dream has no respect for the analyst's conjectures or for the patient's views, fears, hopes, wishes, or illusions; it simply tells how matters stand. However, as noted above, it does not present its message in the form of rational concepts but in symbolic analogies. These analogies may pertain to an external object-related situation, in which case the dream would be interpreted on the object level, or to an inner situation—that is, the dreamer's unconscious psychic configuration—which would call for dream interpretation on the subject level. Whatever its content and level of interpretation, the dream is viewed as a compensatory activity; that is, its function is to expand conscious awareness by sending the ego a message describing a fact that is unknown but potentially vital and that, therefore, needs to become known.

To illustrate, a patient's dream of being threatened by her sister would be investigated on the object level first. In that frame of reference, it might be interpreted as a warning against her sister's behavior, if the dreamer happened to be unaware of her sister's true nature and could see only her loving, friendly side. If, on the other hand, the dream seemed to reinforce a conviction already held by the dreamer—if, indeed, it reflected the dreamer's obsessional paranoid conviction—then it must be interpreted on the subject level through reference to the dreamer herself if its message is to be truly compensatory and tell how matters stand. Interpretation on the subject level would confront the dreamer with her own projection. It would refer to the sister within—the shadow, the unrealized aspects of her personality—to those qualities that the dreamer associates with her sister, such as jealousy or cynicism, while minimizing or being unaware of their existence in herself. However, she may also attribute positive qualities to her sister, such as imagination or artistic talent, that the dreamer herself possesses but devalues for some reason.

GOAL OF TREATMENT

A decisive point is reached in therapy when the psychological situation appears deadlocked, with no rational solution in view that might bring about a reconciliation of the conflicting drives. Sooner or later, dreams or fantasies appear that indicate possible areas for progress and development that could not have been conceived of through conscious thought processes. Thus, in their search for a solution to the rationally deadlocked situation, both therapist and patient would do well to follow the images that arise spontaneously from the patient's unconscious as their guideline. The patient's resulting course of development may not conform to the therapist's standards of normal adjustment. However, this is not the goal of Jungian therapy. Rather, the aim of treatment is to develop the creative potentialities, even if this is only the creative potentiality for living, that lie within each individual patient. Thus, the therapist must decide in every single case whether or not he is willing and able to "stand by a human being with counsel and help upon what may be a daring misadventure." He must have no fixed ideas of what is right or normal, and what is not; if so, he takes something from the richness of the experience. He must try to help his patient find new meanings within by helping him to understand what is actually happening in his objective psyche—"only that which acts is actual." To this end, the patient is not so much told about himself as put in touch with himself. He must make a constant conscious effort to grasp the significance of mediating unconscious images as they emerge in dreams, fantasies, or artistic productions in order to bring about the creative transformation of destructive complexes.

JUNG'S CONTRIBUTION TO PSYCHOTHERAPY

Jung's contribution to therapeutic techniques rests on his view of psychological conflicts in terms of their symbolic significance as well as their symptom content. Psychopathology is seen as the result of the individual's inability to integrate new adaptational needs. However, although the intensity of a psychiatric disturbance may be correlated with ego weakness, this may not be the only factor involved. A breakdown in the capacity to integrate the stream of irrational images and impulses may be caused by the magnitude of the new life within, by the individual's unrealized potentials and talents. When viewed in this light, mental suffering can play a creative role in development if the conscious ego can relate to it effectively.

By making accessible through its symbolism whatever views, insights, and awareness were previously hidden and unconscious, the objective psyche functions not only as the source of psychological conflict and pathology but also as the source of psychological and spiritual guidance. Indeed, by uncovering the guiding aspect of psychological symbolism, Jung undertook far more than the task of relieving overt neurotic and psychotic symptoms. In deciphering the messages of the objective psyche, he showed us that it is possible to come face to face with the creative sources of existence and to unfold thereby the deepest meanings of life.

However, if the creative elements constellated by the archetypes are to be utilized fully, it is not enough for the individual to understand the reality of the autonomous complex intellectually. It must be existentially experienced as an autonomous reality. For it is through actually being touched emotionally that one is moved and thus changed. When the dissociation between conscious and unconscious personalities is healed and redirected, when a true dialogue develops in which both have their say, individuation can then take place; one becomes truly one's self. This is the aim of therapy.

REFERENCES

Jung, C. G. *Modern Man in Search of a Soul*. Harcourt, Brace, New York, 1939.
Jung, C. G. *Collected Works*. Pantheon Books, New York, 1953.
Jung, C. G. *Man and His Symbols*. Doubleday, Garden City, N. Y., 1964.
Whitmont, E. *The Symbolic Quest: Basic Concepts of Analytical Psychology*. Jung Foundation (Putnam), New York, 1967.

CHAPTER FIVE

Karen Horney

JACK L. RUBINS, M.D.

INTRODUCTION

WHAT IS KNOWN as the Horney theory systematizes the concepts formulated by Karen Horney during the last fifteen years of her life, between 1937 and 1952. These were set down, in part, in five books and in numerous journal articles and, in part, were presented in formal and informal discussions and lectures. In this fifteen-year period, Horney's ideas were modified. This chapter refers to the final version of the theory as it is elaborated in her last published volume, *Neurosis and Human Growth*. Other modifications that have occurred as ideas and that were only implied in Horney's original work have subsequently been clarified, defined, and elaborated by her colleagues and successors. Remaining gaps continue to be filled and the Horney theory expanded through its application to areas of psychiatry that were not dealt with previously.

The need for this new theory was based on three categories of clinical observation. (1) The difference in the symptoms of neurosis that were characteristic of the nineteenth century as compared with the symptoms that predominated during the twentieth century and differences in the symptoms that were typical of Europe as compared to those typical of the United States. These differences indicated the need to ascribe greater importance to the influence of sociocultural factors on individual development. (2) The fact that the variation in symptoms from one patient to another could not be adequately explained on a purely biological basis. This raised questions about the validity of certain generally accepted postulates, such as the existence of immutable instinctual drives and developmental phases and of sexual conflict as the root of neurosis. In brief, these questions underscored the need for a more individualistic yet more holistic view of psychic organization. (3) The dissatisfaction with current thera-peutic results. Many patients, after a successful classical psychoanalysis, continued to suffer from residual symptoms—such as discontent, depres-sion, or disturbing personality traits—despite the seemingly good insight they had achieved into their unconscious mechanisms. This apparent paradox demanded a re-evaluation of the nature of neurosis and the pro-cess and goals of therapy.

Accordingly, the Horney theory differs from the classical (Freudian) theory in several respects. These differences are cited throughout this chapter and described in further detail in the specific context in which they arise. For the convenience of the reader, they may be summarized briefly as follows. Horney did not accept the libido theory and the postu-lates derived therefrom—stages of psychosexual development, the Oedipus complex, the economic concept of a fixed quantity of libidinal energy, libido-cathexis, infantile fixation, and regression. Although recognizing the importance of sexual drives, she did not hold these to be universally uni-form or immutable in development; nor did she consider them the cause of neurosis. In their place, cultural factors and disturbances in interper-sonal and intrapsychic development were seen to be the cause of disturb-ances in sexual functioning and of neurosis in general. Horney also rejected the topographical hypothesis of the psyche—id-ego-superego—and, in its place, postulated a more holistic, dynamic concept of the self. A different emphasis was placed on the significance of childhood events; these were not seen as a direct, relatable cause of adult neurotic symptoms, nor were infantile attitudes necessarily the prototypes of adult behavior through the repetition compulsion. Rather, infantile attitudes were seen as initiating neurotic development, which then becomes self-perpetuated. Horney also rejected the concept of transference in its narrow sense, since childhood attitudes, as such, are not carried over into analysis. In its place, the doctor-patient relationship was conceptualized as a complex of current interpersonal attitudes and expectations. The goals and techniques of this psychoanalytic psychotherapy are also different from those of Freudian therapy; these differences are discussed later on.

Horney theory accepts the Freudian concepts of psychic determinism and unconscious motivation (although Horney's concept of the uncon-scious was broader than the unconscious of classical psychoanalytic theory, and the motivating factors are different); of emotional conflict as the cause of neurotic anxiety and defensive maneuvers (although the conflic-tual polarities are broader and may be conscious or unconscious); of re-pression; of resistance; and of the value of dreams in therapy (although these, too, are seen in a broader, dynamic sense).

Horney was primarily an experimental clinician, concerned mainly with therapy. Her theories evolved from observations of her patients and were confirmed by further observations. The Horney theory reflects this clinical orientation. Thus, it includes a philosophy of human nature and morality, theories of human motivation, concepts of normal and pathological personality organization and functioning, and the elaboration of a therapeutic technique.

THEORY OF PERSONALITY ORGANIZATION AND FUNCTIONING

The term "personality structure," which is used interchangeably with character structure, appears often in Horney's writings but is not defined in psychological terms. Its meaning can be inferred from the clinical context in which it appears, however. Thus, the concept has no static model; rather, it is used holistically, functionally, and dynamically.

HOLISTIC VIEW OF PERSONALITY

Holistically, the individual is seen as a unit within a social framework, ever influencing and being influenced by his environment. Particular aspects of personality functioning that are symptomatically significant may appear in the foreground or may be focused on for clinical purposes—physical or emotional factors, intrapsychic conflicts, environmental maladjustments, specific attitudes or behaviors, sexual or work functions—but this isolation is artificial. Such factors can be truly assessed only in terms of the total individual gestalt.

FUNCTIONAL ASPECTS

Functionally, personality may be said to consist of the total attributes that characterize the constantly changing organization of the individual. These include his biological and social needs, behavioral traits, feelings, attitudes toward others and self, self-evaluations and concepts, social values, expectations, inhibitions, and conflicts. The normal personality is defined in terms of generic tendencies, as contrasted with the neurotic. Greater value is placed on some attributes than on others. They vary at different times; some are more easily expressed and experienced; some exert a greater influence on behavior; some are more conscious; some are more subjective, others more objective.

Dynamic viewpoint. The dynamic viewpoint postulates that each attribute has a peremptory force. It is simultaneously created by the individual and acts upon him, demanding satisfaction, producing strivings, or pressing toward action. One attribute may reinforce or conflict with another.

Personality, then, constantly changes in observable ways, in definite directions, with definable rhythms. This concept has been emphasized by Kelman in his continuing studies of the psychoanalytic process. It is partly because of this holistic, functional, dynamic view of personality developed by Horney that Freud's structural theory of personality and his economic theory of a fixed quantity of psychic energy were held untenable. The Freudian concept of the ego, for instance, is considered essentially a reification of dynamic principles, forces, and subjective experiences. On the other hand, Freud's concepts of unconscious motivation, activity, and determinism were accepted by Horney. However, her view of the motivating factors, acting consciously or unconsciously, was quite different from that of classical psychoanalytic theory. According to the Horney theory, motivating factors derive from current personality attributes described above rather than from infantile libidinal strivings carried over from childhood through the repetition compulsion.

TRIPLE CONCEPT OF SELF

Originally, Horney sometimes used the terms "personality" and "self" synonymously. Basically, however, personality refers to just one aspect of the self, and in the later version of her theory, the term "self" almost completely replaced the use of the term "personality." Understanding the triple concept of self is crucial to the understanding of Horney theory in general.

The actual self. The actual self refers to the individual as the sum total of his experience. Temperamental factors—need variations, behavior patterns, primary emotional reactions, abilities, talents, imagination, and humor—are recognized as contributors, whose determinative role is not elaborated. However, their role is less important in neurotic development than are neurotogenic, environmental, and intrapsychic factors. A recent modification of the theory by Rubins stresses the importance of such factors as body image, self-concept, identity, and some temperamental qualities in the maturational process. Vicissitudes in this maturational process modify the healthy and/or neurotic pattern in characteristic ways.

The real self. The real self is defined as a central inner force or principle common to all yet unique in each individual. It is not conceived as a predetermined homunculus with specific attributes but as a source of constructive growth, spontaneity, energy, interest, effort, decision, clarity and depth of feeling, and resourcefulness.

Thus, the real or central self is equated with healthy integration and the sense of harmonious wholeness. Recent developments in Freudian ego psychology—such as the synthesizing functions of the ego and the autonomous, conflict-free sphere of ego functioning—have taken into account some faculties of the central self as they were outlined by Horney in this concept.

Horney maintained that, given such optimal environmental circumstances as parental warmth and acceptance and a certain amount of healthy friction, the child who is normal physiologically and neurologically will develop a healthy personality. This view implies an optimistic, nonjudgmental philosophy of human nature and morality. Thus, according to Horney:

. . . there exists inherently in Man, evolutionary constructive strivings—by his nature and with his own accord, toward realization of his
own potentialities, and . . . he will evolve a set of values therefrom.
The criteria of what is moral hinge on what encourages optimal
growth as a human being, as contrasted with what is destructive or
obstructive.

This statement opposes the notion of the death instinct in that the individual's destructive tendencies are considered to be neurotic rather than
innate.

The idealized self. The idealized self, which is the third concept, is
solely a neurotic manifestation and is therefore discussed below, in connection with Horney's concept of psychopathology.

THEORY OF PSYCHOPATHOLOGY

REDEFINITION OF NEUROSIS

Horney's holistic orientation requires a redefinition of neurosis, with attention shifted from specific symptoms to total personality disturbance.
Accordingly, Horney conceived of neurosis as a disturbance in the total
personality that (1) has its source in distorted parent-child relationships
and is subsequently self-perpetuated; (2) is characterized by distortions in
the individual's relationships with others and self, which stem from emotional conflicts and anxiety, and unconscious dynamic intrapsychic efforts
to avoid the disintegrative effect of these conflicts; and (3) results in discrepancy between potentials and achievement, in rigidity and suffering,
and in impairment of function in most areas of living.

The rigidity of neurotic reactions and their capacity to induce conflict
and anxiety are due to the compulsive quality of the attitudes from which
they derive. These attitudes have a driven quality and "must be abided by
regardless of the individual's real wishes, feelings or interests, lest he incur
anxiety, feel torn by conflict, be overwhelmed by guilt feelings, feel rejected by others." Such attitudes toward self or others are designated as
neurotic trends and may include needs, traits, drives, and expectations.
Other criteria of compulsiveness include indiscriminateness, insatiability,
and exaggerated reactions to frustration.

It is evident that the formation of the neurotic personality involves both
intrapsychic and interpersonal (cultural) factors. Horney was one of the
first psychoanalysts to stress the importance of cultural influences, although in her final volume she accorded greater weight to intrapsychic
processes.

CULTURAL DETERMINANTS OF NEUROSIS

Cultural influences form the framework of neurosis in several ways. As
culture-bearers, parents determine the child's generic values, self-concepts,

and some behavior patterns. However, whether the child conforms to these influences or rebels, imitates, or adapts ultimately depends on intra-psychic processes. If they conflict with the child's natural tendencies, cultural influences may blur or otherwise undermine his identity. In a broader sense, cultural influences determine what is considered healthy or neurotic for a particular society. They also influence the formation of the idealized self, although the specific characteristics are neurotically determined. Specific neurotic conflicts may be reinforced by or reflect similar conflicts between cultural values; for example, competition and success versus brotherly love and humility; alleged freedom of action versus the limitations imposed by society; the stimulation of desires versus the real difficulties that may interfere with the satisfaction of such desires.

PSYCHODYNAMICS OF THE NEUROTIC PROCESS

Early childhood experience, in the overall sense, is believed to play a crucial role in the genesis of neurosis. This is not to be confused with direct causality, however. That is, neurotic symptoms cannot be attributed to specific infantile experiences in a one-to-one relationship through the repetition compulsion, as postulated in classical psychoanalytic theory. The adult does not simply repeat childhood reactions; individual neurotic growth patterns have been superimposed on these childhood reactions. To illustrate, the final form of the small snowball that is pushed and grows larger as it rolls down a hill depends on the slope of the hill, temperature, thickness of the snow, and the strength with which it is pushed. Thus, the form the snowball ultimately takes cannot be related directly to the push itself. Similarly, the infant may be subjected to a wide variety of neurotically determined parental attitudes, including excessive expectations, over-strictness, smother love, and rejection. To counteract these distortions in parental attitudes, the infant develops those reactions and traits that can best insure feelings of security and safety. Despite a universal biological dependency, infants can react to parents in many ways. These possible reactions have been grossly classified as (1) moving toward by accepting love, closeness, and realistic dependency; (2) moving away into solitude, privacy, and self-containment; and (3) moving against through friction, self-assertion, and protest.

GENESIS OF ANXIETY AND CONFLICT

The child who is exposed to rejecting parental attitudes reacts with vague feelings of loneliness, helplessness, and fear of the potentially hostile world that surrounds him. This reaction is called basic anxiety. To avoid this anxiety, he develops attitudes toward his parents that are either compulsively submissive, aggressive, or detached. These attitudes have been called neurotic trends or drives. When one predominates, the others are repressed but continue to exert a dynamic force. Their expression may alternate or be modified by traumatic external events, personal experience, cultural demands, the development of other neurotic mechanisms, or changes in the instinctual drives, particularly the sexual. Anxiety, then, is the mainspring from which these attitudes or neurotic trends gain their intensity and pervasiveness. The existence of such attitudes, which are simultaneously contradictory and compulsive, becomes intolerable and incompatible and creates basic intrapsychic conflict that generates further anxiety. Generally, by early adolescence, this constellation of attitudes is grossly defined in the personality structure, although it may continue to change.

The preceding description challenges the classical psychoanalytic theory of psychosexual development, including the concepts of fixed biological phases of development that are related to specific body regions, the sexual nature of child-parent relationships (Oedipus complex), and regression. In contrast, Horney attributed excessive preoccupation with a genital or other organ function to a parental attitude, such as maternal overconcern or rigidity regarding this function. She ascribed the adolescent's feelings of sexual attraction for the parent of the opposite sex or homosexual tendencies to parental seductiveness or unconscious rejection of the child's given sexual role rather than to inherent libidinal tendencies. Sexuality per se and the conflicts surrounding it were not considered causes of neurosis. On the contrary, neurosis may cause disturbances in sexual feelings, attitudes, and behavior. This viewpoint has been elaborated in numerous articles by Weiss on compulsive sexuality and by Gershman on homosexuality.

There is an admitted gap in the application of these principles of childhood development to the individual child and adolescent. Horney was not a child analyst. Her formulations were developed through reconstruction of the childhood history of adult patients. Only recently has her theory been adapted and applied to this younger age group. Thus, some of her colleagues engaged in this area of practice have described variations in parent-child interactions and consequent modifications in the attitudes of the child. Maturative phases have been schematized and related to the neurotic process by others. Recently, Rubins described characteristic changes in the clinical picture of the neurotic personality in adolescence. These changes are precipitated by aggravation of the neurotic conflict by increased social demands; by intensification of neurotic self-idealization, often with extreme fluctuations, as confusions over identity emerge; by the threat to a previously successful neurotic solution posed by newer reality situations; and by an increasingly acute awareness of the alienation from self.

CHARACTEROLOGICAL DEFENSES AGAINST NEUROTIC TRENDS

To allay anxiety and resolve the conflict between neurotic trends, the child and later the adult must institute further protective measures, an evolution that is the basis for the self-perpetuated neurotic development. These measures consist of characterological defenses or solutions to conflict in contrast with the symptomatic defense mechanisms usually described by the Freudian school, such as repression and denial, which are more limited and focused. There are three general types of solutions or approaches to inner harmony: major, comprehensive, and auxiliary.

Major solutions. The three major solutions—self-effacement, expansiveness, and resignation—extend and expand the original compulsive trend into a way of life. The patient may have some awareness of his use of these solutions, but their ramifications, intensity, resistance to change, and implications in terms of his general adjustment are largely unconscious. According to each orientation, the neurotic assumes certain characteristic personality traits, needs, attitudes toward others and self, values, fears, sensitivities, and inhibitions.

SELF-EFFACEMENT. In the self-effacing solution, love has the greatest appeal for solving life's difficulties. The individual is, in fact, compelled to be loving and lovable, self-sacrificing, compliant, sympathetic, dependent; he sees these qualities as having high value. He needs to be loved, to give in rather than argue, to please, to be approved of. He is oversensitive to and fears criticisms, rejection, and abandonment to the degree that he may anticipate these reactions without justification. He inhibits any expression of aggression, initiative, competitiveness, striving toward success; he considers these negative traits. As might be expected, he can readily admit to weakness or unimportance; he overidentifies with underdogs. Unconsciously, he identifies with his despised self; in contrast, other people are always superior, nicer, more competent or intelligent. His attitudes often cause him to be taken advantage of, and he unconsciously invites such treatment.

In its extreme form, this solution may be manifested as morbid dependency and is often characterized by neglect of self so severe as to result in self-elimination. Helplessness has great appeal; consequently, unconscious acting out through illness, suicide, or sexual perversion may occur. It should be noted that sexual masochism refers to only one aspect of this generally masochistic attitude, which involves the total personality.

EXPANSIVENESS. The expansive solution requires mastery over life and over others in the neurotic sense of domination and self-glorification. Certain personality traits have positive values for such an individual. These include hardness, strength, efficiency, domination, aggression, shrewdness, ambition and success, and insensitivity to the feelings of others. He needs to control, have his way, complete and outdo, and gain prestige. He shuns affection, sympathy, and trust as weaknesses; he is afraid to admit to error or imperfection, even illness, for these represent negative values. He sees himself without limits, confident and superior. He mistrusts others and sees them as potential competitors.

The three subforms of the expansive orientation are based on the particular aspects of the idealized self-image with which the individual identifies.

The narcissistic-oriented person identifies with his glorified attributes. This differs from the concept of narcissism postulated by classical psychoanalysis. The person is not in love with himself (libido cathected onto his own ego) but with an irrationally glorified concept of his self.

The perfectionist-oriented neurotic identifies with the irrationally high standards he has set and is driven to live up to them. Unconsciously, he may experience himself as perfect and look down on others with contempt; at the same time, he is constantly threatened by a fear of failure or by awareness, however subtle, that his high opinion of himself is exaggerated.

The arrogant-vindictive neurotic identifies with his proud self. Irrational pride is common to all neuroses, but it is most intense and evident in individuals who are obsessed by their need for power and domination. It renders the individual most vulnerable to hurt pride reactions, leading to vindictiveness, acute or chronic, and the need for retaliation and triumph. Sadism in this context refers to the vindictive satisfaction associated with fulfillment of the neurotic need to subject others to pain or indignity. Although this need may be related to sexual activity, this is only one area of its expression.

RESIGNATION. The solution of resignation differs somewhat from the other two in its dynamic motivation. Self-effacement and expansiveness emerge after direct repression of contradictory orientation. The resigned person, on the other hand, strives not only for freedom from conflict but for freedom from all emotional feelings; therefore, both of the preceding orientations must be repressed. They continue to exert a conflictual effect from within, however, which may emerge when the resignation is dealt with in therapy. The traits of resignation are mostly negative—aloofness, reduction of material wants, detachment. The individual's needs are for privacy, not to compete, not to be involved or committed; he wants to be self-sufficient and independent. He fears influence, obligation, intrusion, coercion, pressure, change, which he may feel to emanate from others, even if this feeling is without foundation. His need for detachment renders emotional ties intolerable; anticipated closeness through sex and marriage may cause anxiety. All awareness of such attitudes as love or aggression is inhibited. The attitude toward self is one of objective interest and numbness, and others are experienced as strangers. The resigned orientation may take one of three forms.

Persistent resignation includes the traits described above plus inertia, disinterest, aversion to activity (although routine or sporadic work may be well done), and feelings of futility.

In the rebellious form, passive resistance becomes active and is directed against environmental factors or inner restrictions.

In the third form, shallow living, the degree of futility, hopelessness, and emptiness is extreme. To avoid it, the person is driven to constant activity and distraction in sex, sociability, participation in others' ideas. Detachment then deteriorates into unrelatedness; emphasis is on fun without real enjoyment or on prestige or opportunistic success without any sense of accomplishment; or the person may become a well-adapted automaton.

These orientations do not describe a character typology. They indicate forms of development, related groupings of attitudes and peremptory traits that may not be concretized as behavior. They are seldom present in pure form; there may be admixtures or shifting as more conscious solutions are found to be inadequate and others are substituted. Thus, we see the pseudocompliant individual who is dependent in order to manipulate others or the basically resigned person who presents a facade of submissiveness or dominance or alternates between these facades.

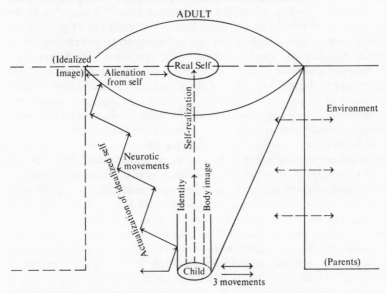

FIGURE 1. *Schematic representation of neurotic development according to Horney theory (modified).*

Comprehensive solution. Even after the major solutions described above have been applied, conflict still exists. The attempt to attain a greater degree of unity, however spurious, requires the more comprehensive solution of self-idealization. This process involves the actualization of the idealized self. Fundamentally, it is a means of avoiding psychic conflict by rising above it. Initially, the glorified image is conscious, limited to certain activities and aspects of self; it is often experienced in fantasy or daydreams, especially in children and adolescents, with awareness, at first, of its irrational, imaginary, exaggerated nature. However, it progressively encompasses more of the personality, becomes more organized, and partly or totally unconscious. "Eventually the individual comes to identify himself with this integrated idealized image . . . it becomes an idealized self" that he is driven compulsively to live up to and maintain. This is so because it satisfies needs, permits avoidance of anxiety and other painful feelings, promises fulfillment of imagined capacities, transforms weakness into virtue, and provides a feeling of identity and unity. Its precise nature in an individual is determined by "his own special experiences, his earlier fantasies, his particular needs, his given faculties . . . and his special solution for his basic conflict." It is irrational and unattainable, aiming toward the ultimate and absolute. It involves specific trends, attitudes, and values: "compliance becomes goodness; love [becomes] saintliness; aggressiveness becomes strength, leadership, heroism, omnipotence; aloofness becomes wisdom, self-sufficiency, independence." It may also involve elements of the body image. Indeed, selective inclusion of parts of the body image in this self-glorifying and self-denigrating process may be an explanatory factor in specific psychosomatic symptoms. (See Figure 1.)

Auxiliary solutions. The total neurotic superstructure remains fragile, giving rise to disruptive feelings of strain and tension. Additional auxiliary measures to preserve inner harmony, sometimes designated as pseudosolutions, become necessary. Only five of the many auxiliary solutions postulated in Horney's earlier work were retained in the final version.

Externalization consists of experiencing inner processes or feelings as occurring outside the self. It is broader than the traditional Freudian concept of projection, in which the individual ascribes his own rejected personal tendencies to others. It may be total, seeing all one's qualities in others; or active, converting one's self-contempt to a contempt for others or anger at one's own faults to anger at these same faults in others; or passive, with inner coercion felt as coercion by external authority. The tendency may be so complete as to constitute a vicarious way of life, experiencing one's self only in and through others. It is particularly evident in those individuals who show a paucity of inner emotional experiences. In such cases, idealized attributes as well as the actual qualities of self may be externalized so that a spurious sense of identity and worth is derived through identification with another person who is seen as ideal. This has been advanced as one of the mechanisms involved in homosexuality.

Compartmentalization, also called psychic fragmentation, is the experiencing of self as consisting of unconnected parts and of one's attitudes as without interrelationship, either cause-effect or contradictory.

Alienation from self is both a defensive measure and a consequence of the neurotic process. It is active, achieving, among other results, the relief of tension by blurring those real self attributes—genuine wants, feelings, and beliefs—that conflict with neurotically idealized qualities.

The measure of automatic control, which is largely unconscious, checks the generation of impulses and feelings and their expression. Instead, these impulses and feelings may be expressed somatically. Physical manifestations may include muscle tightness, constipation, facial tension or tension headaches, and breathing spasms. It may apply to all feelings but selectively permit the expression of some, such as crying, in neurotically exaggerated forms.

Supremacy of the mind (intellectualization) refers to the use of intellect to avoid experiencing emotional conflict. It enables the person to observe objectively what occurs within. Thus, he may accumulate information about himself without applying it to his life. Above all, he values the mystic power of knowledge: "to know is to be able to control." This mechanism, which involves logic and reasoning, may prevent free association in therapy. It may also trigger panic when the individual is abruptly threatened with loss of control by approaching sleep, anaesthesia, or intoxication or when he is forced to let go in sexual activity.

Neurotic claims. Movement toward actualization of the idealized self is expressed differently to the outside world than to the self. The neurotic expects to be treated by the outside world in accordance with his glorified self-concept. Irrational needs—based on fears, inhibitions, and feelings of deprivation—are thus transformed into claims. Unaware of his self-exaggeration, he is not conscious of the excessiveness of his expectations or that the feeling that he is entitled to certain privileges is inappropriate. Such claims are general to all neurotics or specific for each solution. Neurotic individuals may feel that they are entitled to special consideration or deference, that they should be exempt from the consequences of their actions, that they are not vulnerable to illness or mishap, that they are immune to aging or death. They may believe they deserve utter obedience, understanding, or love, regardless of their own attitudes. This egocentricity reveals itself in the expectation of fulfillment without proportionate effort or consideration of the feasibility of one's goals. The clinical effects of long-standing claims may be chronic; the neurotic patient feels he has been treated unfairly and must get back at the world; or these claims may produce chronic inertia, envy, depression, or eventually, a feeling of doubt as to what rights he really does have.

Neurotic demands on self. The neurotic molds and drives himself to live up to his irrational self-concept through a system of shoulds, musts, demands, and expectations, whose specific nature varies with the neurotic structure. These inner dictates grossly determine what the person should or should not be, know, feel, do. They are largely, though not always, unconscious. In any event, the "tyranny of the shoulds" exerts intense pressure on the individual, although there may be some variation in degree of intensity.

The neurotic's reactive feelings about what is, in effect, an inner authority may vary. He may actively accept authority, welcoming a regulatory system that holds in check repressed feelings, the emergence of which might be feared as disintegrative. On the other hand, he may feel ambivalent, passively resist, or actively rebel against such an inner authority. This, in turn, renders him hypersensitive to coercion from external authority. Indeed, his transformation of a rational, guiding external authority into an irrationally coercive one may be due, in part, to the externalization of intense inner dictates. And his attitudes toward authority may be in conflict. The awareness of his need for such authority may conflict with his resentment against it. He may be compulsively submissive in one situation and assume an authoritative, dominating role in another.

This construct has been compared with the classical psychoanalytic concept of the superego, but there are differences between them. In Freudian theory, the superego represents internalized parental-cultural values; it corresponds to conscience. The "shoulds," however, do not constitute a genuine moral code, nor do they represent an attainable ideal. Aimed at some form of irrational perfection, they are always neurotic. The distinction between genuine morality and neurotic pseudomorality and guilt due to failure to reach the absolute has been clarified by Weiss in his papers on psychoanalysis and moral values. Even some religious practices, generally considered to express man's optimal moral code, have been found to be motivated by compulsive, egocentric attitudes rather than genuine religiosity.

Pride system. The idealized image achieves intense value and hold on the individual as it becomes invested with pride. Genuine pride in realistic achievement provides a solid feeling of self-worth; but the neurotic's false pride, based on exaggerated self-concepts and spurious values, is brittle and vulnerable to challenge or threat, as when a claimed attribute is disproved by reality. Neurotic pride may take various forms, specific for each individual. These include pride in prestige, intellect, will power, strength, honesty, lofty standards, lovability, appearance, and sexual prowess. The typical hurt pride reaction consists of shame (failure from within) or humiliation (action from without). This may be automatically, often unconsciously, transformed into secondary feelings of embarrassment, guilt, vague irritability, or degrees of anger, ranging from sullen dislike to rage and hate. When anger must be repressed, fear, anxiety, or psychosomatic symptoms may appear as the only apparent conscious reaction. These reactions may occur not only in response to actual events but in response to anticipated ones as well. They are followed by automatic attempts to restore pride, such as a need for vindictive triumph, withdrawal and loss of interest in the situation, denial or distortion of the event, or exaggerated humor.

The neurotic feels contempt for what he is, for his actual self. Pride and self-hatred, two sides of the same coin, form the pride system. The actual attributes toward which contempt and rejection are directed make up the despised self. They are evidence of the failure to achieve the idealized self and must be repressed. The degree of self-hatred may be extreme, although awareness may include only feelings of inferiority, ugliness, guilt, sinfulness, etc. It can manifest itself in six gross forms: (1) relentless demands on self ("shoulds"); (2) merciless self-accusation through moral condemnation, self-reproach, or self-blame; (3) self-contempt and self-disparagement, often as a result of comparison to others; (4) self-frustration by imposing taboos on positive activity, enjoyment, hope, striving, etc.; (5) self-torture through masochistic behavior or dreams or externalized as sadism; and (6) self-destructive behavior, such as accident-proneness, smoking, addiction, recklessness, psychosomatic illness, possibly psychoses, or actual suicide.

Central inner conflict. Self-hatred is also directed in a unique and often intense way against the real self. Since positive tendencies are particularly threatening to the neurotic idealized self-image, they must be avoided or denied. Taboos are imposed on such qualities as enthusiasm, spontaneity, productive effort, curiosity, and creativity. Although present in all neuroses, this becomes more evident during the final phases of analysis, when such attributes are emerging and the restrictive neurotic superstructure is weakening. This produces a special form of intrapsychic discord, a central inner conflict. Its appearance gives the analysis a special quality. All the patient's symptoms become more intense, but they are less rigid and less threatening and incapacitating. Anxiety may increase periodically, but the patient seems better able to handle it, to stick with it, to work it through. Psychosomatic symptoms may appear or reappear, but they shift rapidly. Previous defensive trends may emerge again, but they recede as the patient becomes increasingly aware of their source, significance, and effects. There is greater awareness of assets, a growing ability to take chances, explore, be spontaneous, accept one's limitations and actual assets.

Alienation from self. Of special importance for understanding Horney's theory of psychopathology is her concept of alienation from self, particularly in view of its recent clinical applications to the sexual perversions; to the problem of identity, which has become an area of interest in every discipline; and to the phenomena of depersonalization and psychoses. Alienation is an active defense as well as the outcome of the over-all neurotic process. The various neurotic mechanisms—compulsive distorted self-concepts, shoulds, claims, self-hatred—all combine to lead to this result. It is a process in which the individual moves away from his experiential center and genuine identity to create a pseudoidentity and pseudoself.

Some manifestations are objectively observable; others are subtle and subjective. Some patients lose awareness of physical activities or body attributes. They may exhibit dullness of eyes or face, few spontaneous body movements, or poor coordination. They may be unaware of visceral sensations. There may be numbness of limbs or an attitude of impersonality toward the body, *la belle indifference*. There may be a lack of capacity to feel, of awareness of feeling, or of depth of feeling. The patient may be angry, happy, or sad without being aware of it, so that he will even express astonished denial if it is pointed out. Some patients are shocked to see themselves in a mirror or to hear their voices recorded. They may have no emotional response to beauty, art, or other stimuli. They may complain of emptiness, deadness, haziness of feelings, thoughts, or relations with others. They may speak of "one" or "you" instead of "I" and describe inner experiences in terms of external events. This vagueness may extend into curious dissociated states bordering on the split personality or trance. Particularly severe forms are the amnesias or depersonalization states.

The vagueness may be experienced as a feeling of discontinuity with the past; these patients may have few or hazy memories or feel little connected with their childhood. There may be a blurring of body image or identity in all its aspects—size, gender, color, body configuration. There may be lessened energy, ranging from unsustained effort to complete inertia, although, at times, there may be neurotically driven hyperactivity in some areas. Directive powers weaken, and indecision and uncertainty become increasingly apparent. Or the patient may be unwilling to assume responsibility for his actions. Primary distortions of the maturational growth process—formation of body image, self-concept, and identity—may produce characteristic modifications of this alienation from self. The degree and nature of such alienation may be of special significance in explaining the causes of certain forms of schizophrenia.

Symptom formation. With emphasis on the whole patient (character structure)—course of development, process, patterns, intrapsychic movements—the isolated pathological symptom recedes in importance. Neurotic symptoms are characterological; they are classified as distorted attitudes or areas of living in which such distortions become manifest. So-called typical symptoms—anxiety, fear, somatic manifestations, sexual dysfunction—are not considered in terms of their biological origins. Specific symptoms are produced by disturbances of personality; they can be studied only in these terms and understood only in the context of the total personality. The character structure and its vicissitudes must be kept in focus at all times. The symptoms are indicative not only of pathology but also of the adaptive measures employed to provide a degree of integration and unity, however shaky.

ANXIETY. It is debatable whether the first basic anxiety could be considered true anxiety. Its precise nature requires further research. However, once the neurotic trends are established, true anxiety is generated. The development of the neurotic superstructure extends the possible area of emotional conflict between opposing trends—the idealized and despised selves, contradictory shoulds, and real self and neurotic attributes. Conflict and anxiety are intimately related, but the anxiety-producing conflict can no longer be seen simply as ego versus id. The Horney-oriented analyst, when confronted with anxiety in a patient, must ask: "What is endangered, and what is endangering it?" In effect, any pride-invested aspect of self that has subjective compulsive value may be endangered, either by a contradictory internal tendency or by disapproval from without.

The absence or presence of anxiety is not an absolute criterion of pathology for several reasons. First, emergent anxiety may be repressed due to excessive control, pride in serenity, or some other neurotic attitude. It may not even arise, owing to feelings of alienation. Or other emotions—such as rage, humiliation, or embarrassment—may replace it in apparent direct response to threat. Second, not all anxiety is neurotic. Healthy, constructive, normal anxiety may be evoked in response to positive movements or when genuine values are threatened, and it is essential for mobilizing constructive activity. In lieu of the term "normal anxiety," Kelman has introduced the concept of tension with a mean variation for each person; neurotic anxiety occurs when the mean limit is exceeded. Instead of normal or neurotic anxiety, the concept of rational versus irrational sources of anxiety has been postulated.

FEAR. Whereas anxiety is the imminent coming to awareness of a threatening, conflict-producing factor, fear is the reactive feeling to the very possibility of such emergence. Fear may be generalized; it may focus on exposure of pretense or duplicity, on failure, on injury to pride, on change in the status quo, on loss of control, etc. Other fear may be more directly related to special neurotic attitudes: fear of success in the self-effacing neurotic, of love in the ruthless, of closeness in the detached, of ridicule in the narcissistic. Fears may occur in special situations, such as public performances, exams, work; or a fear of closeness may arise in connection with sex. The classical phobias are but symbolized projections of general fears onto specific objects or situations.

PANIC. Panic is due to the sudden collapse of a major aspect of the idealized image accompanied by the sudden threatened emergence of intense repressed conflictual drives.

PSYCHOSOMATIC SYMPTOMS. Psychosomatic symptoms arise with the emergence of a repressed conflict, acutely experienced as a dilemma, or a repressed affect—anger, anxiety, joy, humiliation, sadness—that cannot be totally experienced. Such symptoms are nonspecific; the same symptom may be related to different affects, and different ones may relate to the same affect at different times. These affects, in the specific psychological inner configuration of the moment, are externalized onto the unconscious body image, parts of which act as a focus through having been distorted in the self-idealizing, self-denigrating neurotic process. Personality factors—such as pride in strength; control and invulnerability to illness; conflict between shoulds, such as "proper" emotional reactions and intellectualism; inability to participate in emergent anxiety—may contribute to the somatization. Psychosomatic symptoms are also seen to have an adaptive (restitutive) as well as a constructive function.

AREAS OF MALADAPTIVE FUNCTIONING. Specific areas of maladaptive functioning have been studied, such as work, interpersonal relationships, and sexuality.

Difficulty in work may take many forms—impaired relations with one's superiors seen as authority or with one's co-workers; inability to accept or delegate responsibility; inhibition in productivity due to excessive self-demands and fear of failure; over- or underevaluation of capacities; excessive rebellion against rules or limits, resulting in poor organization of time or procrastination; overreaction to routine problems of creating, with resultant anxiety; distractibility or inability to concentrate; or compulsive hyperactivity with scattered interests.

Sexual dysfunctions are explainable in terms of neurotic attitudes. Compulsive use of sex to satisfy neurotic needs to dominate or submit or for closeness is characteristic. Sexual hyperactivity—promiscuity, Don Juanism—may be motivated by inability to form deep relationships, by narcissistic standards of performance, or an insatiable need for triumph. Focal sexual psychosomatic impairments—premature ejaculation, dyspareunia, frigidity, impotence—may be due to unconscious needs to frustrate the partner, inhibitions due to rebellion against perfectionistic demands, or a fear of letting go. Homosexuality is explained by a combination of factors: intense hatred of one's gender attributes, derived from early parental rejection of the child's sexual role and exacerbated by neurotic self-devaluation; actualization of neurotic dependency, domination, or distance needs without related heterosexual conflicts; identification with one's idealized image in the partner; and experience of a more unified identity in an external context.

Other areas similarly studied include schizophrenia, the adolescent psychiatric disorders, drug addiction, loneliness, the nature of creativity, group relations and therapy, mental retardation in children, and determination of individual reactions to therapeutic drugs. These are new directions in the application of the Horney theory.

PRINCIPLES OF TREATMENT

Horney did not enunciate an explicit technique. The theory was still evolving, clinical application was limited, and it was and still is felt that therapeutic techniques depend largely on the analyst's personality and must be adapted to the needs of each patient. Some guiding principles were formulated, however, and these have since been expanded with increased clinical experience.

The theory's redefinition of neurosis, its holistic-dynamic concept of self, and its growth-oriented approach required redefinition of the nature of the analytic process and its goals, with some practical implications, as follows.

With less attention to isolated symptoms, symptom relief is no longer a primary therapeutic goal of the analyst. A decrease in underlying symptom-producing conflictual elements will improve symptoms. The patient, however, seldom wishes basic personality change; this is too frightening at first. He wants to remove symptoms and difficulties but maintain the status quo.

Nor is social adjustment a therapeutic goal. Viewed psychologically, it often embraces compulsive conformity with little regard for the real self. The apparently well-adjusted successful neurotic who actually lives a life of quiet desperation is the antithesis of the goal of greater self-realization.

The concept of curing neurosis makes no sense, since past development cannot be undone. But removal of stifling, distorting influences allows growth potentials to expand; in effect, the neurotic outgrows the neurosis. The aim is movement toward self-realization rather than attainment to a specific degree of a certain kind of healthy attitude. The constructive must outweigh the obstructive. This goal is dynamic, relative, and qualitative rather than fixed, absolute, or quantitative.

Neurosis is a self-perpetuating process, motivated by needs to maintain a distorted unconscious form of personality in order to gain a degree of unity and identity; it is not a simple repetition of infantile attitudes. Emphasis in therapy is on the present, placing recall in a different light. Childhood is important for understanding of the formation of the neurosis and for following changes in character structure and neurotic solutions as encompassed in the adult personality. Nevertheless, recovery of childhood memories is not a primary therapeutic goal but merely helps to expand awareness of current emotional experience as experienced in the past. Present experiencing permits past recall; past recall does not determine present experiencing.

Knowledge by the analyst of the patient's personality and what is occurring dynamically therein at every moment is essential.

To make conscious that which is unconscious is still a basic goal. Conscious knowledge must include not only information but total awareness of inner happenings—past and present feelings and attitudes—now and in all their ramifications as they affect the person's life and being and as they affect others.

Gross movements during analysis take three forms: disillusionment, re orientation, and mobilization of constructive forces. These cannot be easily separated and usually occur to some extent at the same time. The first predominates at the beginning, the last toward the end.

THERAPEUTIC TECHNIQUES

Technique consists of optimal ways and means of applying these principles to produce the greatest possible progress toward these goals. Setting short-term goals is as important as setting long-term ones and sometimes more so, depending on the patient's condition. Immediate goals might be simply to create a supportive relationship with another interested human being to hold the patient's personality together if imminent disintegration, panic, or psychotic break threatens; to go along with or even reinforce some neurotic goals in order to strengthen motivation for continued analytic work, which is particularly important for adolescents; to define and emphasize constructive assets, although doing this too early may be ineffective or even unfavorable; or simply to educate the patient as to what constitutes analytic work.

A formal distinction between analysis and therapy was never clearly spelled out in the context of the Horney theory. Horney used the terms synonymously, often as psychoanalytic therapy. Brief psychotherapies directed at symptom relief or social adjustment are held to be of limited and temporary value. Brief psychoanalysis with a predetermined time limit, intended to stimulate the patient's efforts, has been found ineffective in producing greater change faster. In fact, change may often be due to neurotic "shoulds," leading to intensified pride in achievement of spurious success.

Whether the treatment can be termed analysis is not determined by formal rules, such as daily sessions, use of the couch, or the number of years the patient remains in treatment. Nor is it contradicted by use of short-term goals, since these temporary strategic therapeutic maneuvers may be preparation for or part of further analysis.

Use of the couch. This is not essential; the seated vis-à-vis position may be equally or more effective. It should be the patient's choice; and, eventually, he should feel free to use either. However, the choice may have healthy or neurotic implications for both patient and analyst and serves as the basis for analyzing attitudes. For example, the patient may choose the face-to-face position because he depends on the reactions of others, seeks approval or closeness, or wants to dominate the analyst by staring him down. On the positive side, facing the patient may provide the analyst with a better means of observation. Lying on the couch may be experienced by the patient as submission, humiliation at being lower (inferior), having to do what he should, exposing himself, being distant or sexually vulnerable, or losing control. It can serve the patient positively by permitting greater attention to his feelings without distraction.

Frequency of sessions. Frequency of sessions is another variable. Once weekly is usually inadequate, since the time lapse between sessions allows for dilution of emotional experiences and loss of continuity. Three times a week is usually optimal, though this may be increased if anxiety demands it. Some patients may make more progress on a once-weekly schedule than others do who are seen three times a week.

Fees. Requiring the patient to pay an adequate fee and assume responsibility for broken appointments is essential, not necessarily because of the feelings of sacrifice engendered but to indicate the value of the time, effort, service, and responsibility. Attitudes about payment must be analyzed as an aspect of general handling of money or an expression of the patient's feelings toward the analyst. Compulsive promptness or lateness of payment, forgetting whether payment is to be made on a session or monthly basis, handing it to the analyst obviously, or mailing it unobtrusively can be indices of attitudes of compliance, resistance, perfectionism, claims for special treatment, needs for distance, etc.

Free association. Free association is desirable but not essential. It does not imply uttering everything that comes to mind, as classically stated, but refers to uncensored, spontaneous reporting of all inner experiences—sensations, feelings, thoughts, dreams, etc.—at the same time that attention is directed on such productions. This is seldom done early in analysis, since neurotic tendencies are implicated in speech, and spontaneity and involvement with self are impaired. Speech may be defensive (rambling) or combined with compulsive intellectualism (use of logic and reasoning). Freely speaking may be experienced as letting go, giving up control, closeness to the unconscious and, therefore, may be threatening. As analysis proceeds, however, the capacity for free association usually increases.

The analytic situation is a cooperative process of interrelatedness, functional in that its purpose is working, in which the analyst carries the greater responsibility. It is a constantly changing relationship, each partner influencing and reacting to the other. The patient's attitudes toward the analyst involve more than transference of child-parent attitudes. The analyst is experienced in complex ways, derived from the patient's unique neurotic needs, expectations, and claims, which change at different times. The analyst may be felt as a loving or revered god or magician, punitive judge, confessor, teacher, competitor, tool, co-worker, or friend. Each attitude carries unconscious claims for change through the magic clue of the analyst's power, without personal effort, or through absolution, learning a lesson or being a good patient.

Analyst's role (countertransference). The analyst plays an active role in the treatment in the sense of emotional participation in contrast to the detached, evaluating observer with the classical mirror function. There is a repeated emotional movement between the patient and the analyst that requires understanding, tolerance, and compassion, despite disagreement. Attention must be comprehensive, wholehearted, feelingful, and productive. The analyst's reactive feelings can help indicate unconscious maneuvers of the patient. However, he should be able to distinguish his own neurotic residual feelings. Such neurotic remnants as arrogance and pride, the need to dominate or be self-effacing, to please or avoid friction, or his own detachment may cause him not only to select particular patients but also to overlook or have difficulty in handling those attitudes in his patients present in himself. His relationship with the patient will be governed by his relationships with others.

The analyst's help may take many forms. His mere presence provides general human help. His interest, willingness to understand, faith in possibilities, acceptance of weakness or hostility without criticism or recrimination, and firmness against cajolery furnish a kind of relationship different from any the patient has previously experienced. The analyst attempts in various ways to encourage the patient's interest and involvement. He tries to stimulate awareness of neurotic trends, their intensity and extensity, mutual contradictoriness and destructive potential, their nature as immediate feelings and as past experiences. He utilizes intuitive impressions and detailed observations and notes contradictions between statements, attitudes, values, patterns of the analysis from moment to moment, hour to hour, daily, weekly, and yearly. He notes themes communicated symbolically at various levels of the patient's associations—reality; interpersonal, including analytic; and intrapsychic. He employs dreams as indicators of unconscious processes. All these may at times be conveyed as interpretations.

Interpretations. The analyst's interpretations may stimulate, uncover, focus attention, summarize, repeat, express understanding, and serve as background. Their spirit should be questioning and tentative, intended to stimulate. They may be explicit remarks or implicit signs—grunts, smiles, encouraging gestures. For maximal progress, regardless of anxiety or relief induced, they should be relevant to the most significant issue consciously or unconsciously raised by the patient; meaningful, according to his present condition and traits; timely, for constructive use at the moment. Positive patient reactions include taking the interpretation seriously, finding it pertinent, working further with it. Negative reactions include lack of understanding, undue anxiety or hostility, pseudoacceptance without real assimilation, and blockages.

Resistance. Within the traditional concept, three forms of resistance are described in the context of the Horney theory. Forces interfering with the drive toward self-realization, including the neurosis itself, are retarding forces. However, such obstructive forces need not prevent progress; a neurotic need to know everything can be an incentive to work at something. Such obstructive forces are manifested as defenses, evident in life but more so in analysis when the patient is under attack. The constant question is: "What is he defending, and what is he defending against?" These are the characterological trends and attitudes of the neurotic structure. Specific manifestations of these defenses, arising when they are threatened, are called blockages. They may be personal or impersonal; expressed against self, analyst, or others; passive or active; acute (such as use of alcohol or drugs, silence, listlessness, forgetting, or acute negative therapeutic reaction) or chronic (lessening of curiosity about self, inertia, increased unconscious dishonesty through denial, rationalization, vagueness, complaints about lack of progress).

Dreams. Dreams are a primary tool for furthering analytic insight, to extend beyond just taking into account latent symbolic meanings. The first dream related in the analysis, whether a present or a past recurrent one, is crucially significant. It is the purest, tersest, and most meaningful, often expressing the patient's entire personality structure and attitudes toward life and the analysis; it can seldom be interpreted effectively early in treatment. The form of dreams is important; they may be abbreviated or detailed, disorganized or structured, close to or far from reality, static or full of movement. The rhythm of the dreaming pattern—rare, frequent, cyclic

—indicates psychic activity; why the dream has been presented *now* should be considered. Series of dreams may indicate evolution of some trend or psychic movement. Attitudes toward dreams—actively relating them to self, recall at beginning or end of hour, good recall or forgetting, verbal or written—indicate attitudes toward the unconscious. Content may show symbolic meanings not only as object symbols but as representations of attitudes, conflicts, solutions, directions of movement, active or observer involvement, relationships with others, degree of relatedness (dreams within dreams, movies), etc.

LIMITATIONS OF THERAPY

The limitations of Horney therapy are determined by the goals, by the degree to which any patient can avail himself of it, and by lack of experience of its practitioners with specific diagnostic conditions. It is long-term therapy requiring much time and money; thus, it is limited in the number it can reach, although low-cost clinics and group analysis are increasing this number. An overwhelmingly unfavorable past or present environment may limit the extent of change. A certain capacity for psychological thinking and awareness is required, although this is relative. Also favorable are a certain moral toughness, a tolerance for anxiety or psychic pain, an ability to stay with a problem, a basic desire to change, and a certain intelligence and imagination. Absence of these qualities is limiting. Advanced age is a relative limitation, rigidity of attitude and behavior being more important than chronological age. Use of this therapy with children is still limited; further experience is needed. Application to psychotics and sociopathic or acting-out personalities is largely unexplored, with clinical effectiveness demonstrated in a limited number of cases. Some aspects of certain specific conditions, such as sexual perversions and psychosomatic diseases, have not yet been satisfactorily explained in the holistic framework.

CURRENT PERSPECTIVES

Given these limitations, as well as its already proved empirical value for patients amenable to analytic treatment, what is the future of this theory? On the one hand, its application seems to be growing as the number of its practitioners increases and further usage is explored experimentally. It can be applied to conditions hitherto considered to have a poor prognosis, such as certain forms of psychosis and adolescent syndromes. One indication of its value lies in the number of its ideas being adopted and adapted by classical psychoanalysis (usually without credit being given to Horney), such as the synthesizing ego functions and the significance of pride in neurosis (Hartmann); the expanded notion of neurotic polarities in conflict, leading to further conflict (Kubie); the reevaluation of narcissism and the ego ideal (A. Reich, and Arlow); the concept of a working relationship in analysis.

On the other hand, in its present state Horney theory is not the final answer to our understanding of psychopathology, and it will require continued clarification and modification to increase its applicability to particular mental conditions, such as the childhood behavior disorders and certain forms of psychosis; to particular types of patients, such as the elderly; to lower socioeconomic groups; to the mentally retarded. It must be refined for application to newer settings, such as the clinic; for use with the heterogeneous group and the family; and for use in combination with psychotropic drugs.

REFERENCES

Horney, K. *The Neurotic Personality of Our Time*. W. W. Norton, New York, 1937.

Horney, K. *New Ways in Psychoanalysis*. W. W. Norton, New York, 1939.

Horney, K. *Self-Analysis*. W. W. Norton, New York, 1942.

Horney, K. *Our Inner Conflicts*. W. W. Norton, New York, 1945.

Horney, K. *Neurosis and Human Growth*. W. W. Norton, New York, 1950.

Kelman, H. *The Process in Psychoanalysis*. American Institute for Psychoanalysis, New York, 1963.

Kelman, H., editor. *Advances in Psychoanalysis*. W. W. Norton, New York, 1964.

Kelman, H., editor. *New Perspectives in Psychoanalysis*. W. W. Norton, New York, 1965.

Rubins, J. On the early development of the self: its role in neurosis. Amer. J. Psychoanal., 22: 122, 1962.

Rubins, J. The self-idealizing process during late adolescence. Amer. J. Psychoanal., 24: 27, 1965.

Sheiner, S. B. Schizophrenia: a panel. Amer. J. Psychoanal., 17: 110, 1957.

Sheiner, S. B. On the therapy of schizophrenia. Amer. J. Psychoanal., 24: 167, 1964.

CHAPTER SIX

Harry Stack Sullivan

LEON SALZMAN, M.D.

INTRODUCTION

HARRY STACK SULLIVAN received his training in psychiatry during the early years of Freud's profound influence on American psychiatry. However, he did not go to Vienna for his psychoanalytic experience and training, as did so many of his colleagues. Instead, he worked in the United States with Adolf Meyer at Johns Hopkins, at the Sheppard Pratt Hospital in Towson, Maryland, and with William Alanson White at St. Elizabeth's Hospital in Washington, D.C. He was a founder and charter member of the Washington Psychoanalytic Society and founder of the Washington School of Psychiatry. Both his analytic training and his personal analysis were in the classical tradition.

Sullivan made basic and significant contributions to psychodynamic theory and to the theory of mental disorders, which emphasized the cultural matrix of personality development.

The particular direction and emphasis of these contributions derived from his close association with social scientists—such as Ruth Benedict, Margaret Mead, Edward Sapir, Leonard Cottrell, and Harold Lasswell—and with culturally oriented colleagues, such as Erich Fromm and Karen Horney. In brief, Sullivan worked closely with a group of psychoanalysts and social psychologists who were moving away from the classical psychoanalytic theories because of the biological and instinctual bias of those theories.

HISTORICAL BACKGROUND

Freud believed that man developed out of a matrix of instinctual forces that needed to be restrained and inhibited when confronted by the external world. According to this instinctivist psychology, man was viewed as an animal, overwhelmed by inner forces he must repress or restructure in order to survive as a social being. The focus of study, therefore, was directed primarily toward the elucidation of these inner pressures, which were topographically located in the id. The unconscious, as a reservoir of id forces and repressed impulses, was the source of great interest in psychoanalytic theory and therapy. Freud's system was called an id psychology, in contrast to later theories, which were centered on the psychology of the ego.

There were serious objections to Freud's psychoanalytic theories from the beginning, particularly to the sexual nature of the libido. These disagreements ultimately produced dissensions in the psychoanalytic movement. In the early 1900's and during the period of mass exodus of psychoanalysts to the United States in the 1930's, there was evidence of growing dissatisfaction with Freud's instinct theory and increasing recognition of the significance of ego factors in man's psychology.

These European psychoanalysts—particularly Karen Horney, Erich Fromm, Sandor Rado, and Franz Alexander—were exposed to a new culture, where the predominant values and ethics differed from those they had known in Europe. Some of Freud's theories, which were presumed to have universal application, did not seem to be as significant in the American scene as they were in Germany and the Austro-Hungarian culture. This raised many new questions about the role of culture in personality development. The effect of culture, as opposed to instinct, took an increasingly prominent role in personality theory. The ubiquity of many of the variables in human development, which had been considered biologically ordained, were examined anew in the light of the influence of the social, political, and economic factors in man's growth. The Oedipus complex, for example, which Freud and his followers believed was inherited and biologically innate, could be viewed as a potential development that might be manifested if the social structure of the family or the community stimulated attachments to the stronger members of the household. In other cases, subtle or overt sexually seductive behavior on the part of the child's parents might constitute a precipitating factor in the emergence of this phenomena. In any event, the Oedipus complex could not be viewed as innately present in all individuals regardless of their experience with their parents or the social structure of their environment.

In addition, the climate of scientific philosophizing was vastly altered in the 1900's by the formulations of electromagnetic theory and Einstein's theory of relativity. Freud had formulated his theories on the basis of the prevailing scientific model of the nineteenth century—the mechanical, physical model, represented by hydraulics and energy mechanics. And this was entirely appropriate for the late 1800's, before wave and quantum theory were elaborated to explain the physical world. However, the deficiencies of the mechanical model became glaringly apparent in the 1900's, when the principles of interaction, transactional theory, relativity, and the field theory concepts tended to emphasize the limitations of the mechanical model for the study of the behavior of particles as well as man.

SULLIVAN'S SCIENTIFIC ORIENTATION

This was the setting for Sullivan's intellectual development. The ultimate elaboration of his theories of personality within an interpersonal framework reflected the strong influence of his social scientist colleagues and his talent and interest in science in general. Sullivan was dissatisfied with those psychological theories that depended on extensive extrapolations from hypotheses that could not be tested. He was particularly impatient with those psychoanalytic concepts that could not be validated because they were based on experiences beyond recall or because they required prior acceptance of certain variables, such as the aggressive or death instinct, as universal human attributes. Consequently, he insisted on formulating his concepts entirely from observable data.

METHODOLOGY

For example, instead of postulating a maternal instinct to explain the dominating interest of a mother in her child or the desire of a woman to have children, Sullivan hypothesized that the tension of the infant's needs stimulate anxiety in the mother, which is manifested as tenderness and results in the care and attention that the infant requires. This proposition, which he called the "tenderness postulate," is described later on. It is possible to test the validity of this formulation by studying the effect of the needs of the infant on all adults in his immediate environment and then determining whether the biological mother is actually more involved with the infant than any other person or whether anyone who is capable of tenderness is not equally affected by the helplessness of the infant. Unlike the conception of a maternal instinct, which presupposes an innate interest and tenderness toward one's offspring, this proposition examines the phenomenon of motherhood and tenderness as an interpersonal development, dependent on the stimulation of anxiety in one person by the needs of another.

Similarly, Freud's assumption of an innate aggressiveness, known as an aggressive instinct, predetermines the observation and identification of a piece of behavior, since it is assumed that aggressive behavior is universally present. Sullivan suggested that the notion of an aggressive instinct be put aside and human behavior simply observed. It may be that evidences of aggressiveness will be discovered, but one can then proceed to explore the conditions under which it was produced, whether it is universally present as a primary phenomenon or secondarily provoked by the behavior of another person. This is a critical matter and has been the subject of a great number of genetic, biological, and anthropological studies. The developmental child studies of Piaget, Gesell, and others strongly suggest that aggression is a secondary phenomenon rather than an innate one.

In this sense Sullivan limited his concepts to formulations that were capable of being tested and either validated or disproved. The prior assumption of an Oedipus complex or an aggressive instinct does not permit the investigator to observe human behavior objectively and without prejudice. Consequently, when one begins by assuming the existence of an aggressive instinct, and then aggression is noted in a child, this becomes evidence that such an instinct does indeed exist and only needs to be identified. If, on the other hand, one does not begin with this assumption, then one is free to speculate as to what elicited this specific reaction rather than other possible reactions and what circumstances are likely to produce an aggressive reaction rather than some other type of response.

Many of the early psychoanalytic hypotheses grew out of speculations and global interpretations based on a few intensive analytic studies. Data were then accumulated to affirm these hypotheses. Thus, once the notion of an innate Oedipus complex was proposed, the absence of confirmatory data was described as denial of its presence, and the presence of data to confirm it was accepted at face value. In contrast to this approach, Sullivan suggested that, if the investigator begins afresh, without previous preconceptions, he will find the Oedipus complex present in a great many individuals. However, Sullivan insisted that the investigator would also find it absent in many individuals. Ideally, the investigator would then be stimulated to identify the factors that might account for its presence in one person and not in another, and this would greatly advance the understanding of the phenomenon.

In fact, the situation prevails in large areas of psychoanalytic theory, where present knowledge does not justify reified concepts. This can be demonstrated most succinctly in some of the prevailing notions on the psychology of the female. For example, the concept of penis envy states that the female not only experiences the absence of a penis as a loss and denial but actively envies the male in this respect. This concept is an outgrowth of Freud's notion of the primacy of the male. Accordingly, a great deal of activity in the female, such as competitiveness with the male in occupational or aesthetic pursuits or aggressive striving for status and esteem in so-called male areas of interest, is automatically labeled penis envy and is derogated or viewed as abnormal if it extends beyond certain limits. However, if the female is studied without prefixed notions as to the components of her behavior, one might conclude that her activity derives from many sources, some of which are far removed from sexual envy. Her competitiveness or aggressive strivings may be a reaction to cultural restrictions and prejudices as well as the result of a natural striving for achievement. Feminine interest in male pursuits can be viewed as an unwillingness to accept such distinctions, which, after all, have been categorized in this way by the male. Sullivan did not allow such established concepts about the female to intrude on his investigations; instead, he tried to study the origins of behavior in the context of a specific situation and within the framework of his subject's idiosyncratic personal history.

Clearly, when the observation and examination of data are guided by open-ended hypotheses that are capable of being proved or disproved, this is conducive to a more scientific approach to the study of human behavior. Sullivan's views generally encouraged such an approach.

AREA OF INVESTIGATION

Sullivan defined psychiatry as the study of interpersonal relations that were manifest in observable behavior of individuals. Although he had great interest in what transpired on the inside of an individual, he felt that the individual could be studied only in terms of his interaction with others. Thus, the main focus for Sullivan's study of man was man's transactions with others, particularly the activity that transpired between them. The field of operation—how one person behaved toward another, how each person's behavior was affected by the behavior (both overt and covert) of the other, and the subjective experiences of each—was a valuable area of study. These phenomena could be studied only with difficulty outside of the therapeutic situation, but the process was greatly enhanced when the therapist was one of the participants, for then psychiatry became a transaction between the therapist, who was a participant-observer, and a client whose living was disturbed or disordered. For this reason, Sullivan's theories and concepts tended to be more operational and capable of being tested outside of a subjective framework. Their validity as a tool for scientific investigation was further enhanced by the fact that he took great pains to define his terms and to limit the boundaries of their application.

Not only were Sullivan's theories congenial to social scientists because they stayed close to the traditional scientific methodology, but they were also of interdisciplinary value because his emphasis on the field rather than the individual gave greater prominence to the social and cultural context in which personality develops. This emphasis on the interpersonal and the reliance only on data that are observable through gesture, verbalization, sign, or other communicative devices have constituted the strength of his theoretical constructs, but they have also been a source of criticism. Sullivan felt that there was no way to study the individual's purely private, uncommunicated thoughts and fantasies. Therefore, it has been suggested that he neglected the uniquely personal elements of an individual's personality. This is certainly true to a limited extent, but the fact is that Sullivan believed that such study was the province of literature rather than psychiatry. Thus, he justified his neglect of individuation as a proper concern and goal of human maturation by insisting that psychiatry must deal with those human characteristics that are shared and communicated to others. He felt that these are fundamental issues involved in psychiatric disorders. Consequently, he was the paradigm of the ego psychologist. He saw man as an animal, biologically bound, whose potentialities and possibilities are determined by his culture. In summary, then, Sullivan defined psychiatry as the study of biological and conditioning processes that occur in situations in which the psychiatrist functions as participant-observer, the unit of study being the interpersonal situation.

BASIC THEORETICAL CONCEPTS

Sullivan formulated four basic postulates as the foundation for all his theories.

BIOLOGICAL POSTULATE

This stated that man, as an animal, differs from all other animals in his cultural interdependence. Thus, man's functioning within his cultural matrix differs from the herd behavior characteristic of some animals; nor is the organization of human society patterned on the colonies created by ants and bees. These forms of communal living are instinctually derived, not volitionally determined. In contrast, man's cultural development is a function of his psychological as well as his physiological dependence. It stems from his growing capacity for tenderness, from his ability to develop an interest in another human being that is equal to his interest in himself.

MAN'S ESSENTIALLY HUMAN MODE OF FUNCTIONING

Sullivan maintained that "man is more simply human than otherwise." This postulate implies that man, in the performance of his most diverse activities, is still closer to the human mode of functioning than to that of animals. It emphasizes the basic similarity between the most extreme behavior and the human mode of behavior rather than resorting to analogous animal behavior to explain atypical human behavior. It tends thereby to encourage more simple explanations for complicated distortions of behavior, without evoking unnecessary or unsupported hypotheses derived from myth or instinctual explanations. This does not obviate the value of animal studies or comparisons between animal and human behavior. It only refines and restricts the application of the findings derived from such studies; they are useful only after the explanations deriving from our present knowledge of man have proved to be inadequate.

SIGNIFICANCE OF ANXIETY

This refers to the central role of anxiety in human development. It emphasizes the presence of anxiety to varying degrees in all human functioning but postulates the impossibility of absolute states of anxiety and of absolute states of euphoria. The varying amounts of anxiety present in an individual determine his variable state of euphoria.

TENDERNESS POSTULATE

This basic theoretical formulation has its roots in Sullivan's theories. It is an attempt to conceive of tenderness, in all its various manifestations, as an interpersonal development rather than as an innate feeling present in the form of an instinct or a God-given virtue. Thus, Sullivan states that "the activity of an infant which arises from the tension of his needs produces tension in the mothering one which is felt by her as tenderness." At first glance, this would seem to contradict another of Sullivan's concepts— that tension evokes anxiety, which, in turn, necessitates the creation of defenses against the breakthrough of that anxiety. In this instance, however, the anxiety that the tension of the infant's needs evokes in the mother is experienced by her as tenderness.

Thus, in this postulate Sullivan recognizes that anxiety does not always exert a disintegrating effect; nor does it always constitute an obstacle in interpersonal functioning. The needs of the infant, who is utterly dependent, evoke a response of tenderness rather than irritation. Anxiety, then, can be viewed as a creative force as well as an inevitable accompaniment of human growth. And within this framework the development of tenderness can be visualized as a response to the need of others without exploitative or selfish motives. As pointed out earlier, this postulate is an excellent example of Sullivan's efforts to comprehend the intricacies of human attitudes and feelings as they emerge in the matrix of interpersonal relationships rather than as innate tendencies.

The infant's need for tender concern, in addition to the fulfillment of his physiological needs, has been amply documented by the work of René Spitz, Margaret Ribble, Harry Harlow, and others. Usually, a maternal instinct is postulated to account for the mother's benevolence toward the infant. As mentioned earlier, Sullivan, in his disdain for instinctual explanations to account for global and complicated behavioral patterns, preferred to view the mother's impulse toward tenderness as a phenomenon aroused by the infant's needs. Moreover, this reaction to the tension of the infant is not confined to the infant's biological mother; rather, the tension of the infant's biological needs may evoke a similar response in anyone else in the immediate life space of the infant. The care-taking individual reacts with tension, which manifests itself as behavior designed to meet the needs of the infant. This is described as tenderness and is the prototype of all tender activity in human behavior in which giving is the essential ingredient. As indicated below, Sullivan's concepts of anxiety, love, hostility, etc., are all expressed in interpersonal equations, thereby eliminating instinctual, metaphysical, or theological presuppositions.

GOALS OF HUMAN BEHAVIOR

All human beings have major goals, which Sullivan called end states. The first goal is to fulfill the biological needs of the organism in terms of food, air, sex, etc. The second goal relates to man as an accultured social being and involves those needs that go beyond the purely physiological necessities. These include the need for status, recognition, and a relationship with others. The first goal is called the need for satisfactions, and the second, the need for security.

MODES OF NEED FULFILLMENT (DYNAMISMS)

These needs are manifested as inner tensions, and the characteristic ways in which the individual strives to fulfill them are called dynamisms. The dynamism is the constellation of complex movements that constitute the specific activity designed to fulfill or overcome a need, whether it is a need for food, sex, or self-esteem. The infant's cry, for example, is the simple dynamism used to fulfill his multiple needs. As his needs become more complex, the dynamisms he employs become more complicated and varied. Most dynamisms serve to satisfy the basic needs of the individual, but the self-dynamism or self-system develops as a result of and in response to the basic anxiety engendered by these primitive needs. This is the personality structure that permits the satisfaction of more complex needs at later stages of development.

The dynamism involves a bodily zone, such as the mouth or the genitals, but in the case of the self-dynamism, no bodily zone is involved. The presence of a particular bodily aperture in the dynamism gives it a special coloring. This concept of Sullivan's bears some similarity to Freud's theory of the sexual phases of psychosexual development, but there are also some marked differences. Freud considered these bodily zones to be the central determinant of behavior at specific phases of development. For example, for Freud, the oral phase of psychosexual development evolved around the biological qualities of the mouth as a receiving, sucking, biting aperture. These apertures were important to Sullivan, too, but because they were the areas through which the individual established interpersonal contact. Thus, the infant, whose biological needs are paramount and to whom the mouth plays a crucial role as a vehicle for the satisfaction of his nutritional needs, tends to relate to the environment almost exclusively on an oral level. Therefore, the glottis and vocal cords, the mouth, and a wide variety of sensory and tactile impressions color the infant's experiences. This factor, rather than the accumulation of libido in the oral area, makes the oral aperture a significant area of personality development.

When a dynamism manages to achieve or fulfill a particular need, the tension of the need is removed, and the situation is described as having been integrated, satisfied, or resolved. However, many needs are either unfulfilled or only partially fulfilled by the dynamism. The success of a dynamism in fulfilling a need completely, particularly in regard to the need for security, is frequently interrupted by the presence or development of anxiety in the course of the operation of the dynamism. This is described as a disintegrated situation, in contrast to an integrated situation, in which a need is fulfilled. Because anxiety can be a dysjunctive or disintegrative force when it interferes with the fulfillment of the individual's needs, Sullivan accorded it a central role in human psychological development and its vicissitudes.

NEED FOR SATISFACTION

The failure to fulfill a biological need is not necessarily accompanied by anxiety, although there will be some associated somatic distress, such as hunger, thirst, or cold. These sensations may propel the organism to action, but they do not necessarily result in anxiety. It is primarily the failure to fulfill one's security needs that evokes anxiety. Furthermore, anxiety may be either the cause or the result of the failure to fulfill the need for security. However, the pursuit of biological satisfactions and the pursuit of security are intermingled and cannot be isolated in practice.

NEED FOR SECURITY

In an affluent society, man's tensions are almost exclusively related to his need for security, which can be satisfied only through meaningful interpersonal relationships. If an individual has notable success in fulfilling both his biological and psychological needs and he experiences a minimum of disintegrating situations, he will feel only a minimum of anxiety. The increasing power and confidence he feels with regard to his security will give rise to a feeling Sullivan called self-esteem. A sufficient, albeit minimal amount of self-esteem is required to deal with the realistic feelings of powerlessness and helplessness evoked in man in the course of his lifetime. In more specific terms, self-esteem is directly related to the amount of anxiety the individual experiences in his daily life and his capacity to deal with it effectively. Therefore, mental illness or personality disintegration that results from excessive anxiety is intimately linked to the lack of self-esteem and self-regard and to the feeling of powerlessness in interpersonal activities. Just as there are no absolute states of freedom from anxiety or euphoria, no individual is totally devoid of self-esteem. Massive feelings of anxiety such as panic do occur, but these situations are fleeting and never permanent. Ordinarily, the degree of anxiety present in an individual extends over a broad continuum and is consistent with variations in his mental health or illness.

MODES OF EXPERIENCING

Sullivan's personality theory takes account of the role of cognition and learning in human development. Consequently, he distinguished between various modes of experiencing and their influence on intellectual and emotional development. These modes of experiencing, which depend on the development of cerebral capacities and other physiological skills, permit the development of such psychological functions as differentiation, symbol formation, and other complex intellectual processes to occur. Since much learning occurs in an interpersonal context, the individual's capacity to comprehend such relationships and his mode of experiencing them influence his learning capacity.

PROTOTAXIC MODE OF EXPERIENCING

This is the earliest mode of experiencing and consists of raw, undifferentiated, momentary states. There is no connection between experience and the feelings or ideas within or outside oneself; consequently, such experiences seem to have cosmic and universal connections. They have no continuity of past with present or future and appear to be isolated and incomprehensible. Such experiencing is characteristic of infancy and occurs in mental illness, particularly schizophrenia.

PARATAXIC MODE

In this mode, events appear to be causally related because of temporal relationships and serial connections. However, there need not be any logical relationships. Consequently, since cause is determined by temporal relationships, the opportunities for distortion are manifold. For example, the child who notices that his mother is angry when he enters her room may attribute the anger to his appearance rather than to an earlier dispute she had with her husband. This kind of distorted thinking, which Sullivan calls parataxic, is not uncommon in human functioning, and it is an essential ingredient in the thinking of the paranoid, in whom false referential interpretations arouse feelings of malevolence or danger.

Serial thinking of this kind is a stage in the development of logical thinking and is not, in itself, evidence of mental disorder, although it plays a significant role in the maintenance of suspicious, superstitious, autistic, and paranoid thinking.

SYNTAXIC OR LOGICAL MODE

In this type of experiencing, events are related through logical or rational thinking. It is this experience that has consensual validation and follows a logical train of deductions. Consequently, it is the most mature type of experiencing and represents the highest cognitive capacity of which man is capable. To illustrate, if a group of people begin to laugh when the individual capable of logical thinking enters a room, he looks about and discovers that someone has just finished telling a funny story. In contrast, under similar circumstances, the individual whose mode of experience is governed by parataxic thinking would immediately conclude that the laughter had been provoked by his entrance. Obviously, the capacity for syntaxic thinking requires comfortable amounts of self-esteem.

These three types of experiencing occur side by side in all individuals, and the process of maturation rarely achieves the level where experiencing follows the syntaxic mode exclusively. Typically, most human beings function on all three levels, with a minimal amount of experiencing in the prototaxic mode. The neuroses and psychoses involve a great deal of perceptual distortion, initiated by the nonlogical, more primitive modes of experiencing. Viewed in this light, the cognitive distortions in mental illness appear more comprehensible and less alien to the functioning of normal people with more adequate adjustment.

Sullivan also emphasized the importance of foresight, which involves not only consideration of the future but a consideration of the past in relation to the present and the future. Sullivan held that anxiety might seriously interfere with the crucial role of foresight in human behavior and, concomitantly, interrupt the learning process.

LEARNING

Freud conceived of learning almost entirely in terms of the pain-pleasure principle, but Sullivan amplified its role in personality development. He placed particular emphasis on learning as a way of minimizing anxiety and the ultimate development of a self-system consisting of techniques for avoiding anxiety. In addition, he described a number of factors essential to the learning process, such as empathy, self-sentient activity, trial and error, reward and punishment, learning through imitation, and, ultimately, deduction and conceptualization. Learning, he maintained, was accelerated by lowering the anxiety gradient. On the other hand, he recognized that the initiation and motivation of the learning process depends on the presence of a certain amount of anxiety. Sullivan's description of self-sentient activity was a particular contribution to learning theory. This enables the individual to develop techniques for alleviating anxiety, boredom, or states of deficiency through activities in which he is not only the provider but the recipient of satisfaction. This is true of masturbation or intellectual pursuits, in which the rewards are the outcome of one's own initiative and action. However, this type of learning can be accelerated or impeded by cultural values and attitudes toward activity that provides pleasure through one's own capacities. For example, some bodily manipulations are approved, but others, such as genital and anal manipulations, are strongly condemned. This is true of certain intellectual pursuits as well. As a result, exploratory activity may be abandoned, and interest in one's body and certain cultural areas may cease. Such reactions may produce serious personality complications in later life.

Sullivan's interest in the individual as he becomes acculturated in the human environment encouraged his explorations in learning theory, which is currently playing an important role in the therapy of mental disorders.

ANXIETY

Anxiety is the focal issue in personality development for the neo-Freudians, as it was for Freud himself. Like all other concepts developed by Sullivan, anxiety was seen as an interpersonal phenomenon and was described as the response to the feelings of disapproval from a significant adult. Thus, it can *only* occur in an interpersonal context, even if the other person is not real but a fantasied or eidetic image. The feeling that he is disapproved of can be communicated to and interpreted by the individual in a variety of ways, or it can be falsely interpreted, as would be the case in prototaxic or parataxic experiencing. In any event, since anxiety is a most distressing feeling and may be accompanied by a variety of somatic symptoms and psychological feelings of impending doom, it cannot be tolerated for long and must be dealt with.

In large measure, Sullivan views personality development as a process of learning to handle anxiety by the use of adaptive maneuvers and defensive techniques. Since anxiety stems from the feeling that one's security needs are threatened, these patterns are techniques for achieving security by gaining approval from significant people. They become incorporated into the self-system, which forms the matrix of the personality structure of the individual. When anxiety is widespread, the individual attempts to limit the opportunities for the further development of anxiety by restricting his functioning to familiar, well-established patterns of activity. He avoids new and novel experiences in order to reduce the risks of living. But in doing so, he also reduces his spontaneous activity and is limited to situations where he can predict the consequences of his actions.

In brief, the self-system may restrict and rigidly proscribe the activities of the individual and thereby interfere with learning and motivation. Thus, in attempting to achieve security, the self-system may actually make the individual more vulnerable. For example, in the process of maturation, the individual may develop and incorporate into his self-system a pattern of selective inattention. Selective inattention may enable the individual to focus on the relevant and to dismiss the irrelevant. However, if it is employed extensively, it can become a technique that enables him to overlook any instances of behavior that may be upsetting—that is, anxiety-provoking. In this way, a potentially valuable technique can become destructive and incapacitating if it is used too widely; it can restrict one's horizons and cut off opportunities for learning.

Sullivan's concept of anxiety is particularly valuable in the therapy of mental disorders. The presence of anxiety serves as a beacon to facilitate identification of the patient's problem, and it highlights those elements of the patient's personality that he feels will meet with the therapist's disapproval. Exploration of the anxiety experience is the most fruitful and direct way of uncovering repressions and dissociations. However, as mentioned earlier, although anxiety usually carries a negative connotation, Sullivan pointed out that it may also constitute a positive force, propelling the individual toward learning new techniques and devices for dealing with it.

ROLE OF SEX

In contrast to Freud, who maintained that sexual factors were of major significance from the earliest years, Sullivan felt that sex played its most significant role in the later developmental stages. This is not to devalue its significance in human affairs, since Sullivan was very cognizant of its intense capacity for initiating and sponsoring intimacy and relationship. However, he did not assign it a leading role in motivating the developmental processes, nor did he view sex as the primary source of neurotic or psychotic disturbance. In his view, sex entered the human scene during adolescence, when it served an essential function in integrating interpersonal, heterosexual intimacy. In view of the cultural attitudes and prejudices and the powerful effect of anxiety on sexual performance, the earlier experiences of the individual may produce serious obstacles in the development of adequate sexual behavior. In this way he accounted for homosexuality and other sexual disorders as symptoms rather than causes of personality disorders. Phobic attitude toward the genitals or difficulties in sexual identification can prejudice the sexual performance in later life. Like other post-Freudian psychologists, Sullivan viewed lust as significant but not central in man's behavior. He saw it as a biological function that has special capacities for pleasure. Because it requires physical intimacy, it can serve as the stage on which many other human needs are fulfilled.

STAGES OF PERSONALITY DEVELOPMENT

Personality is a collection of processes that occur as an outgrowth of interpersonal experiences rather than the unfolding of intrapsychic forces. For Sullivan, personality manifests itself only in relation to other human beings. It is embodied in the self-system, and Sullivan described its development in terms of epochs that reflect the changes in the interpersonal environment of the maturing human being. He described six stages, which were subsequently condensed into five. (1) Infancy. From birth to the beginning of language (to two years). (2) Childhood. From language to the need for compeers (two to five years). (3) Juvenile era. From the need for compeers and the beginnings of formal education to preadolescence (five to eight or nine years). (4) Preadolescence. From the beginning of the capacity for intimate relationships with peers of the same sex until genital maturity. (5) Adolescence. From the patterning of genital behavior with the opposite sex until maturity.

INFANCY

This period of development is characterized by utter helplessness and dependence on the benevolence of other humans, particularly the mothering person. The infant's cry and his capacity to arouse tenderness in others are his only tools for satisfying his needs. The oral zone is the area of interaction with the world, and the development of feelings of security and self-esteem depends entirely on the infant's capacity to fulfill his needs.

Anxiety makes its first appearance during this period as a result of the infant's failure to achieve satisfaction of his primary needs. The infant also experiences feelings of security or anxiety through a process of empathy. And he learns some techniques for dealing with anxiety; these include implementing his cry or somnolent detachment or apathy to avoid the tension of needs that produce physiological disequilibrium (dehydration, etc.) or the psychological feeling of total rejection. The cry that achieves such magical results in infancy takes on special significance in later years in the form of language.

This epoch also marks the beginning of symbol formation and the recognition of signs, particularly the forbidding gestures from others, which warn the infant to refrain from those activities that provoke such gestures. Repeated experiences with these forbidding gestures enable the infant to determine in advance which behavior is acceptable and which is not. Thus, the beginnings of the self-system are recognizable in infancy. In addition, the infant begins to develop a set of concepts of himself as well as of others. Some aspects of his behavior that meet with approval are considered to be part of the "good me" personification; those that stimulate anxiety and disapproval are considered to be part of the "bad me." Other items of behavior that produce marked reactions of loathing, shame, or intense rejection may become part of the "not me," which can be repressed and dissociated. These may ultimately come to play an important role in the later development of neurosis or psychosis. Since Sullivan felt that sex does not play a major role in the developmental process until the gonads have matured, these "not me" personifications do not necessarily involve sexual or libidinal transgressions, in contrast to the pregenital repressions that Freud described in such detail. However, the cultural attitudes toward genital and anal manipulation may stimulate enough anxiety in the infant and toddler to produce an avoidance of these areas. Sullivan called this genital avoidance a primary genital phobia, which he subsumed under the "not me" personification.

As mentioned above, the self-system begins to develop in infancy and becomes a technique for avoiding anxiety. However, as it expands, it may tend to restrict further experience if the potential for anxiety is too great. If the self-system becomes too restrictive, it may interfere with the necessary experimentation and risk-taking essential for growth and may seriously impair development in later epochs. The degree of anxiety and the defenses against it that develop in the earliest period of personality development strongly influence the child's capacity to benefit from the experiences in later periods.

Ultimately, the individual's self or ego is made up of reflected appraisals that represent the views that others have of him. If others treat us with respect and tenderness, then we treat ourselves with respect and tenderness. If the individual is viewed by others in a critical or derogatory way or if he believes that others think of him this way, although this may be a distortion in perception, his view of himself may be derogatory. However, the self-system is never completely rigid, and it does allow for alteration and change through correction by later experiences or therapeutic intervention.

In summary, the self-system, which Sullivan preferred to the term "personality," is a reflection not only of maternal and paternal attitudes but of an accumulated set of experiences that begin in infancy and continue for a long period of time.

Infancy is a crucial stage of development; the outcome depends on the nature of the infant's interpersonal relationships with benevolent or malevolent individuals. These relationships can produce the infant's first experiences of trust, faith, feelings of power and esteem; or they may leave the infant uneasy and uncertain, with feelings of powerlessness and helplessness. In infancy, most needs are satisfied automatically with a minimum of stress, and only occasionally is the satisfaction of these needs characterized by restraint or limitation. However, as verbal skills mature and the infant's capacity to comprehend the limits of the environment develops, he begins to experience denial and limitation. When the sphincters mature, training of the bowels and bladder takes place, and the cultural requirements of proprietous eating and socializing are inaugurated. This ushers in the period of childhood.

CHILDHOOD

This is the period of acculturation, when the individual learns the mores of the particular culture to which he belongs. Depending on the amount of anxiety present in infancy and the security operations he develops to reduce and eliminate it, the child can benefit or fail to benefit from the experiences in this era. The development of sphincter control, eating and dressing habits, and behavior toward adults and other children are all dependent on the child's self-esteem and his capacity to deal effectively with the parental figures. Since learning is associated with considerable anxiety through reward and punishment, the self-system begins to expand very rapidly. The development of language and the capacity to sublimate, which permits one to retain unacceptable needs by transforming them into acceptable channels of satisfaction, begin to manifest themselves.

The problem of becoming educated into the requirements of one's culture is often extremely difficult, not only because of unfavorable experiences in infancy but because of the contradictory demands of the culture. The experiences of fear and anger and the value of obsessive verbalization, such as "I'm sorry" or "excuse me," begin to manifest themselves. The need to hold firm by negative or resistive activities also becomes apparent. Willful activity rather than compliant behavior becomes a prominent part of dealing with powerful adults.

During this era a very significant process may occur called the "malevolent transformation," which has serious consequences for future living. When this happens, because the situation may demand it, the child begins to think of himself as bad or unworthy whenever he feels the need for tenderness. In the boy, the need for tenderness is considered unmanly and weak. Therefore, he denies this need, which tends to evoke anxiety. At the same time, the possibility of interpersonal relationships of tenderness and warmth is made impossible, since, when they are offered, they are strongly rebuffed. Tenderness is transformed into malevolence, and the child becomes surrounded by a sea of hostility, which he can deal with only by hostile or paranoid rejoinders.

JUVENILE ERA

When the child begins to manifest a need for compeers, which generally coincides with the beginning of formal education in Western culture, he has entered the juvenile era. Generally, this occurs when he is about five years old. Now his interpersonal range moves beyond his own home and his own parents. He must share a common parental figure in the form of a teacher and deal with other individuals who have equal claims on her. He must learn to deal with new authorities and to cooperate, compete, and compromise with his peers. There is a great expansion of his self-system and an opportunity to correct earlier distortions because of the presence of new significant adults in his life. Behavior that might have been a source of rejection or disapproval previously may now elicit rewards that could modify his earlier reactions.

The development of the capacity for cooperation and compromise provides the background for the competitive skill that is an important ingredient in his ability to face cultural demands in later life. During this period the child develops a clear-cut personality and characteristic ways of dealing with others. So far, he has had little experience with sex except for some expressed preference for friends of the same sex. As the child enters preadolescence, friendships have begun to develop.

PREADOLESCENCE

This period, ranging from approximately eight to twelve years of age, is notable for the development of the capacity for love and collaboration with another human being of the same sex. It is devoid of sexual exchanges, however, since gonadal maturation has not yet occurred. Firm friendships are formed, and loyalty, devotion, and sharing of feelings and closeness with another human being are much in evidence. This era was labeled homosexual by Freud because these relationships are between individuals of the same sex. However, Sullivan felt that the lust dynamism had not yet developed. It is only because people of the same sex are more like one another and therefore easier to understand, with common interests and desires, that these relationships occur. Such intimacies in the later periods of preadolescence may involve sex, but essentially they involve intimacy devoid of sex. One begins to see the world as one's compeers see it. Values are shared, and mutual concerns and interests are aired. Self-appraisals are clarified and strengthened, and the possibility for favorable change is present, since opportunities for tenderness and closeness are more available. One begins to consider the importance of other people's needs as well as one's own, which is the essential ingredient of a loving, tender attitude.

Difficulties begin to manifest themselves toward the end of the era as the sexual apparatus begins to mature and friendships dissolve due to interest in the opposite sex. If there is unequal maturing or if one chum is, for some reason, unequal to the task of moving into heterosexual relationships, then there may be a clinging to preadolescent intimacy, which may become complicated by lust, producing homosexual behavior. However, lust is a very powerful dynamism and generally succeeds in forcing most people out of the comfortable and successful preadolescent friendships that have been established. The tendency to label this era as a homosexual stage of development has produced grave mischief and grief with regard to the friendships and intimacies of people of the same sex. The cultural prejudices and proscriptions that derive from such a view often serve to discourage the development of tenderness, which is necessary in the heterosexual patterning that is to occur in adolescence.

ADOLESCENCE

This is a stormy period in human development. It is the crossroads between the dependent child and the independent adult, with all the complicated patternings of sex, vocation, and future value systems still to be resolved. Even if one enters this period with a fairly solid self-system as an outgrowth of good earlier experiences, it is a most difficult transition. If, however, one arrives at this juncture with weak self-esteem and a tendency toward anxiety in interpersonal encounters, the transition to heterosexuality and adulthood is extremely difficult. Intimacy with another human being is now complicated by lust, and the adolescent must overcome a great many previous restraints on nonlustful intimacies and try to establish sexual involvements as well. In addition, he must separate himself from his family dependencies at a time when he is not entirely independent either economically or emotionally. While still a boy, he is trying to be a man. He must decide upon a career and develop standards and values for the future. Compromises must be reached in accepting the values of the adult world. While he is struggling with all these issues, he is expected to be acquiring and perfecting scholastic or technical skills that will provide him with future economic security. It is a tumultuous period in which one seeks one's own identity as a human being. Now the interpersonal exchanges are confused and ambiguous, requiring the adolescent to make adult decisions while retaining a child's prerogatives.

When heterosexual patternings are established and adult roles are assumed, the period of adolescence draws to a close, and the individual has arrived at adulthood. However, adulthood is not always synonymous with maturity, which is achieved only by a fortunate few. Maturity involves a self-respect that permits one to meet most situations with a capacity for intimate and collaborative relationships and loving attitudes—an understandably difficult achievement.

The foregoing is a brief summary of the development of normal personality. A great deal more learning and experiencing than has been described here takes place during these stages. The limits of such learning are defined by the innate capacity of the individual, the interpersonal atmosphere in which it occurs, and the capacities and emotional integrity of the persons involved in these interpersonal relationships. In addition, cultural requirements and historical, political, and economic conditions also influence the developmental demands on the individual. Sullivan emphasized these factors while he took into account the biological necessities that are so clearly manifested in infancy, childhood, and adolescence.

PSYCHOPATHOLOGY

Although anxiety is the dynamic propelling force for personality development, it is also the essential element in the production of the neuroses, psychoses, and other psychopathological phenomena. The self-system or dynamism described earlier develops in response to anxiety. The techniques and patterns of behavior making up the self-system aim at alleviating and eliminating the distressing effects of anxiety. These security operations are rarely entirely successful, and inevitably the anxiety manifests itself in symptoms that can be noted in all human activity. Such symptoms constitute the bulk of psychosomatic complaints, tics, mannerisms, sterotyped behavior, activity in dreams, etc. They are devices for discharging tensions or minimal outbursts of anxiety, without necessitating the breakdown of over-all adaptive patterns.

In this sense, the self-system, by discharging tensions in acceptable ways and preventing more massive outbursts of anxiety, maintains the individual as an effective functioning entity. However, under extreme stress imposed by external demands or the overwhelming pressures of internal needs, the protective armor of the self-system is inadequate to stem the tide, and more massive disintegration occurs, producing the neuroses and psychoses.

Sullivan's concept of mental disorder arises directly out of his interpersonal concepts. The self-system develops directly in relation to interpersonal needs or the need to avoid disapproval from significant adults. As noted above, in the early development of the self-system, certain experiences are personified in terms of the "good me," "bad me," and "not me." In the same way, individuals are personified as the "good" mother or "bad" mother, and this way of perceiving others is retained as a lifetime pattern, as highlighted in the transference aspects of the therapeutic process. The "not me" personification and often the "bad me" personification lie outside immediate awareness. Mental disorder results when some of these dissociated processes erupt into awareness. The nature of the disorder and diagnosis depend on the way the self-system maintains or fails to maintain itself in the face of these crises.

NEUROSES

Sullivan distinguishes between the substitutive (neurotic) and the disintegrative (psychotic) processes. He believed that in the neuroses certain tendencies are dissociated; were they to manifest themselves in actual living, massive outbreaks of anxiety and panic would result. They are dealt with in substitutive ways, particularly by the obsessional devices of distraction and displacement. These substitutive devices produce symptoms that combine to form a syndrome and are given a particular label. For example, in the obsessional neuroses, the profound insecurities of the individual are held in check by the substitutive devices of magic and control through ritual. In hysteria, the major substitutive technique is a simple process of amnesia in which clear recognition of issues is avoided and somatic substitutions become the major area of relating to others. Sullivan did not concern himself with the conventional, nosological categories; therefore, he did not describe the neurotic disorders under the traditional classifications.

When the process of substitution is used, in order to maintain anxiety at a tolerable level, the individual uses other techniques as well, such as sublimation, that may be broadly defined as a way of making unacceptable impulses acceptable. In addition, there is the ubiquitous tendency toward selective inattention, in which aspects of experiencing that might upset or stimulate anxiety are simply not noticed. As pointed out earlier in this chapter, if this technique becomes too extensive, it may seriously impair perception and learning and be responsible for many major deficiencies in functioning. It may become the basis for considerable distortion in the perceptual process.

The elements of a neurotic process consist of personality devices or techniques, the function of which is to keep out of awareness those responses, reactions, and impulses that, if admitted to awareness, would produce serious personality disorganization. The neurotic symptom, therefore, is an adaptive reaction, the major function of which is to prevent disintegration of personality and promote repair. Sullivan's view of the obsessional disorder gives one a clear notion of his concepts of psychopathology. He studied this disorder in great detail, and it was his work in this area that led to his examination of the schizophrenic process.

Freud viewed obsessive symptoms as a compromise attempt to deal with ambivalent feelings and to prevent the expression of unacceptable aggressive or sexual impulses. The symptom, as he saw it, was not only a displaced substitute for the impulse but also a partial satisfaction of it. Sullivan, on the other hand, viewed the obsessional process as one in which the individual attempts to exert maximal control over himself and the universe in order to guarantee and protect himself against deep feelings of uncertainty and insecurity. He attempts to do this by the personal magic of compulsive ritual or obsessive, ruminative, omniscient thinking. And he strives to achieve perfection, omnipotence, and omniscience so that he may be beyond criticism, rejection, or danger. He avoids commitment and involvement, since these contain emotional elements that cannot be controlled. Most obsessive symptoms can be understood in this framework.

The somatic disorders that frequently accompany obsessional states are the result of the inner tensions produced by these neurotic demands. Sullivan believed that there is very little outlet, even in dreams, for dissociated impulses in the obsessional states; therefore, there is a constant need for control in order to avoid the feeling that one might explode.

PSYCHOSES

When the dissociated impulses actually do go out of control and the self-dynamism fails to retain its integrative capacity, psychosis results. Since Sullivan was primarily interested in the schizophrenic disorders, he focused very little of his attention on the clarification of the affective psychoses.

Psychosis results when the repressed aspects of personality emerge into conscious awareness. These aspects are alien to the ego and disruptive to the usual, conventional, acceptable social processes, and they evoke a sense of loathing and shame. Consequently, their manifestation produces a violent reaction that results in panic. This is frequently followed by the disintegration manifested by an extremely regressed catatonic reaction. In this state the individual withdraws from reality and becomes wholly preoccupied with fantasy, in a cosmic struggle that usually consists of intense rage, stuporous immobility, or a combination of both.

The acute catatonic reaction is generally followed either by resolution of the conflict or by the development of more severe and chronic personality reformulations. The resolution of the conflict and a reintegration of the self-system are possible either through an alteration of the circumstances that led to the disintegration or through a lessening of the demands on one's psyche. The crisis can then be overcome, and the individual can return to his former way of life, albeit with some minor alterations. If, however, the individual attempts to reconstruct or reintegrate his self-system by repressing all doubts about himself or by bolstering his inadequate self-system by invalid referential processes, he may then experience a paranoid reorganization of personality. In this solution to a schizophrenic disaster, the individual achieves some security and certainty by restructuring the world in manageable ways, even if they are viewed as hostile or unfriendly ways. This solution often closes off any therapeutic possibility, unless doubt can be introduced into the self-contained and self-consistent paranoid system.

However, there are other possible solutions as well. Instead of an intellectually organized solution, such as the paranoid formulation, there can be a hebephrenic dilapidation, in which emotional deterioration seems to be central. The individual gives up any attempt to view the world in coherent, systematic terms, and it becomes a totally illogical and meaningless world. Exchange and relationships are made impossible because of his determined effort to ward off involvement.

All these outcomes are elucidated within the framework of Sullivan's interpersonal theory. The various solutions to acute psychotic reactions are seen as attempts to avoid or to set up new interpersonal relationships, and the behavior of both the neurotic and the psychotic patient is made comprehensible by viewing it in interpersonal terms. The neurotic, by his substitutive processes, and the psychotic, through his reconstructive processes, attempt to achieve security and to avoid anxiety by relating to others from the vantage point of the neurotic or psychotic adjustments. The various categories of schizophrenia that are traditionally described as separate disorders were viewed by Sullivan as attempts at solution of the catatonic reaction. In his view, they all constitute restitutive processes rather than nosological categories.

Sullivan developed a psychological explanation for the causes of schizophrenic disorder and brought it directly into the nexus of personality theory by demonstrating that schizophrenic processes were never very far from the normal processes in living. In contrast to the prevailing theories regarding the causes of schizophrenia—which were of an organic, constitutional, or hereditary nature—Sullivan demonstrated that schizophrenia can develop as a direct outgrowth of psychological issues and that it could occur in any individual. Schizophrenia, which he differentiated from dementia praecox, is a personality distortion that grows out of a complicated and warped interpersonal history. He documented this notion in a series of fascinating case histories, in which he might relate a particular delusional development, for example, to a series of interpersonal complications. The anxiety that resulted stimulated defensive operations designed to cope with these pressures. Thus, by demonstrating the origins of schizophrenia in the distortions of personality development, he stimulated the hope of a possible therapeutic resolution of this disorder through an unraveling of the history of its development.

Sullivan's concepts of neurosis and psychosis enabled the therapist to develop skills in dealing with schizophrenic illness through psychological techniques. Frieda Fromm-Reichmann and others have made notable contributions to psychiatry by applying Sullivan's concepts to the treatment of schizophrenia.

TREATMENT TECHNIQUES

Sullivan's views on therapy were a direct outgrowth of his conviction that psychiatry is the study of interpersonal processes, in which the psychiatrist functions as participant-observer. Since his concept of pathology is intimately tied to the self-system that develops out of the need to minimize anxiety, the focus in therapy is on anxiety and the interpersonal context in which it occurs. Sullivan viewed therapy as a succession of psychiatric interviews in which the psychiatrist is a participant in the exploratory process and an observer of trends in the patient that the patient's defensive patterns prevent him from noticing. The focus in therapy is on discovering how the patient came to be the kind of person he is, with his defenses and insecurities that have produced complications and difficulties in living.

Sullivan felt that the manner in which this could be pursued most effectively was through the investigation of anxiety, which permits patient and therapist to see what the patient's insecurities are and where they lie, how they became stimulated in life situations, and what defenses the patient uses to deal with them. This is achieved by dealing with situations in the present that could lead to the recall of earlier experiences. In this way, one can discover what was dissociated and why the patient had to keep it out of awareness. One can then assist the patient to permit the dissociated feelings or attitudes to come into awareness, thereby obviating the need for substitutive devices (neuroses) or disintegrative processes (psychoses). Briefly stated, this is Sullivan's philosophy of therapy.

He introduced a large number of parameters into the classical therapeutic technique. Although he recognized the value of free association, dream analysis, and other symbolic reconstructions, his main emphasis was on the communicative process and what it could reveal regarding the patient's response to anxiety. The genetic reconstruction of the symptom took second place to data of recent origin, which were less prone to distortion. The use of the couch or the frequency of visits depended on the needs of the particular patient—specifically, his dependency, financial status, degree of incapacity, etc.—rather than on predetermined rules of procedure.

Sullivan believed that the process of therapy required the active participation of the therapist; therefore, anonymity was not considered a virtue. His view of transference phenomena differed from Freud's, and he developed the concept of parataxic distortion instead. With this concept he extended the notion of transference to include the multitude of distortions that develop out of parataxic interpretations of one's experience, not only with one's parents but also with other people, such as teachers, friends, and colleagues. Because of the active role played by the therapist, counter-transference becomes an important technique in the therapeutic process. The use of dreams, free association, and other symbolic interpretations play a major role, as they do in classical psychoanalytic treatment. However, Sullivan insisted that such activities be pointed and directed at some particular question being explored at the moment and not used in an open-ended, unstructured inquiry. Values are part of the therapeutic process to the extent that the therapist's feeling and attitudes could not and should not be kept out of the process. Such issues, however, need to be clearly understood and should always be used in the interest of enhancing the therapeutic process. Sullivan himself was a gifted, highly competent thera-pist who made great use of sarcasm and humor and demonstrated the value of such maneuvers in accelerating therapy.

The following is an abbreviated description of the treatment of a case of obsessional neurosis that demonstrates the main outlines of Sullivan's therapeutic technique.

The patient was a 24-year-old man who had spastic colitis and recurrent anxiety attacks. He was a bright, competent individual who insisted on immediate rewards and acknowledgement for skills he felt he possessed but had not yet demonstrated. He was intensely anxious about every piece of work he did and fearful of criticism. He expected his performances to be perfect. He could admit to no deficiency or error and needed to feel omniscient and omnipotent. His rituals were attempts to guarantee superman performances.

Treatment began by obtaining detailed data about his anxieties and the interpersonal relationships in which they occurred, with the aim of exploring some of his dissociated concerns about absolute se-curity and invulnerability. His substitutive devices and rationalized explanations were exposed, and he was able to see the patterns he used in trying to avoid anxiety. His verbal and gestural communica-tions tended to obfuscate and confuse the relevant issues in his dis-order, and his free associations tended to ramble and to be trivial. Active interference was required to bring him back to the point in order to explore any issue at length. To help him recognize what his obsessional patterns were attempting to do, there was a constant ne-cessity to focus on recent data; otherwise, his obsessive doubts would cloud any interpretation in order to reduce its effectiveness. For example, often, his attempts to recall early experiences were clearly related to his wish to avoid exploration of a recent anxiety attack. Direct confrontation, questioning, and intervention were regularly re-quired to keep his communications within manageable limits, lest the interviews become rambling and evasive, with typical obsessional attempts to avoid the significant issues.

The therapist's activities stirred up considerable reactions of anxiety, defensiveness, counterattack, etc., during the therapeutic hour and revealed the patient's typical patterns of behavior. Interpretation of these reactions enabled the patient to see how his perceptions were distorted by his expectations and the extent to which they were influenced by his neurotic needs. In this way, abundant transference data were produced, and the countertransference reactions of the therapist toward the patient's excesses enabled the patient to see how his behavior affected others. Because of his need to be right and beyond criticism, every interpretation was viewed as an attack, and the therapist needed to demonstrate the distortion by becoming personally involved in the issue instead of objectively pointing out the patient's distortion. Dreams and other symbolic material were dealt with only to the extent that they clarified immediate issues and had relevance to current data. Intellectual discussions and the introduction of psychiatric terms were strenuously avoided.

When some clarification of the patient's anxieties was achieved and an understanding of some of his efforts at certainty and guaranteed living was arrived at, the patient was encouraged to test out new patterns of behavior. He received strong support in taking risks and abandoning obsessional security operations, without overidentifying with the results.

Thus, therapy takes on many aspects of a learning experience in which the discomforts of learning new responses must be minimized by support and encouragement. The reconstruction of the individual's functioning without the props of obsessional devices is a difficult and painful process, and the patient must be prepared to experience some anxieties and helped to bear them. Therapy does not continue indefinitely but is gradually abandoned as the individual's skill in achieving improved interpersonal relationships develops. Since one must avoid trying to achieve a total cure or complete reconstruction of the personality—which, in itself, would be an obsessional pattern—the patient must recognize that being human means having anxieties and being vulnerable and insecure at times.

The therapeutic process was, for Sullivan, not only an exploratory process for uncovering repressed or dissociated material but also a learning process in which the restructuring of new patterns must be assisted. There is no special emphasis on sex, other than its role in the patient's life, and the sexual development of the patient is significant only to the extent that it elucidates the growth of his interpersonal capacities. The schema of personality development that Sullivan proposed becomes useful in assessing the interpersonal thwarts and complications and in identifying the stage of development at which such difficulties began.

Sullivan felt that therapy could be terminated when the person's perceptions of himself and others were consensually validated. This is another way of saying that, when a patient's capacity to see himself is validated by the view others have of him and is free of substitutive devices and when his self-respect is adequate to withstand any view of himself by others, he can be considered to have achieved sufficient maturity.

Sullivan made his greatest contributions in the therapy of the psychoses. His notions that the schizophrenic responses were adaptive and restitutive enabled the therapist to understand a great deal of the confused and symbolic communications of the patient. Psychotherapy became recognized as a possible method for reversing the disintegrative process and was widely used, despite Freud's belief that psychoanalysis could not be effective in the psychoses. Sullivan's technique required modification of the classical model, but it made major inroads in the therapy and comprehension of the psychoses.

Since Sullivan believed that schizophrenia, like all other forms of mental illness, was due to some distortion or deficit in the development of interpersonal relationships, his therapeutic approach was similar to that used in the neuroses. However, the modifications introduced took into account the difficulties in communication as well as the schizophrenic's problems in relating to other people. In dealing with the schizophrenic patient, Sullivan attempted to develop his trust and participation by sharing his fear and anguish. He was interested not only in the patient's verbalizations but in his nonverbal behavior as well. And he focused throughout on comprehending the anxiety that pervaded the schizophrenic's functioning and that required such extreme defenses.

He attempted to actively encourage and stimulate the patient's interest in the therapeutic process. To do this, he would freely interpret the symbolic verbalizations or gestures and mannerisms of the patient. He did not hesitate to offer help and guidance in order to stimulate confidence and trust in the process. The goal of therapy was to enable the patient to recognize the source of his anxiety and to overcome his defective patterns by learning to deal with them in a more adaptive way. He was often content to settle for social recoveries—that is, manipulating the patient's life so that he would be exposed to situations that were less demanding and anxiety-provoking. He felt sufficient respect for the schizophrenic dilemma to realize that the passage of time during the illness often permanently incapacitated the patient in terms of his return to a full social existence.

Sullivan's techniques required that the therapist know intuitively what was happening inside the patient and that he achieve rapport with him at that level instead of following some rigid requirement of psychological theory. He would encourage and countenance any maneuver that contributed to understanding the illness, as long as it did not aggravate the illness, arouse anxiety unnecessarily, or show disrespect for the patient. Eventually, he hoped to strengthen the patient's self-esteem so that situations or relationships that had previously stirred up anxiety would be dealt with in a diminished state of tension.

Sullivan did not feel that any limitations had to be imposed on the therapeutic process because the patient was catatonic or uncommunicative or actively paranoid. Instead, he would adapt his communications to encourage the patient's participation by making provocative statements or by actively becoming involved in his illness.

Sullivan also experimented with milieu therapy by providing personnel in the hospital wards who he felt had greater empathy for the schizophrenic patient. This project did not fulfill his expectations; it provided, nevertheless, a strong impetus for later interest in the effects of the environment of the hospital ward on the patient's illness.

REFERENCES

Bullard, D., editor. *Psychoanalysis and Psychotherapy—Selected Papers of Frieda Fromm-Reichmann.* University of Chicago Press, Chicago, 1959.

Fromm-Reichmann, F. *Principles of Intensive Psychotherapy.* University of Chicago Press, Chicago, 1950.

Green, M., editor. *Selected Papers of Clara Thompson.* Basic Books, New York, 1964.

Hall, C. S., and Lindzey, G. *Theories of Personality.* Wiley, New York, 1957.

Mullahy, P. *Oedipus, Myth & Complex.* Hermitage Press, New York, 1948.

Mullahy, P. *Study of Interpersonal Relations.* Hermitage Press, New York, 1949.

Mullahy, P. *Contributions of Harry Stack Sullivan.* Hermitage Press, New York, 1952.

Munroe, R. *Schools of Psychoanalytic Thought.* Dryden Press, New York, 1955.

Salzman, L. *Developments in Psychoanalysis.* Grune & Stratton, New York, 1962.

Sullivan, H. S. *Conceptions of Modern Psychiatry.* William Alanson White Foundation, Washington, 1947.

Sullivan, H. S. *Interpersonal Theory of Psychiatry.* W. W. Norton, New York, 1953.

Sullivan, H. S. *The Psychiatric Interview.* W. W. Norton, New York, 1954.

Sullivan, H. S. *Clinical Studies in Psychiatry.* W. W. Norton, New York, 1956.

Sullivan, H. S. *Schizophrenia as a Human Process.* W. W. Norton, New York, 1962.

Sullivan, H. S. *Fusion of Psychiatry and Social Science.* W. W. Norton, New York, 1964.

Thompson, C. *Psychoanalysis: Evolution and Development.* Hermitage Press, New York, 1950.

Thompson, C., Mazor, M., and Witenberg, E. *Outline of Psychoanalysis.* Modern Library, New York, 1955.

CHAPTER SEVEN

Erich Fromm

SIMON H. NAGLER, M.D.

INTRODUCTION

ERICH FROMM STUDIED psychology and sociology at the University of Heidelberg and subsequently received orthodox psychoanalytic training in Munich and at the famous Berlin Psychoanalytic Institute before he emigrated to the United States in 1933. However, although he has drawn liberally from classical psychoanalytic thought, his focus of interest has been the relationship between man and his society. Thus, his theories reflect the orientation of the social scientist rather than the classical psychoanalyst's concern with the individual per se. Insofar as he has sought to elucidate the relationship between psychological functioning and social milieu, his basic formulations are closely associated with the dynamic cultural positions of Adler, Sullivan, and Horney. Within this frame of reference, Fromm has contributed important insights into individual psychodynamics and their relationship to historical and socioeconomic concepts, which have exerted a significant influence on laymen as well as on psychoanalysts, psychologists, sociologists, and philosophers.

FROMM AND FREUD: MAJOR DIFFERENCES

In general, Fromm has been critical of many of Freud's formulations, which he considers either inadequate or misleading because of their overemphasis on certain developmental phenomena. However, the chief target of his criticism has been Freud's concept of the source and nature of psychic energy, his libido theory. As opposed to the view of classical psychoanalysis, Fromm believes that "the fundamental basis of character is not seen in various types of libido organization but in specific kinds of a person's relatedness to the world," in the action of acquiring things and relating to people. Fromm has also been critical of Freud's failure to devote sufficient attention to the analysis of the mature or genital character, and he has differed sharply with the position of classical psychoanalysis with respect to the significance of dreams. Freud defined dreams as the expression of the individual's irrational aspects, but Fromm assumes that the dream "can be the expression both of the lowest and most irrational and of the highest and most valuable functions of our minds." Fromm has also emphasized his disagreement with Freud's concept of self-love as selfishness. In contrast, Fromm believes that selfishness is actually the opposite of self-love, which is really self-affirmation, which, in turn, is the basis for the capacity to love others.

FROMM'S THEORY OF PERSONALITY

MAN AND SOCIETY

Fromm recognizes that man's behavior is motivated by his biological requirements. However, he contends that man's adaptation is not related solely to the satisfaction or frustration of his instinctual or libidinal needs. Rather, human motivation and behavior are culturally determined, and society generates new needs and problems that are superimposed on man's instinctual needs and are as imperative as the instinctual demands of hunger, thirst, and sexuality, if not more so. To quote from *Escape from Freedom*, the first volume Fromm published in this country in 1941, given the presence of certain universal instincts, "those drives which make for the differences in men's character, like love and hatred, the lust for power and the yearning for submission, the enjoyment of sensuous pleasure and the fear of it, are products of the social process," not a part of a fixed and biologically given human nature. Thus, Fromm believes that society has a creative as well as a suppressing function; that man's passions and anxieties are, for the most part, products of his culture; and that man himself is the most important creation and achievement of the human effort of history.

MAN'S QUEST FOR MEANING

Fromm draws an extensive analogy between individual development and the history of mankind. Man's biological helplessness at birth is the prime cause of the emergence of his specifically human qualities, such as his subsequent awareness of himself as a separate entity, his ability to remember the past and to visualize the future, his capacity for conceptualization and symbolization, and his realization that death is inevitable. These qualities give rise, in turn, to certain existential dichotomies—an awareness of being one with nature, yet transcending it, and the hope for immortality on the one hand and the knowledge that death is inevitable on the other. The human condition drives man to resolve these incompatibilities. Religion, with its promise of an eternal life, represents one such attempt at resolution. There are also historical dichotomies, such as that of abundance versus scarcity. However, these may be resolved through human wisdom and effort.

Above all, man differs from other animals because he has become separated from nature and other men; as a result, he is overwhelmed by feelings of loneliness and isolation. He is compelled to relate significantly to self and others, to give his life meaning through the realization of his powers to reason and to love and of his capacity for productive activity. This provides the necessary frame of reference that will enable him to answer the questions of what he is and how he can best implement his search for meaning and belonging. This human need for meaning and belonging is the key concept in Fromm's theory.

SEPARATION AND INDIVIDUATION

Just as man's history begins with his awareness that he is separate from nature, so the growth of individuality begins with separation of the newborn from the mother; separation occurs first through the physiological birth process and then through the individual's gradual psychological awareness of himself as an entity distinct from mother and other objects. Education, which necessarily involves frustration and prohibition, sharpens this awareness of separateness; once the primary ties of infancy have been broken, the child learns to use his own unique powers. And, gradually, he achieves greater physical, mental, and emotional integration, leading to the development of a structured self, guided by will and reason. Ideally, dependency is gradually surrendered.

On the other hand, the child's primary ties to his parents have given him a sense of security and belonging, which growth and individuation threaten to destroy. Confronted with an external world that appears strong and threatening, the growing child feels powerless and anxious. If his early experiences were unfavorable in that he was deprived of respect, warmth, and affection and if he failed to achieve confidence in his capacities as a result, the child will find the problems of individuation and isolation difficult, if not actually agonizing and insoluble. Generally, there is a lag between individuation and the development of a sense of security based on confidence in one's own capacities rather than the omnipotence of one's parents. During this period the individual whose early environment was unhealthy may find his impotence and isolation intolerable; he may then seek to surrender his individuality and re-establish his dependency through one of several mechanisms of escape. These mechanisms, which include specific forms of neurosis—masochism, sadism, destructiveness, and automaton conformity—are discussed in further detail below as pathological phenomena.

THEORIES OF PERSONALITY DEVELOPMENT

Fromm's theories of personality development are in harmony with his hypothesis that man relates to his world either through acquiring and assimilating things (assimilation) or by relating to people and to himself (socialization). He can take things or produce them himself to satisfy his needs. But he must also associate with others in work, play, and sexual activities. Complete isolation is incompatible with sanity. The specific way in which the individual relates—that is, whether love or hate is predominant, competition or cooperation, freedom or oppression—is an expression of his personality or character.

Socialization may take one of five forms or orientations, which correspond to five types of assimilation. Socialization orientations include masochism, sadism, destructiveness, automaton conformity, and love. And these are correlated with the orientations of assimilation, which emerge as the receptive, exploitative, hoarding, marketing, and productive characters. Thus, for example, the receptive character is a masochistic person. These classifications are ideal constructs. In reality, human personalities are mixtures of these orientations, although one is usually predominant.

Temperament, as the mode of reaction to experience, is constitutional. As such, it influences the character of the activity in the several personality types. For example, the productive or loving personality with a choleric or irritable temperament will react vigorously to love; on the other hand, the sadistic person with this temperament will react vigorously to submissiveness in another. In this sense, personality, through which energy directed outward to the world is channeled, is the counterpart of the instinctual mechanism of the animal.

The family, the psychic agent of society, forms the child's character by compelling him to become a person who wants to do what is required of him as an effective member of society. Thus, the core of personality is the social character, on which the individual orientations are then superimposed. The reason why certain social character patterns predominate rather than others is a sociological problem. In any event, the social and individual character orientations are the end zones of a continuum that ranges from the conventionally patterned to the most idiosyncratic individual, as described below.

The receptive character. The receptive character, whose socialization orientation is basically masochistic, believes that his needs must be fulfilled by an external source, not through his own efforts. In fact, he feels inadequate and helpless. Therefore, he seeks a magic helper and becomes anxious when his supply line is threatened. Feudal societies fostered this orientation, which corresponds to the Freudian oral-passive type.

The exploitative character. This basically sadistic character, which corresponds to the Freudian oral-aggressive personality, attempts to seize what he requires from others, including things, ideas, friends, and mates. He is hostile, manipulative, envious, and cynical. Sociologically, he resembles the feudal robber barons and the adventure capitalists of the nineteenth century.

The hoarding character. Like the Freudian anal personality, the security of the hoarding character derives from his hoarding and saving activities. Spending arouses anxiety. Love is possession. He is orderly and pedantic but generally sterile. Thus, mastery is achieved through order and remoteness. Sociologically, this type corresponds to the bourgeois, Calvinistic-Puritan personality that was a product of the period of transition from feudalism to capitalism.

The marketing character. The marketing character, a product of modern society, is the automaton conformist. In his nonproductive orientation, individual qualities have no intrinsic value. Personality is a commodity for sale, and there are fashions in personality just as there are in other commodities. Moreover, as might be expected, there is no genuineness or stability in human relationships. The classic example is the mythical character of Peer Gynt, who tries to find himself beneath layers of superficial values, only to find that he has no inner core of truth.

The productive character. This is the only productive orientation in Fromm's schema, and thus far it has not characterized society at any stage of its historical development, although Fromm has sufficient faith in humanity to believe that man will ultimately have the courage "to be himself and to be for himself." The criteria of productivity are the ability to reason independently and the ability to love. Love is a human capacity but difficult to realize. As an expression of productiveness, genuine love implies care, respect, responsibility, and knowledge. The ability to love is acquired through loving specific individuals, such as members of one's family. Love for self is not incompatible with love for others; rather, the two are interdependent. Modern culture has produced individuals who cannot love themselves and who, therefore, cannot love others. The productive personality has many virtues; but these do not exceed appropriate limits. Thus, he is adaptable but not unprincipled; he is active but not exploitative. When productiveness is dominant, it tends to transform the nonproductive orientations in the personality. Under such circumstances, a tendency toward submission, for example, becomes devotion.

Authoritarianism is a basic concept of Fromm's thought. It is the most general mechanism of escape from the sense of isolation by seeking external powers, whether personal and direct, as that of a leader, or impersonal, as that of God. All forms of this mechanism serve to avoid personal responsibility and stultify the individual's creative productivity and growth. Basically, "the power to act creates a need to use this power and failure to use it results in dysfunction and unhappiness."

Fromm is averse to the anatomization of personality structure. Simply stated, he believes that only a spontaneous, integrated self can ensure the individual's successful relationship with his world. Therefore, since sex, for example, is only one of man's basic needs, it cannot function as a nuclear explanatory principle, nor can adequate sexual functioning be considered the sole prerequisite for happiness. Happiness is the result of free, productive activity that extends well beyond the limits of this single sphere of activity.

THEORY OF PSYCHOPATHOLOGY

Fromm has not dealt specifically with the differential diagnosis of mental disorders; he is concerned primarily with the role of modern society in the pathogenesis of such disorders. Accordingly, his main theoretical emphasis is on the neurotic mechanisms used by man to escape from the basic dichotomies in human existence. As mentioned earlier, these include masochism, sadism, destructiveness, automaton conformity, and neurosis.

MASOCHISM

Masochism and sadism are usually conjoined in the sadomasochistic or authoritarian personality. The sadomasochistic person in whom masochism predominates feels inferior and insignificant, never experiencing the fulfillment and joy of freedom, which he fears. However, masochism does permit some sense of relatedness to others, despite the fact that such an individual remains weak, helpless, and dependent beneath his mask of love, loyalty, and devotion.

SADISM

Fromm delineates three types of sadistic behavior: (1) making others dependent by wielding unrestricted power over them; (2) exploiting and robbing others materially, intellectually, or emotionally; and (3) making others suffer. Actually, the sadist is not strong and independent but weak and helpless. Unless he is able to dominate someone, he feels isolated and alone. Either trend, masochism or sadism, may predominate in the sadomasochistic personality. Anxiety arises when such a person is neither dominating nor submissive.

DESTRUCTIVENESS

The destructive person tries to destroy or eliminate another person or object who represents a potential basis for comparison or threat. Fromm formulated the attitude of this character type as follows: "I can escape the feeling of my own powerlessness in comparison with the world outside myself by destroying it." Such irrational destructiveness may masquerade as love, duty, or patriotism.

AUTOMATON CONFORMITY

Some degree of conformity is required in any culture, of course. But in automaton conformity, the entire personality is dependent on the cultural pattern, and the individual becomes what others are and expect him to be. His fear of aloneness is overcome by thinking, feeling, and acting exactly like everyone else in his culture or group. A pseudoself is created.

Fromm sees these neurotic and characterological deformations as attempts to escape from the warping, alienating effects of a society that denies man's basic needs for relatedness, transcendence, rootedness, identity, and a stable frame of reference for the perception and comprehension of his world. It is the sick society that drives man into insanity, self-destruction, and antisocial behavior. The family communicates its traditional pathological mechanisms and social irrationalities to the child and reinforces these by communicating its feelings of hostility and anxiety. Treated with hostility instead of warmth and respect, deprived of confidence in his own capacities, the child finds individuation difficult or impossible, and the escape devices described above are called into being.

THERAPEUTIC PRINCIPLES

Fromm has not developed a separate psychotherapeutic method. Instead, he has drawn freely on other systems, particularly Freudian techniques. However, he differs from both the Freudian and the Jungian approaches in his use of dreams as a therapeutic tool. Fromm believes that dreams reflect the rational as well as the irrational aspects of personality. He has also introduced modifications in orthodox psychoanalytic technique with respect to the frequency of treatment sessions, use of the couch, sole reliance on free association; he has, in addition, advocated greater emphasis on current life situations. Fromm contends that the therapist must play a more active role in treatment. This stems, in turn, from his belief that insight must derive from experience that has an affective quality if it is to be therapeutically effective and that this insight will determine the outcome of man's innate struggle toward health. Above all, Fromm is concerned with the requirements for a sane society as a matrix for the creation of the productive, fully human man. Ideally, this would be a humanistic, communitarian society in which man could relate to others creatively as an individual rather than a conformist.

CURRENT PERSPECTIVES

Erich Fromm has not created a separate school of psychoanalysis, although his ideas have been adopted by many psychotherapists. He was chairman of the faculty of the William Alanson White Institute of Psychiatry, Psychoanalysis and Psychology in New York City for many years. At present, he holds the position of professor at the National University of Mexico, where he teaches psychiatry and psychoanalysis, is director of psychoanalytic training, and exerts considerable influence. In addition, Fromm's appeal to the general public remains undiminished, and he spends several months each year in New York City, lecturing to lay and professional audiences.

REFERENCES

Fromm, E. *Escape from Freedom*. Rinehart, New York, 1941.

Fromm, E. *Man for Himself*. Rinehart, New York, 1947.

Fromm, E. *The Forgotten Language*. Rinehart, New York, 1951.

Fromm, E. *The Sane Society*. Rinehart, New York, 1955.

Fromm, E. *The Art of Loving*. Harper & Row, New York, 1956.

CHAPTER EIGHT

Sandor Rado

HOWARD DAVIDMAN, M.D.

INTRODUCTION

DEFINITION

ADAPTATIONAL PSYCHODYNAMICS is the term used to refer to a body of psychoanalytic theory originally formulated and systematized by Sandor Rado and widely disseminated among many generations of psychoanalytic students. Early in his career, Rado worked closely with Freud and achieved eminence as an outstanding classical theorist and educator. Gradually, in the course of his work, Rado became increasingly aware of the need to rebuild classical psychoanalytic theory to conform to the criteria of biological science and scientific methodology. The accumulated clinical observations of classical psychoanalysis have been preserved as the basis of the newer adaptational theory. However, the explanatory principles have been revised so that they may truly serve to clarify and elucidate the data to be organized and explained, and the theory has been restructured to provide hypotheses capable of validation and suggestive of new research. The theory of adaptational psychodynamics also attempts to provide a basis for transoperational correlation with other scientific disciplines. It has been described by Rado as the "introspectional branch of human biology." As such, it postulates a basic theory of the science of behavior of the total organism.

ORIENTATION

Areas of emphasis. During the development of adaptational theory, classical psychoanalytic theory was subjected to meticulous examination and scientific criticism; a partial report of the conclusions drawn from this examination is presented in this chapter. In general, this review served to underscore the importance of literate and detailed descriptions of clinical observations. It often seemed that the more abstract and poetic the theory, the more removed it became from the clinical data from which it supposedly derived. Extensive descriptions of clinical observations constitute the basic data that must then be organized and clarified through theory formation.

The review also pointed up the need for the precise and explicit definition of all technical terms. It was felt that deficiencies in definition and description in the body of classical clinical and theoretical psychoanalytic theory, as reflected in its literature and teaching, had assumed serious proportions. The attempt to preserve outworn theory by increasing patchwork on the libido theory, by refining the definition of energy sources, and by postulating subtler cathexes on subtler structures had led to scholastic dogmatisms rather than recognizable scientific statements.

Finally, adaptational psychodynamics strives to establish a correlation between psychological knowledge gained through introspection and the physiological findings derived from the inspective sciences. Freud believed that psychological functioning would ultimately be explained in organic terms but felt that the knowledge of neurophysiology then available was inadequate for this task. Rado believes that the introspectional and inspectional aspects of brain activity must be correlated by cross-interpretation and that the theory must be open to new knowledge that would continually increase the degree of correspondence.

Psychoanalysis as science. Orthodox psychoanalytic theories served the proper function of scientific theory at the initial stages in the development of the science. They represented a first attempt to organize overwhelming, chaotic, and novel psychic data that had been elicited through the use of a revolutionary technique misnamed "free association." The theories that interpreted these data provoked new questions and stimulated new areas of research and thereby fulfilled the basic function of all scientific theory.

Thus, subsequent direct studies of the behavior of the child were inspired by Freud's retrospectively based hypotheses concerning the emotional life of children and the stages of psychosexual development. The scientific value of classical psychoanalytic theory is also evident in the stimulus Freud's anthropological speculations provided for modern systematic comparative anthropological research into personality development in diverse cultures with varying child-rearing practices. Nor is the significance of this contribution diminished by the fact that Freud's original hypotheses that drew on the meager cultural knowledge then available and those that resulted from his misapplication of Haeckel's law of recapitulation ("ontogeny recapitulates phylogeny") to sociology were disproved later in the light of subsequent knowledge.

On the other hand, classical psychoanalytic theory includes constructs that are inadequate and misleading, such as those that postulate an innate normal progression of pleasure-seeking behavior through various phases, including a homosexual stage and a latency period, that are organized around the specific erogenous zones. And Freud's dual instinct theory is not a scientific theory at all, since it does not permit testable study of clinical phenomena; nor can it be validated by any scientific method. Rather, it represents a philosophical abstract description of the origins of behavior that, according to the adaptational school, is remote from the real motives that govern behavior. Another example of differences with the adaptational viewpoint is Freud's contention that neuroses arise solely as a result of difficulties in the resolution of the Oedipus complex.

Freud's original theory of mental functioning was built around his concepts concerning six elements considered essentially sound by the adaptational school: (1) motivation, (2) pleasure-seeking and pain avoidance, (3) repression, (4) mental mechanisms, (5) mental apparatus, and (6) evolutionary and individual history. However, after 1905, Freud's tendency toward speculation increased, as evidenced by his arbitrary expansion of his sexual theory and his introduction of the animistic concept of instinct. Thereafter, he persisted in the development of mystic animistic concepts, despite his own warning that the instincts were vague and mythological and that his tripartite model of the mind was not to be interpreted literally. Adaptational psychodynamics discards these hypotheses and procedures and reverts to the body of factual knowledge and sound mechanistic theory that were characteristic of Freud's early approach. Only through reorganization that will enable "transoperational correlation with the findings of science" can psychoanalytic theory achieve the goal Freud set for it.

Methodological principles. Adaptational psychodynamics treats the historic concern over the mind-body problem as a paradox resulting from the scientific observer's confusion over his own methodology. The human organism is viewed as an integral unit. The methods of studying the organism vary according to the functions to be studied; the type of information obtainable is determined by the methods available for such investigation. Introspectional material, the product of the reporting function of the brain, is studied by means of a psychological tool such as psychoanalytic exploration. On the other hand, physiological brain functions and other functions of the body are studied by inspectional methods that use structured techniques to measure performance. The psychoanalyst's unique capacity for self-awareness and self-observation is the investigative tool in psychodynamic matters. The psychoanalyst may be a crude measuring rod, but he is the best there is. Confusion has resulted from misguided attempts to explain inspective data by introspectional means and vice versa. There is no validity to the charge that the study of psychodynamic matters cannot conform to the methods of science. Any set of data can be studied scientifically if the appropriate method or instrument is used. Statistical methods may satisfy a primitive thirst for exactitude, but when statistical approaches are misapplied, they can only provide an illusion of knowledge. An introspectional or psychological method is the appropriate one for measuring the cerebral mechanisms of motivation and control, and the complex findings are best expressed by the skillful use of language.

PERSONALITY THEORY

Although Rado recognized Freud's enormous contributions to science, he did not consider Freud's theories immutable. Rather, he believed that the future progress of psychoanalysis as a science depended on the further modification and clarification of classical theory. To this end, he used simpler and less abstract explanations, removed undefined terms and obscure references, and reorganized the material in simple hierarchical terms.

BEHAVIOR AS A TELEOLOGICAL PHENOMENON

Adaptation was postulated as a core concept to emphasize Rado's evolutionary biological orientation. Thus, the theoretical frame of reference conforms to the dictum "adjust or perish," which must be obeyed by both the individual and the species. The emphasis on adaptation has served to refocus attention on the continuing influence on development of mutually reinforcing interactions of ever-increasing complexity between the child and the people and things in his environment. In his later theoretical formulations, Freud minimized this aspect of development and emphasized the role of constitutionally determined internal forces that seemed to operate autonomously.

Adaptational theory conceptualizes and evaluates behavior in terms of its utilitarian and survival functions. Thus, pleasure-seeking is seen as a means to the adaptive end of fulfilling the organism's needs in biological interaction with its environment; therefore, it also serves to ensure the preservation of the individual and the species. Pleasure is not an end in itself. It follows, then, that adaptational psychodynamics is concerned with goal-directed behavior. Behavior is conceived of as a means to an end; it is evaluated in terms of its goal-finding and goal-achievement functions, which are designed to reduce or eliminate equilibrium-disturbing tensions that arise within the organism and to establish a new equilibrium. The observer interprets the adaptive value of behavior in terms of his evaluation of its evolutionary or survival value. Adaptational psychology has adopted the teleological orientation that characterizes modern biology and physiology.

MOTIVATION AND EMOTION

In his early formulations Freud emphasized that behavior must be studied in its motivational context if it is to be understood. However, Freud departed from this fundamental insight in his later theoretical constructs—specifically, his instinct theory, his theory of constitutional bisexuality, and his tripartite model of the human mind. In so doing, he replaced mechanistic concepts with animistic notions that failed to explain behavior in terms of its motivational context. Adaptational psychodynamics does not employ concepts that describe imaginary energy, such as libido, or its cathexis on imaginary structures to explain motivation. Instead, it identifies the forces that motivate behavior as the emotions themselves. Thus, the emotions are defined as the integrating forces that mobilize the organism to take action designed to fulfill its needs.

The only human energy that science recognizes is the conventional metabolic energy studied in physiology and biochemistry, measurable by inspective rather than introspective methods. This is actually the energy underlying brain activity. Psychodynamic phenomena are observed, measured, and explained through the human capacities of introspection, language, and thought. Freud discovered an appropriate method to enable searching scientific exploration of introspectional material and called it "free association." However, Rado uses a descriptive term for it, "communicated deep introspection." The relationship of mind to brain activity is one of congruence, not identity. To quote Rado:

> Consciousness is the awareness of the running report produced as its inward expression by the underlying nervous activity of the brain. The latter may be called the *reporting process*, and consciousness, the *awareness process*. . . . The rest of the brain's activity is nonreporting (i.e., purely physiologic). Nevertheless, even this purely physiologic brain activity may, through proper channels, influence the reporting process and correspondingly, the awareness process.

The extrapolation of introspectional language enables identification of nonreporting emotions—specifically, when the awareness process reveals a gap in motivational understanding and the context in which the gap appears enables the observer to draw the requisite inferences, to describe nonreporting fear, rage, desire, etc. Although this concept recognizes that brain physiology operates on a different level from the psychological concept of motivation, it nevertheless links behavior to brain activity. This dispenses with the obscure connotations of the unconscious.

CONCEPT OF EMOTION

Freud's instinct theory, particularly his libido theory, obscured the primary role of emotions in human life; instead, they were described as secondary derivatives or epiphenomena. In contrast, adaptational psychodynamics places the study of emotions in the foreground as the clearly observable mobilizing forces of behavior on a psychological level and describes their action in introspectional terms. Following the physiological concepts outlined by Cannon, the emotions are divided into two classes.

The emergency emotions—such as fear, rage, shame, guilty fear, guilty rage—are based on present pain or the anticipation of pain. The second class, the welfare emotions—such as desire, joy, affection, love, and pride —reflect present pleasure or the anticipation of pleasure. The welfare emotions stem from pleasantly toned forces of attraction and gratifying interaction with a mothering person.

The emergency emotions provide the organism with an emergency control and protect it from danger and anticipated danger. For example, fear and rage protect the organism by mobilizing it for fight or flight in the face of tangible or rationally perceived danger. If the danger cannot be dealt with and the organism freed from continued fear and threat of damage, the organism will be flooded with inappropriate and excessive emergency emotions that no longer perform a protective function but are damaging in themselves. Examples of the effects of emergency dyscontrol are cases of acute war neurosis and acute neurotic failure. If this reaction cannot be mastered by conscious thought, there follow nonreporting thought, repression, and the other automatic mechanisms of repair—hysteric, obsessive, phobic, and other syndromes. These syndromes are classified diagnostically according to the psychodynamic mechanisms involved. They serve to free the organism, partially, from the painful excess of stimulation produced by excessive insoluble fear. The organism is then able to function once again, although the functioning is constricted.

CENTRAL INTEGRATIVE APPARATUS

Adaptational psychodynamics hypothesizes a central integrative apparatus, which is described in terms of hierarchical levels of central integration and control of the organism's motivations and behavior. This hierarchically organized structure reflects the evolutionary history of the species and is presented schematically as consisting of four levels; (1) hedonic self-regulation (the most primitive), (2) preverbal brute emotion, (3) emotional thought, and (4) unemotional thought.

Hedonic self-regulation. The level of hedonic self-regulation is achieved by the human fetus or the semicomatose adult. In terms of evolution, it corresponds to the integrative functioning of the protozoa. At this level the organism's capacity for foresight, its ability to anticipate the future, is minimal. It simply moves toward objects that fulfill its need and away from noxious stimuli. Nevertheless, there is evidence of discrimination, of awareness of the presence of needed supplies and of other conditions favorable to survival, and, conversely, of the presence of danger. Thus, with respect to evolution, hedonic self-regulation is of obvious survival value. Contact receptors and rudimentary nervous nets are used at the hedonic level. Tension, pleasure-pain, attraction-repulsion mechanisms, and reference to past experience in terms of feeling residues are present. Tropisms and simple conditioned behavior are also manifested by the organism at this level. These forces enable the organism to obtain optimal conditions of food, oxygen, light, temperature, and water and to integrate motor behavior designed to permit it to take and retain needed objects and avoid damaging ones. Hedonic self-regulation is the primitive basis of pain-pleasure physiology.

Pain and pleasure govern the operative patterns of the organism at higher levels of integration as well. For instance, the ability to construct abstract mathematical formulas is also governed by sophisticated application of the pain-pleasure principle. Mathematical thinking produces rewards and punishments, successes and failures, and evokes feelings of pride or provokes a loss of self-esteem, despite the fact that it involves unemotional thought.

In fact, mechanisms for the avoidance of painful stimulation exist at all levels of the psychodynamic cerebral system and in the integration of peripheral (somatic) levels as well. Rado refers to these mechanisms generically as "riddance mechanisms," and he has emphasized their presence in all animal design and at each level of organismic integration. On the physiological level, the riddance mechanisms include such reflexes as vomiting, scratching, lacrimation, sneezing, and coughing; on the psychological level, the primary riddance mechanism is repression. Repression is the automatic riddance of painful thought and emotion through exclusion of the painful processes from awareness.

Preverbal brute emotion. The level of preverbal brute emotion corresponds to metazoan evolution. The emergency emotions of fear and rage appear at the higher level of organization and perform the same adaptive function as pain. The evolution of distance receptors and the increasing specialization of the head end of the organism and of nervous system control at the head end must have preceded the appearance of the emergency emotions. There is "sensory exploration of the shell of the immediate future," speedier motility, evidence of predacity, and an extended period of care of the young. There is increased delay of motor reaction to stimuli as the brain develops at the head as the "manager of muscle" in response to its increased capacity to receive signals and, as a result, greater effectiveness and discrimination of action. The welfare emotions also appear as mobilizers of the organism to action. The emotions are expressed in order to warn of impending danger or elicit cooperation. Thus, they serve as a communicative mechanism on the group level. The emotions are of evident survival value and have feeling tone and voluntary and autonomic expression.

Emotional thought. At the emotional thought level, brute fear and rage are modified and take the form of apprehensive and angry thought. Language and thought processes have appeared, and there is exploration of present, past, and future experience. The cerebral cortex has become dominant. There is greater discrimination, diversity, and flexibility of motor performance. The basic emotions have become differentiable into shadings and compounds of derivative emotions. The learning process is highly developed, and the dependency period is extended. Regulation by reward and punishment is maternal at first and is then governed by society. Reasoning develops; symbols rather than things are manipulated; thought is trial action and provides increased efficiency. Yet emotional thought is selective, not objective; it tends to be self-justifying and feeds the emotion from which it springs and by which it is controlled. Consciousness and self-awareness are present at this level.

Unemotional thought. The unemotional thought level is characterized by rational or objective thought. At the present stage of social evolution, there is continual struggle between rational and emotional thought for dominance in personal and in political life. Unemotional thought corresponds to the transcendence of intellect over emotions. This is achieved by intellectual mastery of the emotions; in the process, intellectual activity becomes increasingly complex. Intellectual activity becomes an exploratory and mastery tool of increasing dependability that can operate in relation to phenomena far outside the "shell of the immediate future." This level provides a fine adjustment of the equipment for survival. Man's complex culture develops from its use, and his social survival now depends on its effectiveness.

CONTROLLING UNIT: THE ACTION SELF

The controlling unit of the entire psychodynamic cerebral system is the action self. Rado identified the action self as occupying an axial position in relation to the four hierarchical levels described above and as deriving from the central importance of the uniquely human capacity for conscious self-awareness. This self-awareness emerges from and is sustained by infantile proprioceptive sensations. The baby, perceiving his muscular activities, discovers himself as the one who acts. The psychological interaction between self-awareness and willed action is the psychodynamic expression of unfolding innate circuits of brain activity. On this foundation, the organism builds its systematic self-image or action self. Combining kinesthetic with other sensory information, the organism learns to recognize itself as a cohesive, enduring being. The self-image is formed as the organism focuses attention on the equipment it uses to control its environment. Changing profoundly as it develops, the action self is originally filled with pleasure by its success in sucking and attributes limitless power to its willed actions; it pictures itself as omnipotent. This is termed the "primordial self." At this stage the infant sees his parents as deputies who exercise his magic powers for him. The tested self develops from the primordial self as a result of continual defeat of this feeling of omnipotence in the face of realistic experience. The self then develops as a reliable, tested self, differing to various degrees from the desired self. This process involves delegatory and emulative identifications, the awareness of one's capacities, and the ability to change the longing for omnipotence into a desire for achievement in socially rewarding directions. These achievements then become a source of self-reward or pride. Emotional self-approval, the function of the action self known as pride, rises and falls, depending on the amount of pleasure the action self consumes. The action self is the supreme decision-maker and controls activity at each of the four levels of the integrative apparatus.

THEORY OF CONSCIENCE

The conscience develops as the preventive branch of emergency control and consists of self-restraining and self-prodding mechanisms that enable the action self to adapt to societal demands. It arises in the dependency situation at the level of emotional thought and enhances the organism's fitness for cooperation, first with mothering persons and then for increasing cultural cooperation. Conscience regulates conduct by self-punishment and self-reward. Cultural rules are transmitted to the child by parental regulations, which are enforced by reward and punishment. The child's reactive fear of punishment restrains forbidden activities. His obedience is rewarded by loving care, to which he responds with heightened pride. These mechanisms, automatized to varying degrees, continue into adulthood in the form of fear of social punishment on the one hand and rising pride in social recognition on the other. Conscience proper derives from the child's belief that his parents are omniscient and his resultant fear of inescapable punishment. When this is automatized, it becomes the fear of his own conscience, and this is the most differentiated and dependable mechanism of self-restraint humanity has achieved. Obedience to the voice of conscience elicits the self-reward of rising pride.

When temptation and defiant rage overrule the fear of detection and punishment, disobedience and efforts to escape detection follow. In submissive obedience, defiant rage is submerged by fear. With growth and loving identification facilitated by the influence of rewards, misbehavior causes guilty fear, which acts as a warning signal that loving care is threatened and must be restored. Thus, the complex emotion of guilty fear consists of self-criticism, the awareness of wrongdoing, and the fear of inescapable punishment, intensified by dependence on loving care, together with repression and retroflexion of defiant rage on the self. When temptation and defiant rage overrule the fear of conscience, disobedience causes guilty fear and falling self-respect or pride. Repair is effected through expiatory behavior taught in childhood and designed to elicit self-forgiveness modeled on parental and social forgiveness. Self-respect is thereby elevated again. Atonement maneuvers aim at restoring self-respect and are modeled on the earlier restoration of parental care and social approval after repentence, at a time when the child was in a state of dependence.

THEORY OF PSYCHOPATHOLOGY

The dynamics of depression are traced to the miscarried application of automatized conscience mechanisms to the repair of the results of serious failures in realistic living.

DEPRESSION

Important failures in realistic mastery cause excess fear and impotent rage that may surpass resolution by the resources of intellectual activity. If fight or flight fails on all levels, hopelessness ensues. Then, on a regressed and inappropriate level, guilty fear and expiation offer the hope that, by self-punishment and forgiveness, concomitant magic help can be coerced. Even when this proves illusory in reality, the hope does not die; rather, there is resort to further and angrier self-punishment to secure the desired end. In the face of realistic failure, this regression to dependent automatized angry expiatory proceedings is the miscarried repair that underlies the depressive reaction.

HOMOSEXUALITY

In adaptational theory, sexual theory has been revised in the light of modern knowledge, since Freud's theory of constitutional bisexuality has been refuted by modern embryological and endocrinological knowledge. Nevertheless, Freud's theory persists in the theory and practice of many psychoanalysts, as evidenced in their search for latent homosexuality. This orientation, when it persists, can be quite destructive; it confuses clinicians and causes despair to many patients who attempt to analyze a mythical constitutional latent homosexuality in the magic hope that this will relieve their suffering, which, in fact, is due to entirely different emotional motivations and failures of function.

Adaptational psychodynamics has re-emphasized the essential heterosexuality of all mankind, based on reproductive anatomy and the institution of marriage, imprinted on the mind of the child early in his development. The fulfillment of the reproductive goal is dependent on childhood learning. Heterosexual function is often damaged by the impact of early parental threats; fears and rages may affect the assertive capacity of the individual—the assertion of his sexual desires, in particular. The partially incapacitated child attempts to repair the damage as he matures; one reparative device, among many others, is the attempt to reproduce heterosexual union in the absence of the frightening and forbidden organ of the other sex. Thus, he is able to avoid fear and guilt, as well as the fear of the humiliation of failure in sexual performance, and achieve orgastic satisfaction nevertheless by means of an illusory or fantasied heterosexual mating between partners of the same sex. Simultaneously, dependent, hostile, and power-seeking motivations are prominent, and usually sexual love is counterfeit. Frequently, as homosexual partners grow used to each other, physical sexual activity becomes increasingly rare. However, homosexuality can only denote behavior motivated by the desire to have orgastic experiences with a partner of the same sex; it cannot serve as a label for all passivity and inhibition.

MASOCHISM

The concept of miscarried repair mechanisms to compensate for failures in the emergency function of the organism is used extensively in adaptational psychodynamics to explain a wide range of psychopathological symptoms. Thus, masochistic behavior is explained in terms of automatized obedience and submission to old parental threats of punishment before forbidden pleasurable goals can be experienced and achieved. This is self-punishment elicited by guilty fear, administered in advance of obtaining prohibited pleasures. Rado describes this as "pain-dependent behavior" that can be observed in all forms of disturbed pleasure-functioning. This explanation is based on the desire for mastery, experience, and pleasure despite inhibitory fear and guilt. According to adaptational theory, it cannot be attributed to death-seeking instincts or sadistic or masochistic components of a sexual instinct.

CLASSIFICATION OF BEHAVIOR DISORDERS

Ideally, the production of emergency emotions—such as fear, rage, guilty fear, and guilty rage—will lead to the realistic resolution of the threatening situations. However, where healthy resolution fails, there develops an overproduction of these emotions, which then presents the organism with an additional threat from within with which it must cope. The overproduction of emergency emotions, termed "emergency dyscontrol," is the simplest form of behavior disorder; other clinical syndromes depart from this source and may be classified in a sequence of increasing complexity of their patterns of attempted self-repair. Rado's classification, as incorporated in his theory of adaptational psychodynamics, provides the following classes of behavior.

Emergency dyscontrol. Emergency dyscontrol includes the emotional outflow; the riddance through dreams; the phobic, the inhibitory, the repressive, and the hypochondriac patterns; and the gainful exploitation of illness.

Descending dyscontrol. Descending dyscontrol may be defined as autonomic discharge of repressed but overflowing emergency emotions into the various component systems—respiratory, circulatory, alimentary, endocrine, etc.—of the whole organism.

Sexual disorders. These include impairments and failures in standard performance; dependence on reparative patterns (such as organ replacement and organ avoidance; the criminal, dramatic, and hidden forms of sexual pain dependence; the formation of homosexual pairs); fire-setting and shop-lifting as sexual equivalents.

Social overdependence. Social overdependence is characterized by the continuous search for an ersatz parent and the mechanisms of forced competition, avoidance of competition, and self-harming defiance.

Common maladaptation. This is a combination of sexual disorder and social overdependence.

The expressive pattern (expressive elaboration of common maladaptation). This pattern includes ostentatious self-presentation, dreamlike interludes, rudimentary pantomimes, disease copies, and the expressive complication of incidental disease.

The obsessive pattern (obsessive elaboration of common maladaptation). In this pattern are included broodings, rituals, and overt expression of temptations; tic and stammering as obsessive equivalents; bedwetting, nail-biting, grinding of teeth in sleep as precursors of the obsessive pattern.

The paranoid pattern (nondisintegrative elaboration of common maladaptation). This pattern is the hypochondriac, self-referential, persecutory, and grandiose stages of the Magnan sequence.

THEORY OF SCHIZOTYPAL ORGANIZATION

Adaptational psychodynamics recognizes that there is a qualitative difference between schizophrenia and the neuroses in terms of organizational deviations that involve the entire organism. It also postulates that schizophrenia depends on a variable but necessary genetic predisposition that is operative throughout the life of the schizophrenic individual. Thus, schizophrenia is not caused by schizophrenogenic mothers; rather, these mothers have been upset by the atypical reactions of their schizotypal babies. "Schizotype" is Rado's abbreviation of schizophrenic phenotype, and his theory holds that the genetic predisposition finds physiological and psychological expression in unique forms. When psychodynamically organized, the clinical data reveal difficulties traceable to a compound of inherited defect, faulty childhood experiences, and miscarried efforts of the individual to repair his deficiency and stay afloat.

According to Rado, schizotypal differentness resides in two fundamental forms of damage. These are an integrative pleasure deficiency and a proprioceptive disorder. The diminished pleasure capacity weakens the motivation for every action of the integrative apparatus throughout life. Normal welfare emotions, which are essential for performance and growth toward enjoyable cooperation and love, are lacking. Consequently, the pleasure deficiency weakens the balance of emergency emotions, and fear and rage rise to an excessive and unmodulated strength. The coherence of the overall control of the action self is disrupted by intense emotion, and self-confidence is undermined because the socially acceptable integration of behavior is so difficult to achieve. The enjoyment of all the complex tasks and relationships of adult life is weakened.

The proprioceptive disorder also damages the action self from the time of its early formation through awareness of willed action in early childhood and throughout life. These two sources of damage to the action self leave it brittle and prone to disintegrative breakdown characterized by thought disorder. The extent of these two defects varies from patient to patient, as do the genetic predisposition and the nature of the traumata of life experience. However, the consequences pervade every area of behavior. The following four processes of automatic repair are described as typical of the organism's attempts to compensate for the defective self.

Extreme overdependence. Extreme overdependence throughout life, together with an inability to give love and affection, is usually accompanied by responses of fear and rage to parental demands and gross obedience or gross defiance, with little in-between range of emotional shading. This dependent craving is resented, and the anger is aimed at those on whom the individual is forced to depend.

Scarcity economy of pleasure. A scarcity of sources of pleasure forces the individual to cling to every morsel of pleasure. Thus, any loss of small pleasure is experienced as a severe blow. However, a favored or routine pursuit may absorb the entire limited capacity for pleasure.

The use of intellect. Intellect is used to do the job ordinarily done automatically by pleasurable feeling. Unemotional thought is used to figure out how to live in the emotional world of other people, whose emotions are not shared by the individual. This attempt to imitate other people's pleasurable reactions may create the impression of oddness, unexpected humor, or creativity.

Greatly increased craving for magic. The preceding three reparative devices may sustain a workable adjustment, but this one miscarries because it defeats adaptation. It provides solace, the individual tends to rely on it, and it can eventuate in delusion.

The clinical outcome depends on the efficiency of the first three repair mechanisms in relationship to the total adaptive resources of the organism. These include intellect, education, privileges of wealth and social position, opportunities, the establishment of achievable goals under the enlightened guidance of parents and psychiatrist, and the capacity for healthy repair. Adaptive failures tend to develop under the stresses of life and the conventional expectations for performance according to the patient's chronological age. As the individual becomes aware of his failures in adjustment, he is flooded with fear and experiences a severe loss of pride; if he finds no acceptable way out, decompensation may ensue with acute schizophrenic panic. He may then resort to more regressed magical methods of repair that produce much of the overtly psychotic symptoms.

TREATMENT TECHNIQUES

Rado's theory of treatment includes the goal of raising the level of the patient's psychological development by remedial re-education, which transcends the removal of symptoms. To achieve this, the therapist must trace the patient's history from the present back to the formative experiences of his early years. It is necessary to overcome the patient's fears and resentments in order to help him communicate fully; the interpretation of the hidden meaning and motivating power of his emerging memories, ideas, and emotions will then prove more fruitful. And to achieve the goal of re-education, the therapist must keep the patient's emotional relationship to him under control. These principles are in accordance with Freud's concepts.

However, Freud's theory of treatment eventually became dominated by the concept of transference, which had its origins in the mysterious force known as the repetition compulsion. Transference is a descriptive rather than a motivational term. Moreover, the abstract power of transference and resistance obscured the motivations of the patient's behavior. The adult patient's childish love and hate of the psychoanalyst derives from the child's pursuit of emotional security in the interest of survival. Whenever he feels helpless, he reverts to the early adaptive pattern of infantile dependence. Under the continued stresses that have induced the adult patient to undertake treatment, he behaves toward the psychoanalyst with the invocatory mechanisms aimed at magic fulfillment that he learned under childhood stress. This behavior does not solve his problem but only creates new difficulties. For example, the classical technique tries to encourage development of a positive transference, which may consist of an overly dependent relationship with a distorted image of the therapist. Once the transference is achieved, the therapist is no longer seen realistically as another human being who is an expert in human relationships and who is to be consulted because he can help the patient work out more effective ways to master his emotions and interpersonal relationships. The dependent and magically idealized view of the therapist may never be resolved in classical technique.

In contrast, the adaptational technique attempts from the start to work against the patient's search for a repetition of a dependent parental relationship. It attempts to prevent perceptive distortions of the psychoanalyst by which the patient strives to fulfill his magical hopes, and it presents the analyst in human proportions. It attempts to help the patient achieve the most realistic level of integration of which he is capable and to help him move to more integrated levels of functioning. Prolonged regression, which is inevitable in classical psychoanalysis, is believed to preclude achievement of these goals.

Rado emphasizes that the undoing of repressions is only a first step in treatment. Once inhibiting fears begin to be relieved, a positive program of emotional re-education is undertaken so that the patient may become aware of his emotional capacities for pleasure, assertion, and competition in reality and thereby learn the lessons he could not master while he was dominated by emergency emotions and inhibition. This is a re-educational process that begins where classical psychoanalysis ends, with development of the welfare emotions while the patient is maintained on the self-reliant or aspiring level. This procedure builds pride based on realistic, successful performance in areas where the patient had failed and in new areas now open to the patient's curiosity and striving.

Adaptational psychotherapeutic technique avoids classifying patients according to specific methods of treatment. Its theory describes the therapeutic needs of all emotionally troubled patients; it does not recognize that certain people are not eligible for analysis. Treatment is designed to meet the needs of the patient after a detailed history-taking and an evaluation of his functioning capacities, the extent and nature of his inhibitions, and his capacity for change.

While elaborating his theory of treatment, Rado offers a deceptively simple and most helpful schema for describing psychotherapeutic methods based on the motivational and integrational level on which they are conducted. The schema obviates the futile argument over whether a treatment is psychoanalytic, based on such criteria as the frequency and duration of sessions, their total number, the posture of the patient, and the material dealt with. Meaningful treatment is based on the application of sound psychodynamic principles that serve as a guide to the psychotherapeutic needs of all patients.

The descriptive schema alluded to above charts the hierarchical order of the patient's designs for cooperation with the therapist. On the basis of the patient's capacity for cooperation, on self-reliant or aspiring levels of function, reconstructive therapy can be done. Patients who employ mainly methods of cooperation based on a search for a parent figure or for magic and who are incapable of a shift to more integrated and mature levels of treatment behavior must be cared for properly by methods integrated on levels suited to them. Thus, there is room in the armamentarium of adaptational psychodynamics for reparative psychotherapy, hypnotherapy, pharmacotherapy, and other techniques that rely for their effectiveness on the forces inherent in these patients' search for magic and for parent figures. The appropriate levels of treatment for each patient must be diagnosed and tested in practice. A proficient psychiatrist should have the ability to provide various types of treatment, according to the patient's need. An appropriate scientific frame of reference provides him with an accurate tool for understanding and communication. The psychotherapy of schizophrenia differs qualitatively in goal and method from the treatment of the neuroses because of the qualitative difference in the psychodynamic integration of schizotypes, as described above.

The scientific understanding of events and changes in psychotherapy requires an accurate theory of psychodynamics and psychotherapy. In addition, there is an artistic dimension to therapy, and apprenticeship methods are required for its mastery. Clinical competence depends heavily on certain characteristics of the individual therapist, such as empathy and insight. The gifted therapist may achieve results even when his frame of reference includes inaccuracies. Psychodynamic science, however, depends on the development of theories that are as adequate and accurate as possible. Adaptational psychodynamics represents an attempt to formulate an organized basic theory that will ensure the accurate understanding of human behavior.

REFERENCES

Davidman, H. The contributions of Sandor Rado to psychodynamic science. In *Science and Psychoanalysis*, J. H. Masserman, editor, vol. 7, p. 17. Grune & Statton, New York, 1964.

Davidman, H. Evaluation of psychoanalysis: a clinician's view, In *Evaluation of Psychiatric Treatment*, P. H. Hoch and J. Zubin, editors. Grune & Stratton, New York, 1964.

Rado, S. An adaptational view of sexual behavior. In *Psychoanalysis of Behavior*, vol. 1, p. 186. Grune & Stratton, New York, 1956.

Rado, S. A critical examination of the concept of bisexuality. *Ibid.*, p. 139.

Rado, S. Mind, unconscious mind, and brain. *Ibid.*, p. 180.

Rado, S. Emergency behavior: with an introduction to the dynamics of conscience. *Ibid.*, p. 214.

Rado, S. Recent advances in psychoanalytic therapy. *Ibid.*, p. 251.

Rado, S. Hedonic control, action self and the depressive spell. *Ibid.*, p. 286.

Rado, S. Evolutionary basis of sexual adaptation. *Ibid.*, p. 312.

Rado, S. Adaptational psychodynamics: a basic science. *Ibid.*, p. 332.

Rado, S. Adaptational development of psychoanalytic therapy. *Ibid.*, p. 347.

Rado, S. Schizotypal organization: preliminary report on a clinical study of schizophrenia. *Ibid.*, vol. 2, p. 1.

Rado, S. From the metapsychological ego to the bio-cultural action self. *Ibid.*, p. 42.

Rado, S. Achieving self-reliant treatment behavior: therapeutic motivation and therapeutic techniques. *Ibid.*, p. 111.

Rado, S. Theory and therapy: the theory of schizotypal organization and its application to the treatment of decompensated schizotypal behavior. *Ibid.*, p. 127.

Rado, S. Rage, violence and conscience. *Ibid.*, p. 147.

Rado, S. Towards the construction of an organized foundation for clinical psychiatry. *Ibid.*, p. 152.

Rado, S. On the retransformation of psychoanalysis into a medical science. Compr. Psychiat., 3: 317, 1962.

AREA C

Other Psychoanalytic and Psychodynamic Theories

CHAPTER NINE

Adolf Meyer

GEORGE MORA, M.D.

INTRODUCTION

BACKGROUND AND TRAINING

ADOLF MEYER WAS BORN in Niederwenigen, Switzerland, on November 13, 1866, the son of a Zwinglian minister. In medical school he was influenced by the psychiatrist August Forel, director of the Burghölzli Hospital for the Insane. Subsequently, during a year of postgraduate study in London, Meyer was particularly impressed by Hughlings Jackson's integrative views of the nervous system and by Thomas Huxley's evolutionary concepts. In 1892, after a period of further study in Paris under the neurologist Déjérine, Meyer decided to emigrate to the United States and to accept a position at the state hospital at Kankakee, Illinois.

EARLY CAREER

Three years after he arrived in this country, Meyer accepted a position as pathologist at the Worcester State Hospital, which at that time was one of the outstanding psychiatric institutions in the United States. Shortly thereafter, he was appointed clinical director of the hospital and began to establish standards for taking and recording detailed case histories of all psychiatric patients. A subsequent tour of various psychiatric institutions in Europe in 1896 resulted in his adoption of Kraepelin's system for the classification of mental disorders. However, nosology was not Meyer's primary interest, for even then he recognized the importance of the psychiatrist's awareness of the dynamic factors that influenced the behavior of the patient and his life situation.

In 1901 Meyer was appointed director of the Pathological Institute by the State of New York, and he proceeded to establish basic standards for the state hospital system. The following year, Meyer moved the institute to Manhattan State Hospital at Ward's Island so that he might have more opportunity for clinical observation. Concurrently, he began to concentrate increasingly on the study of psychopathology.

BASIC ORIENTATION

Instead of emphasizing symptoms, Meyer focused on the types of reaction manifested by the whole individual in terms of his total life experience. In 1903, in an article entitled "An Attempt at Analysis of the Neurotic Constitution," Meyer postulated that mental disorder often had its roots in a personality imbalance that, in turn, was caused by the disorganization of habits. The incomprehensible symptoms of mental illness were viewed as crude and inadequate attempts by the patient to cure himself, which had to be guided rather than suppressed. Dementia praecox, which was then the area of investigation of such outstanding psychiatrists as Kraepelin and Jung, was the testing ground for Meyer's concepts. Contrary to Kraepelin's stress on deterioration as the eventual outcome in dementia praecox, Meyer believed that personality traits, such as withdrawal, preceded the appearance of the disease, and he suggested that prevention as well as recovery might be possible. He conceived of schizophrenia as a twisted maladaptation that could be understood in terms of the patient's life experience and that was characterized by habit disorganization or deterioration.

Meyer recommended that an attempt be made to intervene early in the development of the illness by the patient's school, family, and community. Thus, his early interest in community psychiatry is noteworthy. Moreover, the first applications of the principles of social work to occupational and recreational therapy with convalescent patients and the organization of aftercare programs were inspired by Meyer's work during this period.

In the meantime, psychiatrists in this country had become familiar with Freud's theories, largely through the efforts of Stanley Hall at Clark University. As early as 1906, Meyer evaluated Freud's study of the infantile phase of development as "pathologically important" and warned against premature rejection of psychoanalysis, although he objected to Freud's emphasis on the pathological and hypothetical rather than on the healthy and verifiable aspects of mental functioning. Meyer's theory of psychobiology reflected this conflicting view.

Meyer introduced the term "psychobiological interpretation" during a lecture on dementia praecox at Clark University in 1909, in connection with the different types of disorganizing personality reactions. In the broad context of psychobiological interpretation, Meyer explained, pathological personality reactions could be explained as regression to former, previously protective phylogenetic reactions that were incompatible with adaptation at the later time.

THEORY OF PSYCHOBIOLOGY

BASIC CONCEPTS

Meyer developed the theories that were to be designated as the school of psychobiology during his tenure at Johns Hopkins. There he remained, as professor of psychiatry and the first director of the Henry Phipps Psychiatric Clinic, from his appointment in 1913 to his retirement in 1937. In brief, psychobiology emphasized the importance of biographical study in understanding the whole person. That is, the object of such study is the individual, whom Meyer defined as a biological unit that always functions as a person, whether alone or in groups. Although it changes constantly, the individual's experiential continuum enables him to maintain internal and external homeostatic equilibrium in coping with new situations. In addition, the individual's plasticity allows him a wide spectrum of differentiation in capacity and function and a relatively high degree of spontaneity and responsiveness. Because of the complexity of human functioning, the psychiatrist who attempts to acquire a scientific understanding of his patients must have a combination of attributes: He must be a methodical investigator, biographer, artist, and educator.

In sketching the evolutionary development of the human mind, including its prehistory, largely through the process of symbolization, Meyer noted that the biographical study of man was the last discipline to pass from the stage of intuition and philosophical speculation to that of scientific investigation. This area of study, which he defined as objective psychobiology, consisted of the observation of objective facts, the formulation of predictable conditions in which these may occur, and the testing and validation of methods for their controlled modification. Instead of accepting predetermined hypothetical psychological or metapsychological constructs to account for these facts, he emphasized the soundness of common sense.

Although an analysis of psychobiological assets may reveal the presence of a variety of factors in each individual, Meyer emphasized the basic tendency toward integration that takes place. Because Meyer believed that multiple biological, social, and psychological forces contribute to the growth and development of the personality, he concluded that psychiatrists must study normal and abnormal behavior from many viewpoints.

Meyer conceived of the clinical value of the biographical approach to personality study as follows. It provides a practical and specific guide for eliciting individual data, a means of organizing that data, and a method for checking and re-evaluating data elicited under varying conditions. Recognizing that only a fraction of the total personality could be understood at any particular time, he devised a biological-cultural formula. The denominator of the formula consisted of the total personality record or potentiality of the patient; the numerator was the particular sample of performance.

CLINICAL EXAMINATION

For Meyer, the clinical psychiatric examination included the following components: (1) identifying the motives or indications for the examination, with particular focus on presenting pertinent details in the patient's life history, elicited through biographical study; (2) listing the obviously related personality items, factors, and reactions; (3) careful study of the physical, neurological, genetic, and social status and the correlation between these variables and personality factors; (4) differential diagnosis; and (5) formulation of a therapeutic plan geared to each case. Meyer felt this to be the best way to reconstruct the experiment of nature, which was defined as the reduction of events in the patient's life to the factors in a controlled experiment. In accordance with its common sense approach, psychobiology began with the data that were accessible. Symptoms were viewed as compensatory phenomena. Because data selection was necessary in any examination, Meyer called distributive analysis the study of all the factors in an individual's life that played a significant role, whether favorable or unfavorable, in his adjustment. The formation of better methods of adjustment by the patient, based on his understanding of past maladaptation, was termed "distributive synthesis."

In interviewing a patient, Meyer considered it better to begin by focusing on his chief complaint, which directed attention to the situation that required immediate therapeutic intervention. Later, the psychiatrist would determine the nature and extent of the disturbance in the context of the patient's overall functioning, the previous medical history, and the role played by such factors as constitution, development, and environment. Unconscious material elicited from the patient and information supplied by his family could supplement the psychiatrist's efforts and facilitate his understanding of the situation.

As a general rule, Meyer felt that one-word diagnoses were inadequate in a field as complex as human behavior. Initially, he used the terms "reaction set" and "reaction type" in diagnostic classification. From the early 1920's on, however, he used the word *ergasia*, derived from the Greek word for work, *ergon*, to describe the general concept of behavior and mental activity and its plural, *ergasias*, to denote specific behavioral units. Ergasias were the behaviorally conceived overt and implicit products of psychobiological integration. In the normal personality, of the many potentialities available for adaptation, various ergasias tended to prevail, depending on the internal and external needs of the individual. Meyer defined the individual's overt behavioral response to various situations as "subject organization." He then listed the various ergasias, using a different prefix for each type. At the same time, he warned that these classifications in themselves were not to be regarded as diagnoses; they simply described phenomena that occur under various conditions. It should also be noted that the following list of ergasias is no longer in use but is reproduced here for historical reasons. (1) Anergasias (an = lacking or lost): organic brain reactions, such as general paresis and senile brain disease, in which structural and functional brain deficit and pathology alter behavior; (2) dysergasias (dys = difficult): syndromes due to impairment of brain function, such as the toxic psychoses and delirium; (3) thymergasias (thymo = affective): the affective psychoses, such as manic-depressive reactions, (4) parergasias (para = beside): the form of schizophrenia characterized by regression, abandonment of reality, and delusions; (5) merergasias (mero = part): partial inability to work or function, as in the psychoneuroses; (6) kakergasias (kakos = bad): abnormal, poor, or faulty behavior, used synonymously with merergasias and (7) oligergasias (oligo = few or scant): mental deficiency.

PSYCHOBIOLOGICAL THERAPY

Psychobiological treatment, which began with distributive analysis and terminated with distributive synthesis, was not considered apart from pathology. Meyer believed that the psychiatrist began to treat the patient at the time of his initial contact with the patient's exposition of his problem. This did not mean that diagnosis was not essential. However, the first step in distributive analysis was evaluation of the patient's assets and liabilities. This was best accomplished through the study of his life history, on the basis of current data initially provided by the patient and supplemented by his subsequent reconstruction of past experiences.

Meyer recognized the importance of the patient's cooperation for the success of the psychotherapeutic process: the cooperation of the patient's better self—that is, of the healthier part of the patient's ego—was considered essential. He believed that these healthier aspects of the patient's personality should serve as the starting point for treatment. Therapy was conceived of as a service performed on behalf of the patient; the therapist was obligated to utilize every available opportunity to assist the patient. The basic aim of psychobiological therapy was to help an organism, hampered by abnormal conditions, to make the best adaptation possible to life and change.

TREATMENT TECHNIQUES

In the initial stage of treatment, the therapist's concern focused on the patient's sleep habits, nutrition, and the regulation of daily routines. It was also important at this stage to induce the patient to describe his difficulties in a concrete way and for the therapist to use the patient's ideation and language to communicate his offer of help and advice.

Problems were approached on a conscious rather than an unconscious level. Thus, therapy was administered in the course of ordinary face-to-face conversation in order to implement the psychiatrist's efforts to focus on the patient's current situation and his reactions to his everyday difficulties, as well as long-term life adjustment. At the beginning of each therapeutic session, the patient was encouraged to discuss his experiences in the interval since the last interview, beginning with obvious and immediate problems. Eventually, these problems were explored in greater detail when deeper relevant material had been elicited from the patient. This was accomplished through the use of spontaneous association, a term used by Meyer in preference to "free association" to describe the overcoming of the patient's resistance to verbalizing his basic problems in the unbiased atmosphere of the psychiatrist's office.

The intensity and frequency of treatment sessions depended on the needs of the individual patient. The psychiatrist permitted the patient to arrange his treatment schedule or asked him to agree to a specific therapeutic program. It was the psychiatrist's responsibility to reassure the patient, so that he could function adequately between interviews. This reassurance was conveyed through casual comments and sensitive questioning.

Under the guidance of the psychiatrist, the patient analyzed his personality problems and their relative importance (distributive analysis) and then reconstructed the origin of his conflicts and devised healthier behavioral patterns (distributive synthesis). The psychobiological therapist asked the patient to formulate his life story by means of a life chart, to demonstrate his understanding of the origin of his difficulties and the means he might employ to ensure their resolution and prevent their repetition.

Meyer believed that the essential goal of therapy was to aid the patient's adjustment by helping him to modify unhealthy adaptations; these modifications would lead, in turn, to personal satisfaction and proper environmental readjustment. He called this "habit training." In the process of habit training, the psychiatrist used a variety of techniques, such as guidance, suggestion, re-education, and direction—always with emphasis on the current life situation. Psychobiological therapy was especially valuable with psychotics, although it was also recommended for psychoneurotic reactions. In regard to the treatment of the hospitalized patient, Meyer also emphasized the importance of collaboration of the members of the therapeutic community—physician, patient, nurse, and ward group—as well as the patient's family in providing a setting to safeguard the integrity of the patient's personality functions.

Meyer emphasized that different criteria could be used to evaluate a patient's progress and his return to normality, according to the concepts of different schools of psychiatry. However, he preferred the criteria of the capacity of the individual to follow a constructive regimen of work, rest, and play.

CONTRIBUTION TO PSYCHIATRY

From the opening of the Henry Phipps Psychiatric Clinic in 1913, with Meyer as director, he was closely identified with the psychiatric training program there, which produced a large number of psychiatrists who carried the concepts of psychobiology to medical schools and psychiatric clinics and hospitals throughout the world. Even after his retirement in 1937, until his death in 1950, he remained active in psychiatry.

However, Meyer was not primarily concerned with the dissemination of his theoretical concepts. A large part of his work was dedicated to providing proper training in psychiatry for medical students and residents. This training included the development of techniques for the detection and description of the behavioral signs and symptoms; such techniques provided a common basis for communication. In general, these techniques were based on Meyer's concept of psychopathology as an uninterrupted continuum of normal behavior, as an adaptive reaction occurring through temporal sequences and stages that could be elicited through careful history-taking and formulated by means of a biographical life chart.

Meyer's major contributions to psychiatry might be considered to include: (1) his emphasis on the interactive nature of symptoms and the unity of the individual's psychological and biological functioning, so that psychoses were described as "reactions," a definition used in the first edition of *Diagnostic and Statistical Manual: Mental Disorders* of the American Psychiatric Association; (2) his pioneering biographical and historical approach to the study of personality; and (3) his enthusiasm for social action, especially for community psychiatry. In fact, although community psychiatry has come to the fore only recently, Meyer predicted the establishment of the community mental health center as early as 1913.

As for psychobiology, with which Meyer's name is usually connected, it was never truly a personality theory; therefore, its application declined with the death of its founder. However, the importance of psychobiology does not derive from its application as a system or theory. Rather, psychobiology is important as a trend of thought that paved the way for the acceptance of later psychodynamic concepts.

REFERENCES

Bleuler, M. Early Swiss sources of Adolf Meyer's concepts. Amer. J. Psychiat., 119: 193, 1962.

Diethelm, O. Adolf Meyer (1866–1950). In *Grosse Nervenärzie*, K. Kolle, editor, Bd. 2, p. 129. Thieme, Stuttgart, 1959.

Grob, N. G. Adolf Meyer on American psychiatry in 1895. Amer. J. Psychiat., 119: 1135, 1963.

Lief, A., editor. *The Commonsense Psychiatry of Dr. Adolf Meyer.* McGraw-Hill, New York, 1948.

Meyer, A. *Collected Papers of Adolf Meyer*, 4 vols. Johns Hopkins Press, Baltimore, 1948–1952.

Meyer, A. *Psychobiology: A Science of Man.* Charles C. Thomas, Springfield, Ill., 1957.

Muncie, W. *Psychobiology and Psychiatry.* C. V. Mosby, St. Louis, 1939.

Muncie, W. The psychobiological approach. In *American Handbook of Psychiatry*, S. Arieti, editor, vol. 2, p. 1317. Basic Books, New York, 1959.

Whitehorn, J. C., and Zilboorg, G. Present trends in American psychiatric research. Amer. J. Psychiat., 90: 303, 1933.

CHAPTER TEN

Otto Rank

SIMON H. NAGLER, M.D.

INTRODUCTION

RANK AND FREUD: AREAS OF DISAGREEMENT

RANK REJECTED many aspects of Freudian theory, and Freud considered Rank's concepts to be in conflict with the basic propositions of psychoanalysis. The nature and extent of these differences are described in further detail below. As a means of orienting the reader to the Rankian theory of personality and psychopathology, it may be summarized briefly as follows.

Rank and Freud might be said to have been on opposite theoretical poles. Rank's ideas were relativistic, voluntaristic, and humanistic, in contrast to Freud's mechanistic, deterministic, and reductionistic concepts. Their theoretical differences stemmed, first, from Rank's emphasis on the birth trauma as the crucial factor in the etiology of the neuroses and his concomitant negation of the crucial role played by the Oedipus complex. A second point of theoretical difference involved Rank's concept of the ego as an autonomous representative of the will, in contrast to Freud's concept of the ego as subservient to the id.

Rank also differed with Freud in regard to psychoanalytic therapeutic techniques. In keeping with his theoretical orientation, he emphasized a dynamic relationship between patient and therapist rather than the classical psychoanalytic interpersonal distance and focus on interpretation. He advocated flexibility on the part of the therapist rather than adherence to the rigid rules that then governed the classical psychoanalytic treatment situation. In addition, Rank concentrated on the patient's present difficulties rather than trying to foster insight into his past, as advocated by Freud.

EARLY CONTACT WITH PSYCHOANALYSIS

Otto Rank was introduced to Freud by Alfred Adler as a young student of 21, and shortly thereafter he became a member of the Committee. Recognizing his brilliance, Freud stated that he had acquired in Rank a "zealous and dependable secretary and a faithful helper and co-worker." Rank was encouraged to continue his university studies and "to devote himself to the nonmedical side of psychoanalytic investigation" because of his particular interest in art, philosophy, and the problem of creativity.

DISSENSION AND INDEPENDENCE

Rank remained a member of Freud's inner circle until 1926, long after Adler and Jung had left the Committee to establish their own schools. His departure from the orthodox camp had begun in the early 1920's, however, when he questioned the wisdom of lengthy analyses, which he considered the result of Freud's insistence on intensive investigation of each case, to the neglect of the patient's current therapeutic needs. He also questioned the value of the psychoanalyst's passive role in relation to the course of treatment, and he began to experiment with short-term therapy and to set time limits for the termination of treatment. These changes in practice led to new insights and further theoretical deviations. However, Rank's final break with Freud was precipitated by his publication in 1923 of *The Trauma of Birth*.

Freud himself espoused the concept of birth as a traumatic situation related to anxiety. He expressed these ideas in many of his writings, and they are explicitly stated in a lecture on anxiety in his *A General Introduction to Psychoanalysis*. His opposition arose at least in part in response to Rank's hypothesis that all of life consists of complicated attempts to undo birth trauma and also to the fact that Rank assigned it a crucial role in the etiology of psychopathology. Also, Freud's opposition was directed to the central role accorded the relationship of the child and his mother in psychic conflict, so that all other conflicts, including those deriving from the oedipal situation, merely mask the essential conflicts concerning birth.

BASIC ORIENTATION

In evaluating Rank's theory and therapeutic techniques, one must note several important factors. First, Rank was not a systematic theorist, and he did not share Freud's desire to elaborate a comprehensive theory of personality. Freud ultimately conceded the fact that the available scientific knowledge was not yet sufficient to permit such a finished system, but apparently Rank was much more inhibited by these limitations. Also, Rank was influenced by his lack of medical background. As he had been trained in philosophy, psychology, art, and history, his theories were not elaborated along nosological lines or related to genetic factors. Nor was he bound by the medical tendency to conceive of neurosis as an illness. Consequently, his attempts to find a biological basis for his theory of the birth trauma were soon overshadowed by his concern with the personality as a whole, the self. Thus, his vocabulary is that of philosophy and religion rather than medicine and scientific psychology.

One must also consider the various phases in the development of Rank's ideas. Up to the time he differed with Freud on technical problems of therapy, he had followed basic Freudian tenets more or less. In fact, although *The Trauma of Birth* was a significant break with tradition, it was still in the Freudian spirit, for, as mentioned above, Freud himself had formulated the concept of birth as a psychically significant experience. However, after 1926, Rank became increasingly critical of psychoanalysis and finally reached the point where he no longer considered himself a psychoanalyst.

PERSONALITY THEORY

Rank conceived of personality within a frame of reference that emphasized human values, such as religion and art. He stressed the dynamic dualism in life, the polarities of male and female, individuation and conformity, impulse and inhibition, eschewing the one-sided approach that he considered characteristic of Freudian formulations. Accordingly, Rank's will psychology is essentially an ego psychology, in which the ego functions as an autonomous representative of the will.

CONCEPT OF WILL

The concept of will is, in fact, the core of Rank's psychology, and the problem of willing is "the central problem of the whole question of personality, even of all psychology." Rank considered will to be "a positive guiding [force for the] organization and integration of self, which utilizes creatively, as well as inhibits and controls the instinctual drives." This concept can best be understood if it is considered in terms of its development, beginning with its first manifestations.

TRAUMA OF BIRTH

Freud had emphasized the powerful physiological reactions of birth as the prototype of later anxiety; but Rank correlated anxiety with separation from the mother or, more specifically, with separation from the womb, which represented the source of effortless gratification. He further hypothesized that this painful expulsion results in primal anxiety, which is then subject to primal repression. Thus, any subsequent desire to return to the position of primal pleasure gives rise to anxiety. In a broader sense, however, Rank postulated that all human mental functioning has its origin in the anxiety precipitated by the birth trauma. Thereafter, any change from a pleasurable to a painful situation gives rise to the psychical quality of emotion or feelings of anxiety. In terms of development, Rank suggested that childhood was devoted to the mastery of the birth trauma, although the original or primal anxiety had been displaced onto other situations and objects. Thus, the anxiety experienced in childhood actually represents an attempt to abreact the original traumatic experience.

As the result of the trauma of birth, separation is the most dreaded of human experiences, and the central human conflict derives from the wish to return to the womb on the one hand and the dread of this wish because of the anxiety it arouses on the other. In this frame of reference, weaning is not the frustration of a component instinct (orality); rather, it represents another separation from the mother, with all the anxiety that accompanies such a separation. The frustration of orality, then, is secondary to the fear of separation. And genitality—for the male, at least—is the avenue of return to the mother. The female, on the other hand, can achieve this goal only through identification with her father or brothers or her own child.

INFANTILE SEXUALITY

On the basis of his theory of the birth trauma, Rank reinterpreted other Freudian concepts. Thus, the basic psychoanalytic concept of infantile sexuality was reinterpreted as the child's concern with where he came from and the anxiety that surrounds his desire to return. The boy clings to the notion that all human beings have a phallus in order to avoid the primal anxiety associated with the knowledge of the existence of female genitalia, and homosexuality is rooted in the dread of the female genitalia. Female penis envy is conceptualized as a reaction to the possession of sexual organs and is similarly associated with the primal anxiety.

The masochist transmutes the pain of birth into pleasure. The sadist merely expresses the boundless resentment of one who has been expelled from paradise. The exhibitionist seeks a repetition of the nakedness of the intrauterine Garden of Eden. The theory of the Oedipus complex was reformulated as the result of the attempt to master birth anxiety by accepting the mother's genitals as a source of pleasure rather than pain and anxiety. Sleep, dreams, and even cultural phenomena were similarly explained in terms of the birth trauma and the persisting desire to return to the mother's womb.

GUILT AND FEAR

Separation, which is basic to the development of individuality and the creation of an autonomous will or ego, begins with the act of being born and physical separation from the mother. In the course of normal development, the child learns intellectually and emotionally that he and his mother are separate individuals. Both the child and the adolescent may assert themselves negatively in order to define themselves. In this way, the child learns that he can say "no" to his parents and even to his own impulses. However, this counterwill, which is essential to the process of individuation, tends to destroy the unity with others that is equally desirable. And so it tends to arouse feelings of guilt. Rank called the guilt that stemmed from this source "ethical guilt," to differentiate it from the moralistic guilt aroused by behavior contrary to social commandment. In addition, the process of achieving individuality is beset with life fear—that is, the fear of giving up the support and comfort of symbiotic relationships, analogous to that of the prenatal state. But the developing individual is assertive and potentially creative and views any regression to the womb as a loss of individuality and a threat to life. This is manifested in the death fear, which drives the individual toward greater effort, just as the life fear inhibits. This polarity between the drive toward individualization, which is impeded by life fear, and the drive toward symbiosis and dependency, which is counteracted by the death fear, points up the fact that fear is potentially constructive and not necessarily crippling and that resistance can represent the constructive power of will. Obviously, the ideal is the constructive, creative integration of these opposing trends.

IMPULSE, EMOTION, AND WILL

Rank characterized the personality chiefly in terms of impulse, emotion, and will. The child's impulses seek immediate discharge and gratification. Emotion arises because of the blocking of an impulse from without or within. But the real emotional life of the individual can develop only at the stage of the formation of the will—when impulses are "positively and actively placed in the service of the ego," when they are "under the dominance of the ego" instead of its master. When he learns to master his impulses, as in toilet training, the child begins the process of will development. The will, which is born out of the need to master one's impulse life, is also turned outward and manifested as "negative counterwill in the form of stubbornness, willfulness and disobedience." Inhibition and denial are other expressions of negative will. However, Rank also emphasized the creative nature of will, the creative will impulse, shorn of its Freudian sexual character.

PROCESS OF INDIVIDUATION

The individual goes through three stages in the process of individuation. During the first stage he wills for himself what had previously been determined for him by the values of his parents and society or by his biological needs. The next stage is one of conflict between will and counterwill, in which the individual seeks to construct his own ideals, standards, and goals. The third stage is characterized by a truly autonomous ego, capable of creative utilization of powers and ideas.

The so-called average normal man is fixed at the first stage. There is a relative harmony of personality functioning, but there are few possibilities for creativity. The ideal is to be like others. The second stage, the stage of conflict, gives rise to the neurotic, with his tendency toward self-criticism, inferiority feelings, and guilt. He feels estranged from society, the ideals of which he cannot accept, but he is unable to create his own values, for that would require his self-acceptance. In general, the ideal is to function in opposition to the wishes of others.

The third stage of individuation represents the highest integration of will and spirit. Creativity is pre-eminent. The individual who has reached this level of development accepts his own ideals and values without having to impose them on others. The ideal is to be what one's self is. The ego is not helplessly driven by a Freudian id or restrained by a Freudian superego. It is the autonomous representative of the will in terms of a self-constituted ideal. Rank felt that Freudianism deprived the human personality of its inherent consciousness and potential autonomy, responsibility, creativeness, and ethical sense of duty.

Personality development and individuation are also influenced by two kinds of emotional constellations. These include the uniting or love emotions (love, tenderness, etc.) and the separating or hate emotions (pride, scorn, anger, etc.). The latter prevent the formation of the love emotions. The former lead to a beneficient release of will; the latter cause a hardening of the will. The love emotions lead to a surrender of self-will, a yielding to the will of another. "In love and through love, whether it be divine or human, the individual can accept himself [and] his own will because the other does." On the other hand, force or will compulsion works destructively. Sexuality is the only natural method of healing or, at least, of alleviating the primal ethical guilt because sexuality transforms the negative will into the strongest positive expression of will.

THEORY OF PSYCHOPATHOLOGY

As mentioned earlier, Rank was not concerned with psychiatric nosology. References to various forms of neurosis that are scattered throughout his writings are presented chiefly within the framework of personality types. In addition to the normal man, Rank identified the artistic or creative type, the neurotic type, and the antisocial (criminal and psychopathic) type.

In the creative type, will is the organizing principle. Inhibition prevails in the neurotic. Impulse is pre-eminent in the antisocial individual. These types are characterized by an imbalance of the various motivational trends discussed above. For example, Rank felt that the artist reconciled separation or individualization and the need for union in an essentially constructive manner. On the other hand, the neurotic is a frustrated artist type who has failed to achieve an integration of the opposing trends in life but cannot take the easy (average) way out of the dilemma. Unable to adopt the approach of the average person, he seeks one of two alternate paths: He may become completely involved in trivial experiences to avoid the pain of an independent act of willing, or he may become unduly compliant or consistently rebellious. The neurotic is dominated by a fear of life. He preserves a sense of wholeness by his totalistic, overwhelming relationship with others. The neurotic may become the detached antisocial type in an effort to maintain his ego intact. The death fear is dominant. Such an individual dreads the loss of individuality threatened by any union with another.

THERAPEUTIC TECHNIQUES

The core of Rank's therapeutic technique, which is known as will or relationship therapy, is the concept of relationship. Rank emphasized the relationship between patient and therapist, the emotional dynamics experienced in the therapeutic situation, new developments in the therapeutic situation, attention to the form or pattern of experience as opposed to the content, and the special device of end-setting—the establishment of a time limit for the treatment.

The goal of treatment is to help the patient accept his separateness and will without guilt. Therefore, resistance is accepted as a valid expression of will. Even hostility is to be understood and accepted as an expression of counterwill, directed against the trend toward union and dependence. However, the therapist does not merely tolerate the hostility but utilizes it to help the paient overcome his life fear and gain the courage necessary for separation.

The recognition and utilization of the life and death fears is stressed in Rankian therapy. Progress in therapy, leading to independent acts, may arouse the death fear as well as the primary life fear. Initial success may lead to an intensification of moralistic guilt. The patient must feel the support of the therapist in his new ventures toward independence, even when they do not meet with the therapist's full approval. In brief, throughout the period of therapy, the patient is given quiet assurance that he can be loved without feeling dominated.

But too much acceptance or love tends to activate death fear, since neurotics simultaneously seek and fear close union. An increase in the death fear ultimately leads to an intensification of the drive toward independence, a potentially healthy cycle. However, the therapist must be aware of the death fear early and reveal it to the patient to minimize the swings between trust and fear.

Therapy seeks to develop a more reality-oriented attitude and behavior in the patient. This functionalist view leads to rapid introduction of the reality factor into therapy. Because the neurotic seeks to establish total relationships, the Rankian therapist tries to encourage a more realistic partialization through consistent examination of the real life situation, past and present. Furthermore, the realistic limitations of the therapeutic situation are stressed. The therapist accepts the will of the patient with limits consciously understood by both. The therapist attempts consistently to disassociate himself from the inappropriate, repetitive role assigned to him from out of the past, thereby bringing reality into the therapeutic process.

As soon as a good working relationship is established, however early in the treatment, a definite date for termination of therapy is decided on, subject to change. This technique militates against the excessive dependence on the therapist that is so common in Freudian therapy. Consequently, the patient accepts responsibility for change. Cure is not some remote eventuality. Advance awareness of the time of termination makes the event less traumatic, less reminiscent of the primal birth trauma.

CURRENT STATUS

Although no Rankian school or training institute has been formally established, Rank's concepts have had a significant influence on American social work theory and practice, which is rivaled only by the orthodox Freudian orientation. Rank's theories have formed the nucleus for the Philadelphia or functional school of social work. The University of Pennsylvania School of Social Work has been the center for the dissemination of his ideas, which are particularly suited to social work practice—short-term therapy, a focus on reality factors and current life situations, etc. Rank's influence is also evident in related areas of practice, such as guidance counseling and various forms of group and community work. Recent trends in individual psychotherapy, such as greater activity on the part of the therapist and increasing emphasis on short-term therapy, may also be considered the result of Rank's pioneer innovations.

REFERENCES

Karpf, F. B. *The Psychology and Psychotherapy of Otto Rank*. Philosophical Library, New York, 1953.

Rank, O. *Beyond Psychology*. Haddon Craftsmen, Camden, N.J., 1941.

Rank, O. *Will Therapy and Truth and Reality*. Alfred A. Knopf, New York, 1950.

Rank, O. *The Trauma of Birth*. Robert Brunner, New York, 1952.

Taft, J. *Otto Rank*. Julian Press, New York, 1958.

CHAPTER ELEVEN

Melanie Klein

SIMON H. NAGLER, M.D.

INTRODUCTION

THE AREAS OF DISAGREEMENT between the English school of psychoanalysis, as represented by Melanie Klein, and the Continental school, as represented by Anna Freud and classical psychoanalytic theory, may be delineated as follows.

In contrast to orthodox psychoanalytic theory, which postulates the development of the superego during the fourth year of life, Klein maintained that a primitive superego is formed during the first and second years, the stage of infantile anxiety and aggressiveness.

Klein believed that aggressive rather than sexual drives were preeminent during the earliest stages of development. It is the presence of these aggressive and sadistic impulses and the fear of retaliation that give rise to the primitive superego.

Klein maintained that children two years old could be treated analytically. The couch and free association could not be employed. However, the child might walk about, talk, play, tell stories, describe dreams, etc., and all this material was available for direct, deep interpretation by the analyst from the outset. Such interpretations could serve to allay anxiety. Moreover, the young child is capable of forming a transference. The cooperation of the child's parents is not crucial for the success of treatment, since little significance can be attached to the reality situation in any event. In contrast, Anna Freud emphasized the importance of parental cooperation and of environmental factors in general and advocated the treatment of young children by classical techniques that have been modified to suit the capacities of the child.

In contrast to Anna Freud, Klein believed that environmental factors played a relatively minor role in development.

Klein deviated from classical psychoanalytic theory most sharply in her formulations concerning the Oedipus complex. The onset of the oedipal conflict was traced to the earliest months of life. Further, she believed that the child becomes aware of parental coitus during the first year of life and that this awareness leads to a wide range of sexual and aggressive fantasies.

Klein's formulations concerning the pre-oedipal stages of development, the superego, and fantasy in infants provoked controversy. Her later ideas —particularly her hypothesis concerning a depressive position in the infant, which was considered central to all mental development—were considered major deviations from orthodox Freudian theory.

Klein's intricate theoretical structure developed in two phases. The first phase ended with the publication of *The Psycho-Analysis of Children* in 1932; the second began with her classical paper on the manic-depressive states in 1934.

PERSONALITY THEORY

FIRST PHASE

The concepts formulated during the first phase of Klein's work emphasized the infant's autoerotism and primary narcissism. She considered the infant capable of object relations, despite his poorly defined ego boundaries. Toward the middle of the first year, the infant's oral frustration gives rise to his unconscious awareness that his parents enjoy sexual pleasures, which is initially conceived of in oral terms. This awareness produces oral envy and increased instinctual oral sadism, which stimulate oedipal impulses. At first, these impulses take the form of a desire to penetrate and destroy the mother's body. The child hopes thereby to incorporate orally the father's penis, which he fantasizes as having been incorporated by the mother.

In the girl, the impulse to destroy the mother's body and its contents in various cruel ways gives rise to the fear that her own body will be destroyed in retaliation. In the boy, these aggressive impulses produce castration anxiety. The primitive superego emerges at this stage of development. The incorporated penis serves as a defense against the child's sadistic impulses. These impulses are also projected onto an external object, which is subjected to oral-, urethral-, and anal-sadistic attack. This external object is first represented by the mother's breast; the infant's sadistic impulses are then directed against other parts of her body.

The child also introjects bad objects—those objects that cause the child pain. These evoke a cruel superego that causes severe anxiety. Therefore, in the early anal-sadistic phase the child seeks to eject its superego and even its id. At this time, there is confusion between the fantasied and real dangers of the bad objects, but ejection of the superego paves the way for the introjection of good objects, which provide pleasure and satisfaction.

These early anxieties and defenses are modified by the development of libido and real object relations. In the girl, the turning from the mother's breast to the father's penis is a precursor of the oedipal situation. A similar reaction in the boy may lead to homosexuality unless a reorientation toward the mother occurs. As mentioned above, the ejection of the superego in the early stage of anal development permits the reintrojection of good objects and alleviation of anxiety phobias, which have a paranoid, projective character. In the later anal stage, the superego is no longer ejected; anxiety turns into guilt, and obsessional behavior appears. The infant's belief in creative omnipotence conflicts with his destructive or excretory omnipotence. Obsessional activity is a further defense against early masturbatory impulses, which are mobilized to deal with sadistic oedipal impulses. The normal mechanisms of play augment the pathological defenses, and the creation of a realistic ego-ideal is begun. The development of the libido and superego ceases at the onset of latency. Klein believed that the progressive stages of libidinal development represent the victory of the libido in its struggle against the destructive impulses.

SECOND PHASE

The second theoretical phase revolves around Klein's concept of a depressive position, which she postulated as central to the child's development and its later capacity for love. As noted above, the infant's development is largely regulated by the processes of introjection and projection. The child introjects good and bad objects, and the latter are conceived of as dangerous to the ego. A paranoid position automatically develops at the age of about two to three months. Specifically, projection is employed as a defense against internal as well as external persecutors. Since the infant is in the oral phase of development at this point, the aggressive fantasies projected onto the mother are those of biting, tearing, and sucking out.

At the time of weaning, the infant begins to recognize the mother as one person, both good and bad, and becomes concerned about the threat to the introjected good object, now the loved object, from the introjected bad object and from the id. There is also a danger that the good objects will be expelled along with the bad. This evokes an increase in the introjection of good objects and a need to make reparation for the destroyed objects. The child is filled with anxiety lest the love object be lost due to his own destructiveness. Whenever the mother makes the child angry, the good internal object is threatened with destruction. This conflict is the basis of the depressive position, in which guilt arises as the precursor of conscience. The guilty child uses magic in an effort to convert the bad mother into a good one and to protect the introjected good objects against the bad.

Owing to the suffering, discomfort, and anxiety that accompany the depressive position, the infant is prone to revert to the paranoid position, in which feelings of omnipotence, overactivity, and denial of reality may be used as defensive measures along with projection of internalized bad objects and denial of external ones. Eventually, the perfect good mother and the unrealistically dreadful bad mother merge into the image of the realistic one. According to Klein, the real aggressiveness of the parents is unimportant as compared to the aggressiveness the child projects upon the parents as a result of his own innate destructiveness. Thus, Klein's theoretical formulations served to underscore the extent of man's innate aggressive instinct, postulated by Freud as the death instinct. Only psychoanalysis can eliminate or, at least, diminish this aggression and the anxiety it gives rise to and the mutual reinforcement between man's hate and man's fear. If analysis does not reach and work through this stage of infantile anxiety and sadism, it must be considered incomplete.

Klein's theories were inferentially based on her psychoanalytic treatment of very young children through play technique. Her critics considered her formulations clinically unsubstantiated and described her concepts as "subjective fantasy," "speculative," "hypothetical," "metaphorical," "dogmatic assumption," and "confusion of hypothesis with fact."

THEORY OF PSYCHOPATHOLOGY

Freud maintained that infantile anxiety could be epitomized as the loss of the loved person, particularly in the girl. In the boy, castration was the chief source of anxiety. Klein considered these phenomena to be later modifications of anxiety that arises at an earlier stage of development. As mentioned earlier, in the boy, the earliest anxiety situation arises from the attack on the mother's body with its incorporated penis. The infant's extremely cruel superego perceives the parents as sadistic. Consequently, the girl's sadistic attitude toward the mother's body gives rise to profound anxiety lest she suffer the same fate.

Klein considered sadism a determining factor in mental conflict. The paranoid and depressive positions were fixation points for possible subsequent psychotic disintegration. She believed that the presence of excessive anxiety in infancy and the predominance of a very severe superego from the period of its genesis were the fundamental determinants of subsequent development of disturbances of ego development and psychosis.

The ego deals with the depressive position in two ways. A flight to the good introjections carries with it the danger of a later denial of reality and schizophrenic psychosis. A flight to the external good object is the characteristic forerunner of neurosis and a possible weakness in ego functioning with marked dependency on the object. Inability to deal successfully with the infantile depressive position may lead to the dominance of one of these mechanisms. Again, failure to identify with the introjected and real love objects can result in psychotic disorders, such as paranoia and manic-depressive states. The persistence of an extremely primitive superego may account for the antisocial personality.

THERAPEUTIC APPLICATIONS

Hug-Hellmuth first suggested that the play of children might replace the free association technique that was the basis of the analysis of adults. Klein developed such an analytical play-technique, employing small toys of a primitive type—such as little wooden men and women, carts, motor cars, trains, houses, paper, pencils, and scissors—which were usually placed on a low table in a play room.

Careful observation revealed that the child expresses its fantasies and real life experiences in a symbolic fashion through its play with these simple toys. This play can be analyzed in the same manner as a symptom or dream may be, taking into consideration the meanings of the separate symbols and the mechanisms of the dream work. The play elements are interpreted to the child in minute detail. The child also talks while he plays, and these words have the value of the associations produced in the classical free association technique. Children readily accept the interpretations offered.

For a successful treatment of a child, however young, Klein believed that the child should use language in the analysis to the full extent of his capacity. However, the direct interpretations described are adjusted to the child's level of development, in terms of speech and thought, to facilitate comprehension. For example, if the child talks about a swing that dangles and bumps, this is interpreted as reflecting his preoccupation with the way "Daddy's and Mummy's thingummies bump together." A child, three years old, is reported to have accepted this interpretation without the slightest difficulty.

Klein believed that children form positive and negative transferences in the classical sense. Negative transference is manifested by fear in the younger child and by mistrust, dislike, and reserve in the older child. As anxiety is resolved through play and its interpretations, pleasure in play is renewed, and positive transferences are formed. Resistances that are difficult to resolve may occur if anxiety and guilt are released from the deeper psychic layers. In general, however, action, which is more primitive than thought, is the child's chief mode of expression. As a result, the child often reveals experiences spontaneously and directly through action, which the thinking adult can only recall through reconstruction.

CURRENT STATUS

Melanie Klein's followers have continued to practice and disseminate her theories since her death in 1960. The so-called English school has gained the support of such prominent British analysts as Susan Isaacs, Joan Riviere, and D. W. Winnicott. Ernest Jones was Melanie Klein's staunch supporter from the outset. In the United States, however, the traditional concepts of classical psychoanalysis, as applied in the treatment of children and as represented by Anna Freud, have continued to prevail.

REFERENCES

Brown, J. A. C. *Freud and the Post-Freudians*. Penguin Books, Baltimore, 1961.

Klein, M. *Contributions to Psycho-Analysis, 1921–1945*. Hogarth Press, London, 1948.

Klein, M. *The Psycho-Analysis of Children*, ed. 3. Hogarth Press, London, 1949.

Klein, M. *Our Adult World*. Basic Books, New York, 1963.

Klein, M., Heimann, P., Isaacs, S., and Riviere, J. *Developments in Psycho-Analysis*. Hogarth Press, London, 1952.

CHAPTER TWELVE

Wilhelm Reich

SIMON H. NAGLER, M.D.

INTRODUCTION

WILHELM REICH COMPLETED his formal medical training at the University of Vienna in 1922 and quickly rose to prominence in the psychoanalytic movement. In the late 1920's, as director of the Vienna Seminar for Psychoanalytic Therapy, he initiated searching discussions of analytic technique, which subsequently paved the way for modern ego psychology. But for most of his career, he was deeply involved with the quest for the biological basis of the libido theory. Unfortunately, in this search he made numerous bizarre and pseudoscientific claims in the course of time, including among these the discovery of orgone energy as the basis of life.

According to classical psychoanalytic theory, character represents a habitual and relatively constant reaction that reflects the way the ego combines its various tasks in order to find a satisfactory solution to the conflict between instinctual demands and environmental forces. Reich placed special emphasis on the influence of social forces in determining character structure, particularly on their repressive and inhibiting effects.

This view of character structure as socially determined is currently widely accepted. However, Reich's early social and political views were considered rather radical, and his efforts to apply these views to psychoanalytic theory, which was supposed to be nonpolitical, were strongly opposed. First indications of a possible estrangement on this score appeared in 1932, when, to Freud's great distress, Reich published an article in which he advocated the amalgamation of psychoanalysis and Marxism. Reich's continued political fanaticism led to increasing personal and scientific estrangement from Freud until, in 1936, he left the International Psychoanalytic Association.

Nevertheless, neither the extremism of Reich's early social and political convictions nor the bizarre pseudobiological claims he made subsequently can diminish the significance of Reich's contribution to the body of psychoanalytic theory. In addition, his early interest in political and social forces as an influence on human development was an important stimulus for the development of the cultural schools of psychoanalysis. Thus, his hypothesis concerning character structure and the technique of character analysis have been further expanded by Horney, Sullivan, and Fromm.

THEORY OF CHARACTER STRUCTURE

DEFINITION

It should be noted that Reich's theoretical contributions with regard to character structure were made within the framework of Freud's libido theory. Reich's basic concept is that character is a defensive structure, an armoring of the ego against both instinctual forces within and the world without. It is the individual's characteristic manner of dealing with these threats. As a defense that becomes an automatic mode of reaction, it acquires a rigidity that produces a loss in psychic and physical elasticity. The degree of persisting elasticity determines the difference between the healthy and neurotic personality. The affect-inhibited compulsive personality is the prototype of the rigid, neurotic character.

At the core of the formation of character are the incestuous wishes and their inevitable frustration. Thus, character formation represents an attempt to resolve the conflict. It is precipitated by the fear of punishment that is produced by early sexual education. Society imposes its demands for a certain solution that, in turn, produces a certain kind of character structure. It is through its repressing effects on the libidinal needs that society establishes its authoritarian order: "Character structure is the crystallization of the sociological process of a given epoch."

CHARACTER FORMATION

The rigidity of the ego is the result of several processes. First, there is an identification with the frustrating person and his prohibitions. The aggression aroused by the frustration then gives rise to anxiety, which inhibits motor expression and leads to the inhibited nature of the character. The ego employs libidinal energies to ward off the prohibited sexual impulses. Character armor thus formed serves to alleviate the pressure of the repressed id forces and lends strength to the ego. But the armoring may also become the basis for later neurotic conflicts and symptoms, for the determining pathogenic factor is not the conflict but the manner in which it has been solved. The solution, in turn, is largely determined by society—the family—by the intensity of the fear of punishment aroused in the child, by the degree to which instinctual satisfaction is allowed, and by the character structure of the parents themselves. The outcome of the oedipal phase determines whether the individual will be capable of a satisfactory sexual life, free from neurotic problems. When the ego is excessively rigid, there is an increasing stasis of sexual energy that, eventually, can no longer be controlled by reaction formation. Neurosis can only be prevented by the development of a character that permits genital sexual gratification.

THE GENITAL VERSUS THE NEUROTIC CHARACTER

The final quality of character structure depends on the stage of libidinal development at which character formation was most decisively influenced and on the degree of sexual stasis produced. The genital or healthy character differs from the neurotic character in that the genital character employs genital orgasm and sublimation to bind anxiety, and the neurotic character employs pregenital forms of gratification and reaction formation. In the neurotic character, the basic infantile instinctual conflict remains unresolved beneath rigid, automatic character attitudes, which are reflected in stereotyped postures, facial expressions, tones of voice, and patterns of mobility.

THEORY OF PSYCHOPATHOLOGY

Reich described several types of pathological character formation, such as the hysterical, the compulsive, the phallic-narcissistic, the masochistic, and the neurotic.

THE HYSTERICAL CHARACTER

This type of character is the result of fixation at the phallic phase of libido development. This character is strongly expressed in bodily behavior. Movements are soft and sexually seductive, with a special kind of agility. The hysterical character has little tendency toward sublimation of reaction formation. There is little actual sexual satisfaction and little anchoring of sexuality in the character. Sexual tensions are discharged somatically or in the form of anxiety.

THE COMPULSIVE CHARACTER

The compulsive character is orderly and thrifty and tends to ruminate. Outwardly, he is extremely controlled; inwardly, he is distrustful and indecisive. His affective reactions are diminished almost to the point where affect is completely blocked. These characteristics are the result of fixation at the anal-sadistic level, due to overly strict or premature toilet training. The strong inhibitions created at this stage interfere with progression to the genital or phallic phase and, instead, bring about a regression to the earlier stage of anal interests and aggression. In latency, anal-sadistic reaction formations are intensified to form the final character.

THE PHALLIC-NARCISSISTIC CHARACTER

The phallic character does not regress to the passivity of the anal phase. Rather, he is confident and arrogant. Moreover, these traits plus aggression and sadism are manifested overtly, since reaction formation is absent. He is attractive as a sexual object, although he may be orgastically impotent. The male always has contempt for the female and has great phallic pride, but the phallus is in the service of aggression, not of love. The formation of this character type is usually attributed to frustration of the child's attempts to win the love object through display of the phallus at an early stage of development and his consequent identification with the rejecting person. For such a man, the sexual act becomes a demonstration of sexual potency and a means of degrading or destroying the woman.

THE MASOCHISTIC CHARACTER

Reich disagreed strongly with Freud's concept of a death instinct, and he was particularly opposed to Freud's reference to the death instinct as the basis for masochistic phenomena. Instead, the masochistic character, according to Reich, is the result of the repression of exhibitionistic impulses at the onset of the genital phase of development. Typical masochistic character traits include a chronic sense of suffering, a tendency toward complaints and self-depreciation, and a compulsion to torment others, which results in self-torment. Also included in this character is an awkward manner in dealing with people. However, the masochistic character rarely develops a masochistic perversion. Reich believed that the specific psychodynamic basis for the formation of the masochistic character was a fear of an increase in pleasurable excitation. This fear immediately inhibits any strong pleasure sensation and converts it into pain. Thus, it constantly adds to the store of rejection and displeasure that the masochistic personality feeds upon. Actually, the masochist has an excessive demand for love and an unusual vulnerability to anxiety in the face of frustration. The masochist, because he projects his own insatiable demands, gives what he would like to receive.

THE NEUROTIC CHARACTER

Reich distinguished several phases in the development of the typical neurosis. During the infantile phase of development, there is conflict between the fulfillment of libidinal needs and their frustration, in the course of which these needs are repressed. A breakthrough in this repression—through the formation of a phobia, for example—leads to a weakening of the ego. The phobia is overcome by a neurotic character trait. When adolescent conflict is complicated by the inadequacy of the character armor, the phobia or a corresponding symptom reappears. Reich considered the character neurosis to be more serious than the symptom neurosis.

TREATMENT

Reich's most enduring contribution, the technique of character analysis, is based on his hypothesis that certain resistances are inherent in the character structure of the neurotic patient. These resistances are evident in the patient's specific ways of acting and reacting and may take the form of extreme passivity, ingratiation, argumentativeness, arrogance, distrust, and certain motor activities. These neurotic resistances must be eliminated before the unconscious infantile material from which they derive can be recovered through the classical techniques of free association and dream analysis. Therefore, every analysis must include a character analysis.

Character Resistance

Character traits are much more complex than symptoms and are more easily rationalized. As a totality, they form a compact resistance against therapeutic endeavors. The nature and extent of character resistance vary from patient to patient, of course; however, it remains qualitatively unchanged in any single patient until it disappears with the neurosis. The character resistance is separated out from the total analytic material and resolved by interpretation rather than education to analytic candor and cooperation elicited through exhortation and persuasion. The patient is repeatedly confronted by his character traits until he begins to experience them as painful symptoms or foreign bodies requiring removal.

The Analytic Process

Thus, there are two phases in an analysis. During the first phase there is a focus on character analysis, "education to analysis by analysis." Once the character resistance has been diminished or removed, the second phase begins, with its emphasis on the analysis of repressed infantile material so that the libido may be freed to form a genital fixation. It is important to note in this context that—in contrast to the culturalists, who consider character analysis the main objective of therapy—Reich viewed it as an essential preliminary step toward the main task of analysis, the working through of repressed infantile sexual material.

Reich made other contributions to technique within the framework of his theory of character analysis. He emphasized the danger of overlooking a negative transference that the overly obedient patient of the passive feminine type or the affect-blocked compulsive type might conceal behind a positive facade. He also warned of the danger of premature deep and unsystematic interpretations before resolution of the character resistance.

Up to the time of his death in 1957, Reich had many followers who practiced his theories of orgone or vegetotherapy in the United States. He established an Orgone Institute and set up his own press, the Orgone Institute Press, in New York. He had an estate in Rangeley, Maine, where he directed the activities of the Orgone Institute and the Wilhelm Reich Foundation, publishing the *Orgone-Energy Bulletin* and the *Annals of the Orgone Institute*. The sale of his orgone box or accumulator brought him into conflict with the United States government. This and his subsequent death dealt a severe blow to his followers.

Although Reich's later therapeutic innovations have failed to gain acceptance, his earlier contributions to psychoanalytic theory and technique in regard to ego psychology and the influence of cultural forces on character development have proved to be of considerable value.

REFERENCES

Brown, J. A. C. *Freud and the Post-Freudians*. Penguin Books, Baltimore, 1961.

Harper, R. A. *Psychoanalysis and Psychotherapy*. Prentice-Hall, Englewood Cliffs, N.J., 1959.

Reich, W. *The Function of the Orgasm*. Orgone Institute Press, New York, 1948.

Reich, W. *Character Analysis*, ed. 3 (enlarged). Orgone Institute Press, New York, 1949.

CHAPTER THIRTEEN

Jules H. Masserman

SIMON H. NAGLER, M.D.

INTRODUCTION

BIOGRAPHICAL DATA

JULES H. MASSERMAN—originator of the biodynamic theory of behavior and prominent psychiatrist, psychoanalyst, and experimentalist —received his training in psychobiology under Adolf Meyer and in psychoanalysis under Franz Alexander. Since 1946 he has taught at Northwestern University, where he now holds the appointment of professor of neurology and psychiatry. In 1957, in recognition of his important work on experimental neurosis in cats, dogs, and monkeys, he was elected president of the Society of Biological Psychiatry.

SCIENTIFIC ORIENTATION

Masserman has published two volumes on the principles and practice of dynamic psychiatry in which he has attempted to integrate and synthesize various psychological and physiological concepts of behavior. As a result, the term "biodynamics," a term generically applied to the branch of physiology concerned with the vital functions of all organisms, has come to represent a unique system of psychoanalytic psychiatry, despite Masserman's disavowal of any intention of establishing a new school.

In brief, it is Masserman's thesis that animal studies can help to uncover fundamental biodynamic principles of behavior and thus contribute materially to behavioral sciences and psychotherapy. On the basis of his investigations of dynamic psychology and the experimental neuroses, Masserman has formulated four basic biodynamic principles concerning motivation, adaptation, displacement, and conflict. He has attempted to correlate these biodynamic principles with psychoanalytic concepts and to consider their relevance to psychotherapy.

APPLICATION OF BIODYNAMIC PRINCIPLES TO PERSONALITY THEORY

MOTIVATION

The principle concerning motivation states that all behavior is stimulated by physiologic needs of varying intensity—such as survival, growth, dominance, procreation, even esthetic creativity—and is directed toward the satisfaction of these needs. In support of this principle, Masserman has pointed out that Freud recognized the influence of somatic demands on mental functioning and the operation of an indeterminate number of instincts, other than the libidinal ones. And W. McDougall named two dozen or more instinctual drives.

Experimentally, any physiological need can be utilized to activate behavior. The hunger drive is particularly suitable for experimental purposes and has been shown to be related to sexuality, dominance needs, and herd behavior to substantiate further the concept of the biological origins of social behavior. In numerous experiments it was demonstrated that no learning takes place without relevant motivation; unless training takes the animal's needs and capacities into account, adaptive, contented behavior cannot be effectively established.

Masserman believes that, if we disregard the formulation of the death instinct, "Freud's categorization of the phases of Eros is essentially biological." Thus, for the most part, biodynamic and psychoanalytic concepts relative to motivation can be reconciled. He admits, however, that our understanding of man's esthetic needs on the basis of instinctual strivings and their sublimation is still inadequate. Similar reservations have also been applied to other correlations of biodynamic and psychoanalytic concepts.

ADAPTATION

The second principle states that organisms react to and define their environment on the basis of their unique needs, capacities, and experiences; their reaction is not determined by some ultimate reality. In terms of the human organism, this implies that the individual's adaptation to a situation is determined by his own perception of that situation. His reaction is not based on evaluations of the situation by other observers; nor is it based on objective reality. Reality is, in fact, highly relative. It is dependent on biodynamic factors unique to the species and the individual, and it is subject to many modifications within this framework as the result of specific needs, past experiences, and present integrative capacities. Although an individual may appear to behave in complete accordance with social norms, he nonetheless nourishes numerous idiosyncratic attitudes and conceptions of his particular universe. Confusion or conflict between social norms and the individual's idiosyncratic concepts leads to disturbed or neurotic behavior. In this sense, neurosis might be defined as the persistence of behavior patterns that no longer serve an effective adaptive function.

This second principle is readily demonstrated in experiments in which the animals' responses appear to be paradoxical. For example, these experiments showed that monkeys avoid bananas when their odor is associated with an unpleasant experience. On the other hand, the cats studied suffered increasingly severe self-administered shocks in order to obtain the reward of food. This response could be interpreted as indicating that the goal of masochistic behavior is not self-punishment; rather, it is reward-seeking. Such investigations point up the value of biodynamic findings for the elucidation and clarification of psychoanalytic formulations.

DISPLACEMENT

The third biodynamic principle postulates that the blocking of goal-directed behavior leads to altered efforts to achieve the same or compensatory objectives. Masserman considers this principle to be in harmony with psychoanalytic formulations. The vicissitudes of the instincts (such as reversal, repression, and sublimation) and the defense mechanisms of the ego (such as displacement, condensation, reaction formation, symbolization, and fantasy formation) illustrate the principle of adaptive substitution in the face of frustration.

In animal experimentation such substitutive behavior might take hostile and destructive forms. Nevertheless, it is still directed toward satisfaction of the animal's needs. The optimal environment for such experiments should be sufficiently challenging but not so frustrating as to lead to deviant behavior. When frustrating obstacles are removed, the organism reverts to normally effective behavior, showing that the effective patterns have only been inhibited, not eliminated.

Many animal experiments in this area also demonstrate the prevalence of dominance hierarchies among groups in search of satisfaction of basic needs. Thus, those organisms that constitute the lower order of a group react to their superiors as if they were barriers to the achievement of need fulfillment. As such, they must be submitted to cooperatively or eliminated aggressively. It is significant that cooperative as well as parasitic relationships were observed in feeding experiments on an animal level.

CONFLICT

The fourth principle relates to the all-important concept of conflict—that is, the clash of two or more strong motivations accompanied by increasing tension and anxiety, resulting in maladaptive behavior, as in the neuroses and psychoses. Pavlov and others had induced experimental neurosis in animals by simultaneously presenting positive and negative stimuli that could not be differentiated. Masserman demonstrated that opposing stimuli that were approximately equal in terms of motivational strength would result in conflict that might even lead to persisting disturbance in the behavior of animals. Moreover, this behavior resembles the neurotic anxieties, depressions, and inhibitions that arise in human beings when they are faced with conflicting positive and negative choices.

Masserman produced neurotic behavior in animals by producing conflict between the hunger need and fear by pairing food with an aversive stimulus, such as an electric shock or a toy snake. The degree of neurotic disturbance varied with the urgency of the motivations in conflict, the possibilities of avoidance, the availability of alternate solutions, etc. But the effects of the conflict were remarkably uniform: They consisted of pervasive anxiety; psychosomatic disturbances in respiratory, genitourinary, and gastrointestinal functioning; phobic behavior; stereotyped compulsive movements; sexual behavioral deviations; withdrawal and hostility; and even regressive behavior, such as abnormal dependency.

BIODYNAMIC PRINCIPLES AND THERAPEUTIC INTERVENTION

The factors that accentuate or reduce neurotic disturbance were investigated experimentally. First, it was demonstrated that those variables which increased the basic conflict or hindered its solution increased the neurotic disturbance, even to the point where it threatened the animal's survival. Secondly, Masserman demonstrated that experimental neurosis was ameliorated by such factors as satisfaction of conflicting needs, removal of the animal from the conflict situation (a procedure analogous to a rest cure or vacation), or forcing a solution to the conflict (such as making food particularly attractive to the animal).

Successful attempts at spontaneous solution of conflict were also observed in these experiments. And these efforts probably parallel the manner in which human beings resolve their problems spontaneously— that is, through re-exploration of the problem and discovery that mastery is possible. Indeed, this concept is implicit in the training and education of children to cope with a wide variety of problems to achieve mastery.

In psychotherapy, the protective and permissive atmosphere of the therapeutic situation fosters the patient's self-confidence, which can then be utilized for more successful interpersonal relationships and adaptation. The therapist is perceived as a helpful parent-surrogate with whom the patient can explore and resolve his difficulties. Similarly, it was possible to re-educate neurotic animals through handling by a gentle trainer with whom the animal had had positive experiences.

A form of social therapy was investigated as well, in which a neurotic animal was placed in a cage with a well-trained, normal animal, which it could observe operating the proper switches to obtain food with impunity. This is analogous to placing a neurotic child in a foster home or residential school in the hope that he may be favorably affected by his observation of and interaction with normal children.

Masserman and his colleagues also conducted extensive investigations of the effects of organic intervention in the form of drugs, electric convulsive treatments, and neurosurgery on the course of experimental neuroses in animals. It is of clinical interest that the efficacy of neurosurgery in their animals depended less on the site and extent of the lesion than on the preoperative personality and experience of the animal and the methods used for its postoperative care and rehabilitation.

Above and beyond these biodynamic considerations in his approach to psychotherapy, Masserman stresses what he has termed man's "urdefenses." These are man's faiths, albeit his delusions. The first of these defenses is man's belief in his immortality and invincibility. Numerous religious systems attest to the fact that, from time immemorial, man has refused to believe in the eventual complete end of his existence. The second ur-defense is his belief in the omnipotence of his servants or helpers—his parents, physicians, clergy, various authority figures, etc. The third faith concerns his confidence in the protective function of society—that is, his belief in man's ultimate concern for his fellow man.

Man needs these faiths to live by and the therapist should not try to abolish them. Instead, Masserman insists, we need only assist the patient "gently to find happier beliefs and more creative applications of them. . . . The best therapist is he who helps troubled men rebuild, largely on their own terms, their faiths in themselves, in their fellow men, and in their selected philosophic or theologic systems."

REFERENCES

Masserman, J. H. *Behavior and Neuroses.* University of Chicago Press, Chicago, 1943.

Masserman, J. H. *Principles of Dynamic Psychiatry.* W. B. Saunders, Philadelphia, 1946.

Masserman, J. H. *The Practice of Dynamic Psychiatry.* W. B. Saunders, Philadelphia, 1955.

Masserman, J. H. The biodynamic approaches. In *American Handbook of Psychiatry,* S. Arieti, editor, vol. 2, p. 1680. Basic Books, New York, 1959.

CHAPTER FOURTEEN

Existential Psychoanalysis

EDITH WEIGERT, M.D.

INTRODUCTION

Role of Philosophy in Psychiatry

Psychiatry, more than any other medical specialty, requires elucidation of the philosophical premises that guide the psychiatrist's efforts to understand his patient. According to the psychiatrist-philosopher Karl Jaspers, this understanding is based on a combination of two main trends of investigation. The first of these, objective cognition, refers to the psychiatrist's efforts to follow the chains of cause and effect from the past into the future and, thereby, to establish diagnosis, prognosis, and plan of therapy. The second trend of investigation, emotionally inspired intuition or empathy, is defined as the psychiatrist's ability to understand the patient by identifying with him, by putting himself in the patient's place. Emotional participation or identification with the patient may lead to wishful or fearful falsification, which will lead the psychiatrist astray. Indeed, when carried to extremes, intense involvement may lead to a *folie à deux*. Objective cognition also presents certain pitfalls when the psychiatrist is primarily interested in verifying his premises. The reductive method of analysis illuminates important partial aspects of the patient's personality, but the totality of the subject's integrated existence may escape the analyst.

Contribution of Phenomenology

The phenomenologist, Edmund Husserl, has recommended that every scientist detach himself intermittently from his premises, setting aside his system of preconceived ideas in order to gain a new perspective of the phenomena under observation. Inspired by Husserl, a descriptive phenomenology has emerged to enrich psychiatry, as elaborated in the works of Eugene Minkowski, Ludwig Binswanger, Erwin Strauss, Maurice Merleau-Ponty, and others. Minkowski stated that insanity is nothing more than the exaggeration of the individual's habitual character. The vital impetus toward integration (Bergson's *élan vital*) is reduced in mental illness; the crucial contact with reality seems distorted to the observer. In brief, the patient exists in a world of his own that cannot be fully shared by people who are oriented to common sense standards and values.

Out of the phenomenological philosophy grew the various forms of existential philosophies or *Dasein* analytic studies, each carrying the imprint of the originator's personality. Martin Heidegger conceived of a new synthesis of idealism and realism. Jean-Paul Sartre's writings are characterized by radical nihilism, atheism, and voluntarism. Karl Jaspers, Max Scheler, Martin Buber, Gabriel Marcel, and Nikolai Berdjajew emphasize humanism and theism as opposed to naturalism and materialism. Although their views of the world are frequently contradictory, all these philosophers share in common a desire to bridge the gap between subject and object; therefore, their ideas are of vital concern to the modern psychiatrist.

CULTURAL INFLUENCES

The upheaval of two world wars, revolutions and counterrevolutions, and the threat posed by the development of atomic weapons have destroyed our illusions of a lawful and harmonious cosmos that had previously been accepted as reality. The absurdity of fate has permeated Western culture and has become an almost universal theme of literature, art, and philosophy. Freud anticipated such developments when he wrote *Future of an Illusion* in formulating his concept of thanatos, the death instinct, as the counterpart of eros, the life-affirming instinct. But are thanatos and eros instincts? Freud's reformulation of his dual instinct theory seems to resemble the existential dualism of Sartre's *Being and Nothingness*. Sartre agrees that he has much in common with Freud, but he also disagrees with him on many issues and has created his own theory of existential analysis.

THEORIES OF EXISTENTIALISM

Phenomenology and existentialism were introduced into American psychology and psychiatry by Rollo May and his associates. May has characterized Sartre's theory as "a nihilistic, subjectivistic extreme in existentialism which invites misunderstanding." On the other hand, he considers Martin Heidegger the fountainhead of present-day existential thought. Heidegger's concept of being-in-the-world embraces the inseparable polarity of man and world in the here-and-now situation, in which his *Dasein* ("being-there," the field of being which is his existence) aims at authenticity. Being-there implies concern about being that Heidegger has called

Sorge (care), a concept that encompasses anxiety as well as love. We are reminded here of Sullivan's definition of love as concern for another as well as concern for one's self. The anxiety component of *Sorge* (care) stems from the fear of not-being—specifically, the fear of death. Man knows that he is destined to die, but he is inclined to forget this. Heidegger sees the authenticity of being-there in the resolution to accept one's destiny, to accept death as a constantly present possibility.

Paul Tillich, the theological interpreter of existentialism in the United States, has defined authenticity as the "courage to be," despite the threat it presents of non-being. But the constant threat of non-being tended to splinter care in the concerns of daily living, and the potentialities of authenticity are squandered. Being-there is translated in the sense of the "man," the German impersonal pronoun which is the equivalent of the English "one." The "man" is not fully present. He is preoccupied with his desire to conform to public opinion, the playing of expected roles, meaningless distractions, and aimless small talk. And these preoccupations give rise to a feeling of "being lost to the world" that arouses anxieties and guilt feelings because it undermines the experience of freedom and responsibility.

Sartre has evolved more lucid but often paradoxical existential formulations. Being, the basis of existence, is an enigma to man; but he can objectify the world of things. He can study and handle the technical aspects of the environment, *Umwelt*. He can deal with his fellow man as an object in the *Mitwelt* (being with others). His fellow men become objects of his emotions, desires, and fears. He objectifies them in the processes of cognition and manipulative action. For the other person, according to Sartre, man is an object. The other self "presents himself, in a certain sense, as the radical negation of my experience, since he is that person for whom I am not subject but object." As a subject, however, man remains elusive, partially shrouded in unawareness.

Consciousness, which Hegel called "unhappy consciousness," splits the subject from the object. The other person can objectify the subject more accurately than the subject himself, who is frequently the victim of self-deception. Nietzsche had stated that every man is most remote to himself. Self-consciousness is experienced as an inner split, a loss of face. The self-conscious person loses his mask before the look (Sartre's "regard") by which the other person objectifies and evaluates him; the esteem of the other person makes the subject's conscience conscious to himself. The subject plays the role that common sense dictates, but he does not experience the role he plays. When he becomes self-conscious, he is embarrassed, ashamed, guilty because, in Sartre's words, "he is not what he is and he is what he is not." This paradox interferes with the subject's stable identity.

Man is not the automatically functioning product of nature or of human fabrication, an *en-soi* (in-himself), the passive recipient of fate. He is *pour-soi* (for-himself), a project into the future, transcending the present situation with its contingencies and necessities. Man is thrown into the world, dependent on his heredity, his fellow men, and his luck. Yet he is forced to be free. His desires and fears force him to choose, to take the risk of participating or not participating in each given situation. And by refusing to make a choice, he indicates that he decided not to decide. His emotionally inspired magic imagination rejects and rebuilds the world into which he is thrown, and therewith he transforms himself. The vertigo of freedom confronts him wittingly or unwittingly with the horror of nothingness. Not only is man afraid of the realistic external dangers of his situation; he is equally frightened by the possibility, arising from his imagination, that he may fail to master the situation. He vacillates between faith and lack of faith in himself. He may choose to avoid the danger by repressing his desire, or he may elect to confront the danger by denying his anxiety. But at the moment when he represses or denies. he is not true to himself; he is in a state of false faith. Man deceived himself by making himself believe. Belief, in Sartre's formulations, is always make-believe, because when belief enters man's self-consciousness he represses his doubts. And when he conciously tries to appear honest, he represses his dishonesty.

In the situation of erotic intimacy, man feels liberated from the anguish of nothingness through the high value of love that confirms his existence. But as soon as he makes himself believe that he loves and is loved, doubt creeps into the love relationship. This doubt makes the other person an object of his desires, threatened by the frustration of nothingness, and, similarly, he becomes an object to the other person. The love relationship deteriorates into the master-slave relationship described by Hegel. In Sartre's system, human reality is a passion. In the projects of the *pour-soi*, man yearns for God as the source of protection from the anguish of nothingness; or, in his more solipsistic designs, he tries to be God, a superman, *pour-soi* and *en-soi* at the same time. "Man loses himself as man to give birth to God. But the idea of God is contradictory and we lose ourselves in vain; man is a useless passion."

THEORY OF PERSONALITY DEVELOPMENT

Karl Jaspers, Ludwig Binswanger, and Medard Boss have integrated the concepts of existential philosophy into European psychiatry. Victor Frankl has developed a therapeutic approach related to existentialism, called "logo-therapy." These psychiatrists attempt to apply philosophical concepts in evaluating and understanding their patients' personality structure and functioning; thus, their interest is not restricted to the causes of mental illness. The objective study of mental mechanisms and dynamics by the reductive method of psychoanalysis had illuminated the personal history of mental patients. The existential psychiatrists have utilized these methods in pursuing their interest in the subjective experience of the total personality of their patients.

Yet the total personality is elusive because it is constantly in the process of becoming, in the process of integrating, disintegrating, and reintegrating, of rejecting and rebuilding its self and its world. Even the brain-damaged person is rebuilding his personality and his world out of fragments of perceptions, emotions, impulses, and memories, driven by the horror of incapacitation, which Kurt Goldstein has characterized as the "catastrophic reaction." The neurotic and, to a greater extent, the psychotic individual are also victims of partial fragmentation of the self and alienation from the world, owing to heredity and/or environmental influences, both past and present.

The basic symptom of all mental illness is a partial withdrawal from the surrounding world into a world of one's own. This trend toward egocentricity, solipsism, or autism can be enriching or impoverishing. The world is enriched by the creative personality, who is able to share his values with others. Being-in-the-world is distorted and alienated in the mentally ill person. The world of the hysteric and the distortions in his bodily functions are transformed by the intensity of his egocentric preoccupations. The world of the obsessive person is regulated by rigid, legalistic rituals intended to exorcise the dangers of decay and dirt, which represent death and destruction. Psychopathological transformations are ascribed to the existentialist psychiatrist's intuitive entrance into the patient's subjective experience. Boss tries to enter also into the subjective experience of the dreamer, whose images impress him as fragmented attempts to transcend a situation of stress. Boss sees, even in the most extreme perversions, the patient's attempt to transcend the defensive walls of egocentricity.

Binswanger, in contrast to Boss, uses Heidegger's concept of care only to refer to the manipulation and organization of things and men in political, economic, scientific, or ecclesiastical institutions, which are engaged in purposeful action, directed toward the common welfare. But in an institution, man remains an object, a cog in the wheel, manipulated by managerial skill into encompassing structures. The will to power is tamed by established hierarchies of law and order. Binswanger distinguishes between such transcendence by objectivation and transcendence through love. Gabriel Marcel calls the basic solidarity of men "intersubjectivity." It manifests itself in Martin Buber's "I-thou relation" of mutuality, which uses verbal and nonverbal communication, not for defensive concealment or anxiety-driven adaptation, domination, and appropriation but for the liberating revelations of communion. This communion, according to Berdjajew, transforms the "individual" into a "personality" who chooses and grants to the "I" and the "thou" the freedom of optimal development. In each meaningful encounter this spontaneous integration of personality arises unplanned and unpremeditated. In the parent-child relationship, in friendship, in the enthusiasm of erotic union, in marital partnership, and in personal religious experience, personality reveals itself not only as the boundary of nothingness but as a potentiality of encompassing communion. Karl Jaspers emphasizes that love, a symbol that loses its value in everyday verbal usage, is not merely an epiphenomenon of sexual libido or a product of mature sublimation. Love is present from the very beginning of existence as a potentiality, initially revealing itself in the cry and smile of the infant. It is present in every stage of development as a possibility for mutuality. However, the psychiatrist is always aware that intersubjectivity can deteriorate into the master-slave relationship that Sartre has described.

According to the existentialist view, the regression to infantile forms of adaptation not only is a sign of psychopathology but may also imply a search for a new beginning. The child is full of potentialities and good faith. But if this faith is not confirmed during the process of maturation by relationships of mutuality, existential anxieties and guilt feelings build up walls of defense. The growing child and the adult may then revert to the infantile role in bad faith to escape from the freedom of decision and responsibility in the face of frustration and rage. Existential anxieties and guilt feelings alienate and distort these separated individuals and imprison them in an autistic shell surrounded by the horrors of nothingness. At every stage of human development, however, the healing power of love can transcend the anxieties of defensive egocentricity.

On the one hand, love implies the risk of surrendering self-identity in the desire to approximate the identity and ideals of the beloved. On the other hand, love enriches lovers through the process of identification by fostering in each a renewed self-esteem of authenticity and mutuality.

APPLICATION OF EXISTENTIALISM TO PSYCHOTHERAPY

The psychotherapist may select the orientation that suits him best from the various forms of existential philosophy. He does not force any philosophy on his patient by sermon or subtle persuasion, but, inevitably, he radiates the philosophy he lives by. He tries to know himself and his world in order to be flexible enough to enter into the world of his patient. There is no reality valid for all. The psychotherapist is aware of his own limitations, and he will know if the world of his patient is too strange for him. In that event, he will not be able to establish a bond of solidarity with the patient. Solidarity represents a basic trust in his own potentialities and those of his patient for a meaningful collaboration. This does not mean that the psychotherapist should force himself to develop feelings of empathy, nor can he rely only on his emotionally guided intuition in his attempts to understand his patient.

The existentialist respects the scientific method, although he may regret the development of a scientism that deifies science, where traditional deities have been discarded as illusions. Scientific objectivation is the basis of every therapy. We must study the patient's past development if his *Dasein*

—his present being—is to be opened to the possibilities of the future. The psychotherapist tries to remove the barriers of illusion that are products of the compulsion to repeat past anxieties and habits of escape.

Existential anxiety manifests itself in numerous variations—in castration anxiety, in anxiety about loss of physical or psychological integrity, in separation anxiety, and in the fear of death, destruction, and helplessness. Such anxieties and the defenses that are erected against them in the form of autistic withdrawal, persisting symbiosis, or overbearing egocentricity are re-experienced in the psychotherapeutic encounter until mutual trust between patient and therapist is established. For example, the Oedipus conflict persists as an egocentric desire for unlimited parental gratification and/or vindictive triumph over the therapist as rival. In the face of the inevitable frustration of these desires, the unresolved Oedipus conflict is re-experienced, with various degrees of anxiety, as an unauthentic protest against destiny.

The psychotherapist need not provoke existential anxieties. The patient who suffers from a traumatic neurosis relives the shock of the trauma in his dreams, although he may have forgotten it in waking life. Similarly, every neurotic patient tends to relive the hell of past anxieties, although he may have built up walls of defensive protection against such anxieties. Nevertheless, the repressed tends to return from repression. The patient would not seek the help of the psychotherapist if he had not begun to doubt the bad faith that has motivated his defenses.

The attention of the therapist is directed, therefore, toward the patient's hidden anxieties and guilt feelings, which indicate that the patient seeks to free his thwarted potentialities. The patient should not receive false encouragement or comforting support of his defenses, lest he become a mere object of custodial care. Some patients seek comfort in repetitive accusations of past injustices, such as protest against the schizophrenogenic parent. The patient may build up an illusion that exploration of the past could magically alter his destiny, but there is no redress for past injustice. Death, evil, and destruction cannot be abolished. As he relives the anguish of annihilation in a raging protest against destiny, the adult discovers that he can tolerate frustration that was too much for the child. The patient may then find another way out of the dead end street of impotent protest, for he has in him the freedom to make new decisions that transcend the nothingness implied in every experience of frustration.

Transference presents the possibility of sharing anxieties and the rage of frustration with the therapist, but positive as well as negative transferences provide illusionary solutions to unresolved conflicts. This applies to the countertransference as well, which indicates the degree to which the therapist is affected by the patient's anxieties without facing them squarely. Transferences in Freud's terminology are resistances; Sartre conceives of them as manifestations of bad faith—self-deceptions in the face of challenging frustrations, an escape from the deadening aspects of life through denial or distortion of the present situation with its necessarily frustrating limitations. Every psychotherapeutic encounter is a situation of limitation and stress. Erotic attraction can play a role in fostering empathy and intuition, but erotism is transcended in a relationship of responsible care. Recognition and expression of rage, anger, and hatred may clear the way for an encounter of solidarity and trust. Out of bad faith the original good faith can be reborn—that is, the patient's trust in life, the source of renewal, and the freedom for authenticity and mutuality.

Existentialism has not introduced new methods into psychotherapy. Its emphasis in the therapeutic encounter lies in the transcendence of excessive anxieties. The deepest repressed anxiety is directed against the risk of genuine trust. The care of the therapeutic encounter is not a defense against anxiety; it is neither appropriation nor surrender. This trusting care does not recoil from the limitations of the therapeutic situation but wrestles with its frustrations. And it enables both patient and therapist to endure periods of failure. The therapeutic trust can endow both patient and therapist with a new freedom that allows them to develop their potentialities in meaningful collaboration. Through insight into past and present situations, the patient can be freed to transcend his protesting nihilism in the face of frustrations by making responsible decisions that will transform the future. In liberating the patient, the therapist broadens the horizon of his own understanding and therapeutic creativity.

REFERENCES

Berdjajew, N. *Das Ich und die Welt der Objeckte*. Holle Verlag, Darmstadt, 1933.

Binswanger, L. *Grundformen und Erkenntnis menschlichen Daseins*. Max Nichaus, Zurich, 1942.

Boss, M. *Psychoanalysis and Daseinsanalysis*. Basic Books, New York, 1963.

Buber, M. *I and Thou*. Charles Scribner's Sons, New York, 1958.

Frankl, V. E. *The Doctor and the Soul: An Introduction to Logotherapy*. Alfred A. Knopf, New York, 1957.

Heidegger, M. *Sein und Zeit*. Neomarius, Tübingen, 1949.

Husserl, E. *Die Krisis der Europäischen Wissenschaften und die transzendentale Phänomenologie*. Martinus Nijhoff, Haag, 1954.

Jaspers, K. *General Psychopathology*. University of Chicago Press, Chicago, 1963.

Marcel, G. *The Mystery of Being*. Henry Regnery, Chicago, 1960.

May, R., Angel, E., and Ellenberg, H. E. *Existence, a New Dimension in Psychiatry and Psychology*. Basic Books, New York, 1958.

Merleau-Ponty, M. *Phenomenologie de la perception*. Librarie Gallimard, Paris, 1945.

Minkowski, E. *La Schizophrenie*. Payot, Paris, 1927.

Sartre, J. *L'être et le Néant*. Librairie Gallimard, Paris, 1948.

Scheler, M. *The Nature of Sympathy*. Routledge and Kegan Paul, London, 1954.

Strauss, E. W. *Vom Sinn der Sinne*. Springer Verlag, Göttingen, 1956.

AREA D

---

*Personality Theories
Derived from Psychology*

CHAPTER FIFTEEN

Personality Theory Derived from Quantitative Experiment

RAYMOND B. CATTELL, Ph.D., D.Sc.

INTRODUCTION

EXPERIMENT AND MEASUREMENT IN SCIENTIFIC THEORY

THE BIRTH OF MODERN SCIENCE is frequently placed around the year 1600, when Galileo began to apply quantitative methods to mechanical observation. It is recognized that chemistry separated itself from alchemy and entered a new phase of vigorous development when Dalton, Lavoisier, and others began to apply quantitative methods to establish laws in chemistry. Indeed, it is generally accepted today, as Mach has said, that "the aim of science is to find the formulae which express the relations among observed phenomena." By these touchstones, what is the status, as a science, of psychiatry today?

That it lacks the stability of concepts, the maturity, and the practical effectiveness that are characteristic of a developed science based on quantitative laws and experiment is surely evidenced by the considerable divergencies of theoretical viewpoints represented in this book. However, this is even more apparent in the excessive swings of emphasis in approved practice, such as the recent change from psychoanalytic therapy to behavior therapy and from the predominance of psychoanalytic treatment in private practice to chemotherapy in mental hospitals. Young and uncertain sciences characteristically seek to create the illusion of progress by concentration on rapid movement. As to progress, Eysenck, in an expectedly unpopular but nevertheless sound survey (Eysenck, 1960), has pointed out that in the 1960's psychotherapy has failed to demonstrate that it can bring about recovery at a more rapid rate than would occur spontaneously, without treatment. At this moment no refutation satisfactory to a scientist has been given to the assertion that the number of recoveries due to psychotherapy do not exceed those to be expected from chance. However, to argue this point would serve little purpose. Even more optimistic psychiatrists will, as realistic practitioners, readily admit that present methods of diagnosis, control of treatment, and insights into the necessary tactical steps fall far short of the standards required of a developed science.

The present chapter takes the position that psychiatry is an applied science. As such, it has elements of artistic skill; but in its essentials it must be based on what the sciences of psychology, physiology, and sociology offer. Among the most recent developments in psychology, those that are most relevant concern the concepts, laws, and predictive powers arising out of the experimental and, especially, the sophisticated quantitative studies that have been conducted in the last fifteen years. Psychology, like psychiatry, has never lacked theories; indeed, it has assembled an orchestra of resounding scholarship that enjoys a considerable scientific reputation.

The correlation between the development of a technology and the development of pure theory in science cannot be perfect; but it is also true that impressive technological development cannot occur unless the basic scientific theory possesses real potency. If we use an acid test, as proposed here, clearly our technological capacity to eliminate mental disorder or reeducate delinquent personalities does not provide convincing evidence that we have made more than elementary advances in the basic science of psychology.

Unification of Theory and Measurement

The twin pillars that psychology offers in its support of the development of psychiatry are personality theory and learning theory. Until fifty years ago, personality theory developed mainly as a result of clinical observation —as exemplified by the formulations of Kraepelin, Freud, Jung, and Janet, for example—or was based on what might be called literary and general human observation, as exemplified by the work of William James, McDougall, Allport, Klages, Spranger, and others. The subsequent quantitative and experimental phase, which is the primary focus of this discussion, initially framed its questions in terms of the theories inherited from the earlier clinical and literary phase. More recently, however, it has built upon a theoretical structure of its own. To date, it has failed to produce scientific laws that can aspire to the scope and elaborateness of the scientific speculations derived from the earlier phase. But there is every indication that it has constructed a very sound foundation. It is the kind of foundation that will produce definite results, expressed as basic laws and having predictive powers. We can expect these to develop in applied science with increasing rapidity in the next decade.

MULTIVARIATE PERSONALITY THEORY

Preliminary issues. One reason why the message from the quantitative, experimental approach has not yet come through as clearly as it might is that the dust of conflict hangs over the area, sustained by a battle between the bivariate and the multivariate schools of experimental design. The former follows the classical plan of experiments in physical science; typically, it deals with one independent and one dependent variable. For example, it manipulates a stimulus and measures a response, trying and often claiming to hold all else constant while doing so. Wundt, Pavlov, and Skinner are among the advocates of this method, which has been inherited in its entirety by the reflexological school of learning.

The second school of experimental design, favoring the multivariate method, springs from Sir Francis Galton, Spearman, and Thurstone; and it is more concerned with correlational methods and the simultaneous study of measurement of many variables.

Advantages of the multivariate method. The Galton tradition, enriched by the contributions of many mathematical statisticians in the multivariate field, has recently given us remarkably enhanced access, by the electronic computer, to problems that were previously unapproachable. Thus, the multivariate method has two major claims to superiority over the classical bivariate experimental design. First, the multivariate experimentalist can grasp wholes—complex pattern entities, such as the clinician deals with—whereas the classical experimentalist usually deals with a single atomistic variable, which is often of minor importance and incapable of representing a complex concept. Second, the multivariate method can claim to uncover complex causal relationships without the actual manipulation of people and circumstances that has always been considered essential to classical experiment.

Manipulation in the life sciences has two serious drawbacks. First, it is apt to upset the very phenomena it wishes to study. For example, a dog whose adrenal glands have been dissected out is suffering from something more than the removal of adrenalin from his bloodstream. Secondly, manipulation in the life of human beings of those cardinal emotional attachments that are typically involved in clinical generalizations is practically and ethically impossible. It is primarily for this reason that the experimentalist who understands only bivariate designs has turned increasingly to animal experiments. But, even under the most ideal circumstances, application of conclusions drawn from animal experiments, which do not include cultural concepts or concepts of self, to happenings in the minds of men propels the scientist toward speculative reasoning to a degree grotesquely out of keeping with the precision that characterized his animal experimentation.

The three-cornered argument. Clearly, then, the familiar cleavage, noted above, between the clinical observer on the one hand and the laboratory experimentalist on the other hand is not the most important dichotomy in research methodology. Actually, there is a three-cornered argument in progress. Or rather, although it might serve a purpose if it were an argument, actually, it is in danger of becoming a mere regression into three camps isolated from each other—clinician, brass-instrument experimentalist, and multivariate experimentalist. Curiously, in some respects, there is a stronger bond between the clinician and the multivariate experimentalist than there is between the multivariate and the bivariate experimentalists. Both the clinician and the multivariate experimentalist are concerned with seeking generalizations while keeping the totality of behavior in view through the formulation of hypotheses that cannot be caught or operationally represented by a single variable. For example, both can handle the concepts of drives and of such multifaceted personality structures as the psychoanalytic concepts of ego and superego. But in another respect, the multivariate experimentalist has more in common with the bivariate experimentalist than the clinician, in that both the multivariate and the bivariate experimentalists demand that concepts be referable to measurable operations and reproducible experiments, whereas the clinician makes no such claim and is, very often, prepared to proceed without the kind of recorded and statistically treated results that the experimentalist regards as indispensable.

Then the third side of the triangle becomes shorter once again when one realizes that the relatively sophisticated mathematical models and statistical analytical procedures used by the multivariate experimentalist are stranger and more remote from the clinician's training than are the experimental and control groups used in the typical bivariate experiment, despite the fact that the multivariate experimentalist's methods are comparatively simple. One of the unfortunate results of the development of mathematics in the multivariate approach has been that, although the clinician and the multivariate researcher are very close in principle and in their formal modes of reasoning, when the clinician has attempted to carry out an experiment, all too frequently he has reverted to the simple designs of the bivariate methodologist. Since, except for a few brilliant examples, psychiatrists cannot also be mathematicians, the effective interdisciplinary organization of research today requires the multivariate experimentalist to convey to the clinician the emerging structural concepts but not their detailed mathematical support. His task, then, is to equip the clinician with measuring instruments that correspond to these concepts. The clinical researcher can use these in all manner of criterion experiments, employing a purely logical comprehension of the dimensions measured rather than a mathematical one. After all, the psychiatrist's unique skills involve the application of these measuring instruments in conjunction with his ability to communicate with the patient. It is as unreasonable to expect him to exhibit equal competence in every area of the field of mathematical, quantitative behavioral research as it would be to expect the multivariate experimentalist to be able to conduct a psychiatric interview competently.

To be realistic, it will certainly be a long time before the mathematical prediction of behavior reaches such a level of comparative completeness that it no longer requires supplemental data from the human intuitive arts. However, there is every reason to believe that the results and implements of multivariate experimental research can ultimately be made available for intelligent use by those not engaged in the research on their production and that they will add accuracy to psychiatric procedures. Thus, one can hope that future training in psychiatry will integrate these new concepts. This is certainly a possibility, but it is equally certain that very little has been done as yet to bring this about. Indeed, too many teachers in the field of personality theory still are not facing in the direction from which the advances in integration of diagnostic measurement and theory are most likely to come.

STRUCTURAL MEASUREMENT VERSUS PSYCHOLOGICAL TESTING

The preceding discussion emphasized the fact that theory and measurement need to be closely united. But it should be made clear that the quantitative approach to psychological theory involves much more than psychological testing. Psychologists have constructed projective and nonprojective scales for thousands of variables, and laboratory workers have measured myriads of described variables. Nor is this surprising, for the number of aspects of behavior susceptible to being measured by a scale and labeled is literally infinite, and there is small chance that even two or three of the finite number of psychologists will choose to think the same variable important. Nevertheless, few of these scales have uncovered anything of theoretical importance, and most lie forgotten in professional journals.

Wherein lies the escape from this triviality of measurement? Certainly, as in any science, important concepts must be established, essential in the sense that they wield more predictive power and basic in the sense that they can be correlated with more psychological laws than concepts less happily chosen. Even when they are found, they may not incidentally correspond operationally with some single variable. For example, anxiety score does not correspond with counted beads of perspiration on the brow but may correspond to the average measure of a whole pattern of manifestations. But how are these more vital concepts to be discovered and the choice of variables most suitable for their measurement determined?

Applications of factor analysis. There are essentially two ways in which a science can move toward development of its truly efficacious concepts. One is by the process of conceptual trial and error, in which investigator after investigator pits his brains against the obscurities of nature and tries out concept after concept until one is found that fits the facts better than any other and provides more accurate predictions. The second is to develop a representative experimental design in which one samples variables according to some sampling technique and then uses a mathematical method, such as factor analysis, to isolate the comparatively small number of underlying influences responsible for the observed relationships of covariation among the individually measured variables.

In such sciences as physics and chemistry, the former approach has been quite successful and not unduly arduous or wasteful. The concepts of mass, time, temperature, radiation by wave transmission, valency, etc., were, in general, the survivors of no more than half a dozen alternative hypotheses. But unfortunately, it is a fact of history that psychology has not achieved a comparable degree of success, and students of behavior should realize that they are confronted by quite a different kind of problem, requiring a different method. The number of influences to take into account in deciding whether the home team will win a basketball game or whether Mrs. Jones will decide to speak to Mrs. Smith at a cocktail party or whether patient X will try to commit suicide is of a greater magnitude than the number of influences that affect the orbit of Neptune or the rate of the emission of electrons from a heated filament. Clearly, something more drastic must be done if we are to cut our way through the thickets of primal phenomena in order to reach the significant variables or concepts, concepts that, at the same time, will not be too numerous to make prediction possible.

It is vital that the reader understand the philosophy and the impact of multivariate experimental methods if he is to grasp its revolutionary implications for behavioral research. Unfortunately, space limitations preclude further development of this theme. Perhaps it is enough if the evaluator of theory realizes that methods now exist, particularly in factor analysis, that, when they are used flexibly with rotation to simple structure, are capable of reducing the multitudes of variables to a limited set of underlying functional unities capable of predicting those variables. However, correlational methods and factor analysis must be employed with the added restrictions of a scientific method rather than the bare postulates of a purely mathematical method. Only then are they capable of isolating underlying structures and influences in complex phenomena. Even those critics who have doubted this have agreed that factor analysis is capable of predicting—that is, of accounting for the variance in large numbers of variables by identifying the variance in a comparatively limited number of intervening or underlying variables.

A simple demonstration of the method was provided by Dickman and Cattell, who made 32 physical and kinetic measurement observations on the behavior of 100 balls; the factor analysis of these 32 variables yielded 4 factors—weight, diameter of the ball, elasticity coefficient, and the length of the string on which the balls were swung. These are the concepts that the physicist would use in formulas to explain the 32 measurements. The clinician may not be able to spare the time to follow the mathematical argument in detail. Yet he can be reassured at the common sense level by demonstrations of this kind that, through behavioral measurements, the method is capable of elucidating the same root influences he perceives clinically as accounting for individual differences in behavior.

SURFACE AND SOURCE TRAITS

For a hundred years psychiatry has struggled with the opposing views that taxonomic schemes are its main stock in trade and that understanding the individual patient through insight makes diagnostic categories unnecessary and even misleading. Finding that pigeonholing patients in types of syndrome grouping did not immediately provide such insight or reliable criteria with regard to therapeutic indications, many psychiatrists suggested the elimination of diagnostic procedures altogether. Instead, they advocated deeper, direct understanding of the dynamics of each case.

To get the full value from diagnostic approaches, such as those developed by Kraepelin and Bleuler, the real need was to press beyond the concept of gross syndromes to a more sophisticated taxonomic system rather than to retreat. The statistical, quantitative methodology of multivariate experimentation described above provides a means of doing this with the mathematical model concepts that are briefly designated by the terms "surface trait," "source trait," "type," and "process."

DEFINITIONS

A surface trait is simply a set of behaviors observed to go together, to appear together, and to disappear together; as such, it has the form of a simple correlation cluster. A syndrome is one form of surface trait. Computer programs such as Taxonome are capable of rapidly finding such clusters among the observations fed into a computer. In contrast, the source trait is defined as a simple structure factor, one of the underlying influences that we indicated above may be located by factor analysis. As will be seen below, examples of the source traits found by factor analysis generally include intelligence, the primary mental abilities described by Thurstone—anxiety, surgency, ego strength, and superego strength—and a number of drive patterns, technically called "ergs." The relation of source to surface traits will be discussed below; essentially, the surface traits are heapings up of behavior that derive from interactions of underlying source traits.

It may be useful to review the developments in personality theory that have already occurred through the application of the concept of surface and source traits. Typically, the multivariate experimentalist measures approximately 300 people with regard to 80 different manifestations in behavior. He then produces a correlation matrix among these 80 variables and by factor analysis finds the factors, the source traits, underlying the variables. When he finds, say, a dozen source traits, he is moreover reasonably sure that he is finding patterns that have a high likelihood of replication as patterns by others and that will have psychological predictive value.

This empirically derived emergence of structure provides the dependable concepts for the construction of testing devices. Indeed, it provides a statistical psychometric basis for hitting the bull's eye of such conceptual targets. Herein lies the vast difference between ordinary psychological testing and what might be called functional psychological testing. In psychological testing, one simply constructs scales for a priori notions or for quite specific bits of behavior; in contrast, in functional psychological testing, one discovers the structures to be measured first. That is, one unearths the inherent dynamic, temperamental, or ability structures—the source traits—in the human personality and then sets out to devise functional factor tests that will permit the precise measurement of these structures and nothing else. We are now concerned with personality theory built on experiment with functional measurement.

FACTOR DIMENSIONS

Thirty years of psychometric research in the personality field, using all three possible media of human observation—namely, behavior rating in situ; introspective evidence, as in the questionnaire or the consulting room; and objective test evidence by laboratory or performance measurements—have yielded a steadily increasing harvest of new concepts in personality theory with which the psychiatrist needs to become acquainted.

Analyses of rating and self-rating (introspective) data yield much the same concepts, around 20 in number. These source traits were indexed initially as factors "A," "B," "C," "D," etc., in much the same way the vitamin researchers first indexed their vitamin influences. A period of time must elapse between the simple identification of a behavior pattern as behavior and its thorough interpretation and understanding.

DESCRIPTIONS OF SOURCE TRAITS

It is reassuring for clinicians to find that the first broad factor found by multivariate experimental psychologists had been observed clinically by

Kraepelin, Bleuler, Kretschmer, and others. Kretschmer called it the "cyclothyme versus schizothyme dimension." Every factor must have a convention as to positive direction of score, although mathematically it is a toss-up. Thus, at the positive pole we find easy expression of affect, good contact with people, and a tendency toward mood swings. At the opposite pole, we find aloofness and rigidity, together with some dissociation of affect from cognition.

It was pointed out above that, for the most part, factor analytic work is based on observations of normal subjects. Consequently, there is no reason to suppose that intrinsically either the cyclothyme or schizothyme temperament connotes abnormality. Historically, they were merely first seen in their pathological dress, and it is possible that what was seen was in each case a specific disease process superimposed on an essentially normal deviation. Certainly, the expressions of the "A" factor pattern within the normal range are sufficiently different from schizophrenic and manic-depressive phenomena to justify a more conservative terminology. Consequently, in normals, the "A" factor dimension has been called "affecto-thymia versus schizothymia." The term schizothymia is derived from a Latin root meaning "flatness," which is characteristic of the schizothyme temperament, apart from any abnormality. After this first major "A" factor, a second source trait, "B," which connotes intelligence, was found to have the greatest influence quantitatively on a random set of behavior variables measured in regard to individual differences. Then, in the third place, comes the ego strength factor, indexed as "C," which has most of the properties assigned to it by the psychoanalyst. Factor "D" is a general excitability dimension. Source trait "E" is clearly recognizable as a dimension of dominance versus submissiveness that has also been studied in mammals and primates and has been correlated with hormone concentration. The "F" factor is called surgency-desurgency; at the surgent pole, it seems to be related to creative capacity, which is associated with comparatively little general inhibition; at the desurgent pole, we see a pattern with many features of what is clinically recognized as depression.

The personality theorist who wants to get a real grasp of this field should study the exact nature—that is, the magnitudes of factor loadings in various behaviors—of from 15 to 20 source traits until he recognizes them easily and understands their mode of expression fairly thoroughly. Some of the most important source traits are set out in bipolar form in Table I. For example, he might be particularly interested in the "G" factor of superego strength, which has all the ineluctable categorical imperativeness of the Freudian superego and has a special relationship to anxiety. As he studies this factor, he will encounter a number of interesting refinements, such as the correlations among factors and the existence of second-order factors, which will be commented on here only briefly. For instance, some patterns show themselves more obviously in overt behavior ("L data"), whereas others emerge clearly only in the questionnaire and consulting room ("Q data") responses. A "Q" prefix is used for the latter,

TABLE I

Brief Descriptions of Some Primary Source Traits Found by Factor Analysis[a]

Low-Score Description	Technical Labels		Standard Symbol	High-Score Description
	Low Pole	High Pole		
Reserved, detached, critical, cool	Schizothymia	Affectothymia	A	Outgoing, warmhearted, easygoing, participating
Less intelligent, concrete thinking	Low general mental capacity	Intelligence	B	More intelligent, abstract thinking, bright
Affected by feelings, emotionally less stable, easily upset	Lower ego strength	Higher ego strength	C	Emotionally stable, faces reality, calm
Phlegmatic, relaxed	Low excitability	High excitability	D	Excitable, strident, attention-seeking
Humble, mild, obedient, conforming	Submissiveness	Dominance	E	Assertive, independent, aggressive, stubborn
Sober, prudent, serious, taciturn	Desurgency	Surgency	F	Happy-go-lucky, heedless, gay, enthusiastic
Expedient, a law to himself, bypasses obligations	Low superego strength	Superego strength	G	Conscientious, persevering, staid, rulebound
Shy, restrained, diffident, timid	Threctia	Parmia	H	Venturesome, socially bold, uninhibited, spontaneous
Tough-minded, self-reliant, realistic, no nonsense	Harria	Premsia	I	Tender-minded, dependent, overprotected, sensitive
Trusting, adaptable, free of jealousy, easy to get on with	Alaxia	Protension	L	Suspicious, self-opinionated, hard to fool
Practical, careful, conventional, regulated by external realities, proper	Praxernia	Autia	M	Imaginative, preoccupied with inner urgencies, careless of practical matters, Bohemian
Forthright, natural, artless, sentimental	Artlessness	Shrewdness	N	Shrewd, calculating, worldly, penetrating
Placid, self-assured, confident, serene	Untroubled adequacy	Guilt proneness	O	Apprehensive, worried, depressive, troubled
Conservative, respecting established ideas, tolerant of traditional difficulties	Conservatism	Radicalism	Q$_1$	Experimental, critical, liberal, analytical, free-thinking
Group-dependent, a joiner and sound follower	Group adherence	Self-sufficiency	Q$_2$	Self-sufficient, prefers to make decisions, resourceful
Casual, careless of protocol, untidy, follows own urges	Weak self-sentiment	Strong self-sentiment	Q$_3$	Controlled, socially precise, self-disciplined, compulsive
Relaxed, tranquil, torpid, unfrustrated	Low ergic tension	High ergic tension	Q$_4$	Tense, driven, overwrought, fretful

[a] In ratings and questionnaires, and now embodied in the Sixteen Personality Factor Test.

and prominent among them in the Sixteen Personality Factor Test (16 P.F. Test) is Q_3 or self-sentiment strength. The score on this measures the development of the sentiment developed about the self, which seems to indicate the extent to which the individual's behavior is determined by attitudes that evolve from a consciously precise self-concept.

The Q_4 factor, called ergic tension, seems to represent the general persisting level of drive frustration in the total drive endowment of the individual. As far as one can judge from its correlations and manifestations, this does not merely indicate undischarged libido level in the Freudian sense but represents the amount of undischarged drive from sex, pugnacity, and any other ergs that may be encountering some of the frustration inevitable in our culture in the personal life of the individual.

Assessment of Source Traits

Questionnaire versus the objective-analytic battery. Granted that these structures and concepts give precision and potential measurability to some of the older, important parameters that are the basis for our understanding any individual, how is the practitioner to assess them? In part, he will want to do so directly by clinical interview. In normals, such as officer candidates for the Air Force, they have often been evaluated by careful rating procedures. In administering tests, one can use either questionnaires or objective, miniature situation performances (the Objective-Analytic Battery or O-A). The latter is ideal but cumbersome, so that, in all probability, the most convenient way to assess source trait levels in individuals is by a questionnaire, provided the questionnaire can be constructed with sufficient ingenuity to avoid excessive motivational distortion by faking. The Sixteen Personality Factor Test has been used widely in both clinical and occupational situations to evaluate the level of the individual on 16 of the 20 factors that have proved most relevant and most reliable. The test yields 16 scores, each on a 10-point scale. However, the psychologist or social worker who has not received sufficient training in this area should be warned that, in assessing personality source traits either by this method or by the Objective-Analytic Battery, he is not dealing with a profile of immutable levels, which he is likely to associate with I.Q. tests or ability measures, but with personality traits that can develop and be modified by life circumstances, psychotherapy, etc. Nevertheless, repeat measurements with these scales at intervals of one or more years have shown that, when life circumstances remain fairly stable, most of these traits demonstrate considerable stability from the age of 10 on.

The original factor analyses that showed these patterns in normal adult subjects have been applied in the past 15 years to groups of abnormals and pathological subjects and at different ages, specifically, at 12 and 13 years of age, at 11, at 7, and, recently, at 4 and 5 years of age. The evidence produced in the questionnaire type of response clearly indicates that most of these factors have a continuity of form—that is, of loading pattern—over the whole age range and in groups representing different cultures.

Thus, high and low surgency is a recognizable pattern at all age levels that have been investigated to date, as are the affectothyme versus schizothyme temperament dimension, ego strength, and the various other factors. Furthermore, studies performed in Italy, Germany, Japan, India, and Australia have shown that the essential form of these patterns survives cultural translation. Therefore, the evidence accumulated to date supports the view that these functional unities are relatively fundamental dimensions of human personality that may undergo some modification in expression with age and cultural changes but that retain a real continuity. This has been an important consideration in recent years for the planning of developmental studies, which will be referred to below.

Essentially parallel findings appear when personality source traits are measured through the objective (performance or laboratory) type of test. There are some interesting modifications, however, due to the difference in the power of the eyepiece, so to speak. Some magnification occurs in questionnaires, so that second-order factors in the questionnaire realm (very broad factors that take the form of groupings of primaries) emerge only as first-order factors (narrower in the total field) in the objective test realm. For example, the single general anxiety factor that appears in objective laboratory test measures fractionates into an interrelated set of subfactors in the questionnaire—namely, the factors of ego weakness, guilt proneness, tension, etc.

In general, the use of objective test batteries, as exemplified by the Objective-Analytic Battery, eliminates some of the shortcomings of the questionnaire, such as the question of reliability of response. But they require more time, skill, and apparatus for administration. Consequently, to date, the objective test measurement of personality factors has not been used in clinics or mental hospitals as frequently as have the questionnaire measurement techniques, though more exact work in the future will require them.

CONSTRUCTION OF THE THEORETICAL MODEL

Elaborate personality theories that do not offer, as a basic prerequisite, the ability to measure recognizable trait structures involved in the theory will not get very far. On the other hand, a system that has nothing to offer but a set of traits cannot be considered potentially significant, no matter how these traits describe the natural history of the observed species. It follows, then, that psychology must experiment with models that will account for trait interaction and development, for the role of situations, etc., and that will permit accurate prediction of the outcome of trait combinations and conflicts.

Moreover, this model must have diagnostic validity, and it must be applicable to pathological phenomena, despite the fact that, as pointed out above, at least half the data on which it is based are derived from observations of normal subjects. Obviously, there may be special disease processes described in clinical material that are never manifested in any aspect of normal behavior. This problem will be discussed below. A description of the main model is our first concern. This is called the "intersection model," for it treats any behavioral event as something that can be accounted for only in terms of concepts of personality, of situation, and of on-going process. Each of these variables is clearly represented by a specific formula.

INTERSECTION MODEL

Any act is considered, as far as personality is concerned, to involve the total personality—that is, the whole profile of source trait scores. The simplest mathematical way of handling this is to assign various appropriate and experimentally obtained weights to the action of specific traits in each given situation and then simply add these contributions together to get the total strength of the final response. However, if one suspects that the relation obtaining in nature is more complicated than a linear one, then the formula may be modified by introducing, for example, products or exponentials among the trait scores. But, so far, this has not been necessary, and the basic equation in this intersectional factor analysis model remains what is sometimes called the linear specification equation. It can be represented for "k" traits as follows:

$$a_j = b_{j1}T_1 + b_{j2}T_2 + \cdots + b_{jk}T_k \qquad (1)$$

where T_1, T_2 . . . T_k are an individual's scores on the traits; a_j is the act as we want to predict, and b_{j1}, b_{j2} . . . b_{jk}, are behavioral indices or weights for these traits when they are manifested in the context of the situation "f."

CONCEPT OF THE LINEAR SPECIFICATION EQUATION

This is a simple linear equation. As explained above, it states that the magnitude of any particular behavior manifestation (a_j), such as a symptom, is determined by a whole set of source traits or factors, here indicated by the letters "A," "B," "C," etc., from Table I. So far, this is in accordance with good psychiatric principles, which postulate that most behavior is multiply determined and is not due to the independent action of any single trait or dynamic need. The weights or behavioral indices that express the extent to which each of the standard common factors is involved in performance are determined by experiment, followed by a factor analysis, and can be assigned any values, ranging from $+ 1$ to $- 1$. The application of this specification equation can be illustrated by two examples. The first of these is an equation discovered by Pierson and Kelly for the probability of recovery from delinquency in adolescent children. The second is also an empirically derived equation and expresses the success of psychiatric technicians, evaluated in their own institutions, as a function of their personality factor scores on the 16 P.F. Test. These may be stated (see Table I for trait identification) as follows:

$$\text{Response to treatment} = .1B - .5C + .3D - .1F + .6G$$
$$-.2H + .2I + .2J + .2O - .3Q_2 + .2Q_4 \quad (2)$$
$$\text{Psychiatric success} \quad = .2A + .5C - .2E + .3G + .3H$$
$$-.3M - .2O - .3Q_1 + .3Q_3 - .2Q_4 \quad (3)$$

It should be noted here that in any actual calculation the values for the source trait scores—which, typically, represent the values on a 10-point scale, based on the "stens" in the test score—always represent the individual scores on these common traits. ("Sten" is an abbreviation of "standard ten," meaning a standard score in which sigma equals 2 and the total range is 1 to 10.) The I.Q., the affectothyme ("A"), and the ego strength ("C") factor measures would be familiar instances of such source trait scores. The T's in the first equation above are replaced with letters to denote particular source traits in the second and third equations. The meaning of these letters was given earlier, in Table I. It should be noted that, whereas the T values, which express the unique qualities of the individual, constitute the profile of his trait scores, the values that define the situation in which he stands are represented by the b values or behavioral indices. And these indices are unique to the particular situation, not an individual. They can be identified only by factoring data that include that situation. These behavioral indices describe the extent to which the given situation evokes certain personality traits. It becomes more evident at this point that we have called our general approach the intersection theory because it considers the act as the intersection of a multidimensional personality with a multidimensional situation. This, of course, is no figure of speech but refers to an equation for actual computations that can be applied to any related problem. The validity of these modes of representation of the individual and the situation can be tested in other ways as well.

PREDICTIVE VALIDITY

The theory has a practical, testable application. Thus, the practitioner can take the particular scores of a patient on a test, such as the 16 P.F. Test or the High School Personality Questionnaire (HSPQ) or the O-A Battery. After entering these figures in a familiar equation, obtained by previous researches, for some important situation, he can make a rough prediction of the patient's response. For example, the psychiatrist might be interested in the way a particular individual will respond to a certain therapeutic treatment; provided general research has been used earlier to establish the behavioral indices for this situation, he will be able to make an estimate that is probably much better than one that could be made from intuition

alone. The accuracy of the estimate can, of course, be calculated by finding the magnitude of the multiple correlation obtainable from the given
weights.

Some psychometrists have been content to use personality source trait
measurements and ability factor measurements in just this way, restricting
themselves to purely actuarial statistical methods. But this is not utilizing
the resources of the intersectional theory of behavior to their full capacity.
Surely, the very characteristic that distinguishes a good psychiatrist or psychologist from an accountant or a computer is his desire to use psychological laws as well as those laws that are merely actuarial and statistical. And
here, once again, we encounter a substantial advantage of functional psychological testing over mere psychological testing. If these source traits are
the natural structures of personality, which we have every reason to believe
them to be, or if they correspond to functional states—such as anxiety,
stress, elation-depression—which we know them to be in other cases, then
we can project the prediction beyond that which is possible actuarially.
We can reason and predict to future dates and different occasions by
adding to the formal calculation or to an estimate that is made in one's
head what we know about the way in which these source traits will change
with time and situation and as a result of other influences.

MODIFICATIONS IN SOURCE TRAITS

With this potential capability it becomes important for personality theory
to develop, as soon as possible, its repertoire of laws and resources of information about these source traits. One of the obvious and immediate directions of possible research is to find the way in which each source trait
changes and develops characteristically with age. When it became known,
for example, that the general intelligence factor, as defined by Spearman,
grew rapidly in early childhood and reached a definite plateau at about 15
or 16 years of age rather than at a much later age, as generally assumed,
then predictions about learning rate and future achievement began to be
made with much greater reliability and insight. In the last few years, as
information has accumulated about the life course of several well-known
personality factors, many psychologists who had sat on the fence too long
and looked askance at factors as mere mathematical abstractions became
convinced of their reality. For one sees that each shows a highly characteristic age course, quite different from that which would arise from a mere
averaging of any mathematical but unpsychological set of subtest scores.
For example, when the anxiety factor is scored on the eight subtests found
to load it most consistently, we discover that anxiety is high in adolescence, then drops steadily until the age of about 35, after which it stays
low until old age, when, apparently, it rises again. The ego strength factor
also follows an unstable course in adolescence; thereafter, it continues to
rise very slowly and steadily with life experience. The provision of such
norms should also help to enhance the psychiatrist's understanding of how

far individual cases may be deviating from the normal development.

In the 1970's, however, research on intersection theory has many other important things to explore in regard to source traits. Central among these is the relative importance of constitution and environmental learning in determining individual differences. Preliminary research certainly shows great differences among them in this respect. Personality theory could also be pushing ahead to manipulative, bivariate experiments carried out on factor measurements, such as anxiety, ego strength, surgency, and superego strength. Since measures are now available, no factor analysis would be necessary; the aim of such research would be simply to determine, for example, which physiological influences and family learning situations determine levels of these primary structures.

DIAGNOSIS AND PROGNOSIS BY THE INTERSECTION MODEL

In regard to the establishment of the patterns of functional unities in personality that we call traits, the contention of the factor analyst is that he really needs no check from clinical—nonmetric—types of observation, although he welcomes the enrichment of meaning given thereby to the bare bones of his framework. He has rested his case on the most fundamental principle for establishing functional connections in science— namely, what John Stuart Mill called "the principle of joint variation." Thereby, causal and other connections can be proved, and it can be shown that certain elements of behavior do, in fact, go together when examined by more precise methods than are available to the clinician's eye and memory. Consequently, it is not surprising that the factor analytic experimental methods first elucidated some of the major patterns that have been observed clinically, for the clinician is using the same principles but without benefit of a computer. Correlational investigations have confirmed the validity of such concepts as ego strength, a general factor of anxiety, superego strength, schizothyme tendency, ergic tension, etc.

Although the basis of the newer concept is different, more precise, and more verifiable, these new factors have been given the labels by which the vaguer shapes that preceded them have been clinically recognized. For example, there can no longer be any justification for several different views of the exact pattern of ego strength expression or for conflicting views about whether ego structure is a single pattern or several. These issues can be quickly decided by experiment, and in Cattell's *Personality and Motivation Structure and Measurement*, precise loadings are given for the various expressions of ego strength, schizothyme tendency, anxiety, etc. Table II shows, for example, how various introspected and observed anxiety manifestations load the anxiety factor.

TABLE II

Psychiatric Symptoms Expressive of Anxiety
A. *Self-Rating*[a]

Item Number	Correlations with Pure Anxiety Factor			Symptom
	Average of 1 and 2	Research 1 (Sample of 90)	Research 2 (Sample of 150)	
1	+.40	+.32	+.48	Jumpy, nervous
2	+.39	+.32	+.45	Feel lonely
3	+.38	+.36	+.39	Want to get away from it all
4	+.36	+.29	+.43	Worry
5	+.36	+.32	+.40	Do foolish or clumsy things, say the the wrong thing
6	+.36	+.27	+.45	Nervous movements (finger tapping)
7	+.36	+.31	+.41	Feel depressed or despondent
8	+.34	+.36	+.31	Excitable
9	+.34	+.32	+.35	Have silly, groundless fears
10	+.33	+.30	+.36	Have a fatalistic attitude
11	+.31	+.36	+.26	Lack of self-confidence
12	+.31	+.32	+.29	Irritable
13	+.31	+.22	+.39	Heart pounds when excited
14	+.31	+.29	+.32	Easily distracted
15	+.30	+.28	+.32	Daydream
16	+.30	+.21	+.39	Get confused for certain lengths of time
17	+.30	+.26	+.33	Tense
18	+.29	+.33	+.24	Cry
19	+.28	+.30	+.25	Pulse rapid
20	+.27	+.21	+.32	Easily embarrassed
21	+.26	+.23	+.29	Get cold shivers
22	+.26	+.46	+.05	Moody
23	+.25	+.33	+.17	Have rapid emotional changes (hate to liking)
24	+.25	+.28	+.22	Can't concentrate
25	+.25	+.24	+.26	Get tired easily

[a] From Cattell and Scheier, 1961.

B. *Psychiatrist's Ratings*

Symptom	Correlations with Pure Anxiety Factor
Irritability	+.42
Anxiety	+.33
Depression	+.32
Phobic behavior	+.22
Sleep disturbances	+.13

Universal Index Series

The factor analyst usually uses indices for traits to avoid possibly false connotations in popular labels. For example, in the Universal Index series, U.I. 24 corresponds to the general anxiety factor. After this pattern is tied down, the psychometrist must also show how U.I. 24 measures behave in clinical situations. In this case the factor behaves exactly as the popular conception of anxiety has always behaved. That is, measurements on the U.I. 24 show that the measurements for neurotics are decidedly higher than they are for normals. They show that under psychotherapy and chemotherapy the score on U.I. 24 is reduced. They show that U.I. 24 measures increase in individuals subjected to anxiety-provoking situations. The exact identification of a measurable behavioral pattern for anxiety, U.I. 24, permits these associations to be demonstrated and, incidentally, also permits more precise research to uncover those physiological variables related to anxiety. Understanding of physiological associations has been enhanced since factor analytic separation of the response patterns has shown that a stress reaction pattern exists, now called effort stress. This resembles and was frequently confused with anxiety before the advent of correlational factor analytic evidence, but it behaves very differently in several ways. For example cholesterol in the blood stream seems to be related positively to effort stress measurements but not to anxiety measurements.

Diagnostic Criteria

The difference between the theories developed from multivariate quantitative research and those based on clinical observation does not stop at some variations in emphasis in descriptive patterns, some greater clarity in the separation of distinct concepts, and the possibility of resolving otherwise unending verbal disputes by reference to quantitative experimental results. It may alter the whole theoretical picture, as has happened through findings on the number and nature of the factors involved in a specific process, as in neurosis. It would appear that clinical observation has succeeded in locating only the more grossly obvious of these functional unities and that a much larger number must be considered. Whereas Freud believed that "anxiety is the central problem in the neuroses," and many psychoanalysts continue to treat neurosis as if the main problem were to reduce the deviant degree of anxiety, the factor analytic approach by the intersection model has identified at least seven primary factors that distinguish diagnosed neurotics from normals beyond the $p < 0.01$ level of significance. According to current tentative labels, these include "C−" (ego weakness), "E−" (submissiveness), "F−" (desurgency), "H−" (threctia), "I+" (premsia), "O+" (guilt proneness), "Q_3−" (inadequate self-sentiment development), and "Q_4+" (high undischarged ergic tension level), as presented in Table I.

In the Objective-Analytic Battery, seven factors have also been found that distinguish the neurotics from the normals with the same statistical potency ($p < 0.01$), although they cover a broader area than was measured in the questionnaire. The degree of separation of neurotics and normals that can, in fact, be obtained just by the use of the O-A Battery is shown in Figure 1.

If we examine these factors in terms of their clinical association, we recognize that classical psychoanalysis has designated ego weakness, guilt proneness, and ergic tension as factors in the neurotic breakdown, but it

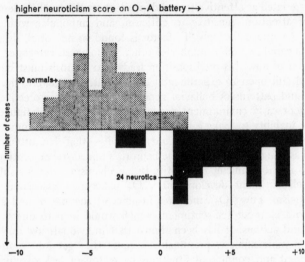

FIGURE 1. *Frequency histogram of the linear discriminant function, showing degree of diagnostic separation obtainable for 30 normal and 24 neurotic subjects on objective test personality factors.* (From Cattell, R. B. The Scientific Analysis of Personality, *p. 331. Penguin Books, Baltimore,* 1965.)

has said nothing about "H—" factor (threctia), "I+" factor (premsia), or "Q₃—" (deficient self-sentiment). The evidence produced by studies of twins is that "H" factor is largely hereditary and represents a general autonomic sensitivity to threat in the low score direction—hence the name threctia. Presumably, this finding of low "H" in neurotics merely indicates that the individual who is highly susceptible to external threats also reacts excessively to threats from internal forces or impulses. It may be that Freud considered this temperamental component too obvious to state, but in any actual calculation of individual differences in neurosis it cannot be overlooked.

The concept of premsia versus harria ("I" factor), on the other hand, adds an entirely new dimension to the theory of neurosis. This factor is largely environmentally determined, although some association has been shown with blood groups. It appears to represent the extent to which the individual has been brought up in an overindulgent and unrealistic environment as opposed to a disciplined, more self-restrictive atmosphere. The term premsia is an acronym from "protected emotional sensitivity," and the ratings given to children and adults high on this factor stress sensitivity, plaintiveness, dependence, preference for art and drama over science and mathematics, and a tendency toward fussiness in personal relations. In school, these children are rated as attentive to and dependent on the teacher, demanding of attention, sensitive to criticism, and unpopular with their peers. An unusually high "I" factor is found in neurotics, drug addicts, alcoholics, and a number of other pathological categories. The question of how this predisposition leads into neurosis must be considered still open to experimental check. But, presumably, the attitudes and patterns of behavior generated by this overprotective and indulgent early environment produce the neurotic hesitation—that is, the inability to make a firm decision either to give up some satisfaction or to accept its consequences fully—that has often been noted as one of the origins of the neurotic's unrealistic perceptions.

It is not too difficult to identify the mechanisms whereby subnormal self-sentiment development ("Q_3") becomes associated with neuroticism. Low "Q_3" indicates insufficient shaping of and attention to a clear-cut self-sentiment, which would help to direct decisions and actions. It has been shown that individuals low on "Q_3" develop more anxiety, presumably because they get into more unstructured and conflicting situations by reason of lack of guidance from the more decided self-concept present in the high "Q_3" individual. Lack of integration follows because behavior is not referred as readily to a defined self-concept.

Similarly, operational explanations have been put forward for the action of others of the new source traits identified through this experimental approach. Space limitations preclude discussion of these traits here, but the hypotheses they have given rise to have already been put to experimental check in some cases. In the main, within the limits of this chapter, we are reduced to a bald statement that certain source traits have been found and that certain significant score differences have been found among various pathological groups, which, consequently, have resulted in certain diagnostic potencies for the scales concerned. But, in addition, rich theoretical developments have occurred with respect to these concepts in these last few years that require further validation from measurement and experimental findings.

Some clinicians may justifiably feel that, in terms of stimulating clinical research, the approach of the psychometrists has been an unduly cautious one. More specifically, most experimentalists have been very conservative in speculating about the nature of these entities. Although there is no question that these functional entities are real, one hesitates to name and theorize about them until additional criterion evidence has appeared. And this evidence has not appeared nearly as rapidly as it should because of the communication gap between the clinicians on the one hand—who have been inclined, when they take to testing, to use some clinically derived test, regardless of its factorial base in research—and the statisticians on the other. The statisticians, whose skills and realm of action have not included the trial of these tests in clinical situations or the testing of them against psychiatric diagnoses, have in the main constructed factor-pure tests and then simply left them in the clinician's lap. However, now that these factored scales and batteries have been made available in formal publication, in such instruments as the 16 P.F., the HSPQ, the IPAT Anxiety scale, the various factor depression scales, the Objective-Analytic Battery, and the Motivational Analysis Test (MAT), we can certainly anticipate a more rapid accumulation of checks against standard psychiatric diagnostic judgments and evaluations of therapeutic gain. From the theoretical point of view, this will result in a much greater understanding of each functionally unitary source trait, which, though we know it already to be established indubitably as a functional unit, lacks definitive interpretation with respect to its relationship to age, family background, neurological associates, and finally, the degree to which it may be modified by therapeutic procedures.

THERAPEUTIC GUIDELINES

Any personality theory worthy of the name should have intimate contact with the principles and practice of psychotherapy. The traits connected with functional testing and the general intersection theory do indeed give guidance on the strategy and tactics of the individual therapeutic procedure. But discussion of this relationship will also reveal a gap in relation to what have been called unique traits.

COMBINATION OF SOURCE AND SURFACE TRAIT MEASUREMENTS

Attention must be focused for a moment on the relationship between surface and source traits. Prior to the advent of basic research in personality structure as implemented by the factor analytic experiment described above, most psychological scales consisted of measurements of surface traits or of attempts to relate behavior to a particular test by a kind of blind empiricism. For example, the Minnesota Multiphasic Personality Index (MMPI) was directed to syndromes (surface traits) that had been recognized previously by the psychiatrist. Thus, the test served as an aid in assessing the severity of the symptoms of that syndrome in a given case. Essentially, the Rorschach has had a similar aim: to provide independent evidence as to the severity of a particular syndrome and, thereby, help to classify the individual's disorder. Ultimately, a host of clinical psychologists discovered many blind empirical relationships between pathological syndromes and response to inkblots.

This approach to diagnosis through special-purpose tests is the exact opposite of what we have described here as the goal and orientation of the *general* purpose *structural* test. In the latter, meaningful structures are found first, and tests are then directed to the elucidation of these concepts. However, a surface trait, such as an MMPI scale may offer, can be as much a natural structure as a source trait outlined in the 16 P.F. Test, for example. Therefore, some reference must now be made to the possible advantages of insightfully combining surface and source trait measurements in diagnosis. It is denied by psychologists, such as Wiggins, who have examined the MMPI by correlations that its scales have the homogeneity required by the surface trait definition. But in a clinical sense they may have the homogeneity of correlations with actual psychiatric case syndromes. It was pointed out above that a certain correlation cluster or surface trait, such as the severity of a conversion hysteria syndrome, may be created by several fairly different patterns of source traits. This can be illustrated by the two following specification equations, each of which describes a group of anxiety reaction symptoms of the same severity. The first makes the general statement that, typically, anxiety (*a* in the equation) is due −.4 to ego strength (+.4 to ego weakness), +.5 to guilt proneness, and +.5 to ergic tension (frustrated drive level). Other factors are omitted for simplicity of illustration.

$$a = -.4C + .5O + .5Q_4$$

Let us now take two individuals, *J* and *K*, with the following scores on the 16 P.F. Test.

	C	O	Q$_4$
J:	.5	.2	.8
K:	.5	.8	.2

When these values are substituted for "C," "O," and "Q$_4$" in the specification equation, one gets the following result.

$$a_j = (-.4 \times .5) + (.5 \times .2) + (.5 \times .8) = .3$$
$$a_k = (-.4 \times .5) + (.5 \times .8) + (.5 \times .2) = .3$$

In one case, this high anxiety reaction score of .3 (0 is average) can be ascribed to a higher guilt proneness and in the other to a greater ergic tension. In general, this illustrates that the same surface trait score (overt symptom level) can be understood in terms of different source trait profile scores. It is the latter that provides the understanding essential for effective therapeutic intervention, and the whole movement of recent years to discount the docketing of cases by surface trait scores rests on this fact. On the other hand, experimental examination of the personality factor profiles of psychiatric patients assigned to a given syndrome group does reveal a certain similarity of profiles. For example, as indicated above, neurotics tend to be low in ego strength and surgency, high in ergic tension ("Q_4"), high in guilt proneness ("O" factor), and high in premsia ("I" factor). Moreover, this still leaves enough room for individual differences. In one patient the level of overt severity of symptoms—the surface traits—may be accounted for by a marked ego weakness and a relatively minor guilt reaction; in another, the test results will show that, although the patient's ego strength is not deficient to any conspicuous degree, his reaction is much more severe.

Scores expressed simultaneously in surface and source trait structures should be of great value to the therapist in planning his campaign of therapy for the individual patient. Table III provides the weights necessary to estimate the typical MMPI surface trait scores from the 16 P.F. source traits. Thus, the former can be analyzed in terms of the latter. To date, this computational approach has had relatively little impact on psychiatric practice. However, several articles now appear in the literature in which a different prognostic outcome has been established experimentally on the basis of one individual's source traits profile as compared with another's, when the actual syndrome measurement by a surface trait scale, such as the MMPI, has been equally severe in both cases and undistinguishable. This does not mean that surface trait measurement, such as the MMPI, should be dropped. The purpose of this discussion is to point up the value of a good two-handed use of surface trait (MMPI) and source trait (16 P.F.) measurements in what has been called psychometric depth analysis. One needs to ascertain as accurately as possible both the severity of the actual symptoms and what combination of source traits is most involved in their production. The typical relationships for general surface-source traits have already been established for the average patient, as indicated in Table III.

Knowing the causal nexus in a particular patient at the level of source trait structure is of obvious value from both a theoretical and practical standpoint. It can be illustrated from actual measurements by the work of Pierson and Kelly on young delinquents, referred to above. This study showed that in a group of delinquents whose antisocial behavior (surface trait) was equally severe, those with greater ego strength were less likely to modify their behavior in the foreseeable future. On the other hand, subjects who scored high on "D" factor (excitability) were more likely to return to normal behavior.

Table III

Predictions (Average Makeup) of MMPI Surface Trait Scale Scores in terms of 16 P.F. Source Trait Scale Scores with Various Attenuation Corrections

For any row in the figures on 16 P.F. trait measures, the weights (rounded to one decimal) are given to apply to the 16 P.F. source trait scores to get the best estimate of the MMPI surface trait scale. The values in the last four columns are the multiple correlations, showing how far the 16 P.F. can be expected to estimate the surface trait syndromes. For example, psychasthenia and anxiety are pretty well estimated, but hysteria and masculinity-femininity are not. These values are based on studies of a normal group of three cases and should be taken as tentative until checked against the findings derived from investigation of a mixed group of normal and clinical subjects. N = 300.

MMPI Surface Trait Estimates	A	B	C	E	F	G	H	I	L	M	N	O	Q₁	Q₂	Q₃	Q₄	Corrected for MMPI Scale Unreliabilities Only	Corrected for 16 P.F. Scale Unreliabilities Only	Corrected to Ideal Scales for Both	Uncorrected
Anxiety	0	0	−1	−2	0	0	−1	0	0	0	0	2	0	0	−1	3	49	64	68	58
Lie "L" scale	0	−1	2	−2	0	1	0	−2	0	1	1	−1	0	0	0	1	27	35	40	32
Validity "F"	0	−1	0	1	−2	−1	1	2	0	1	0	−1	0	1	1	1	46	58	73	51
Correction "K"	1	0	1	−1	0	−1	0	−1	0	−1	1	2	1	0	−1	1	37	49	55	43
Hypochondriasis	0	0	−1	0	0	−1	1	1	−1	1	0	2	0	0	−1	0	42	55	62	49
Depression	0	0	0	−1	−1	−1	0	−1	0	1	0	−1	1	0	1	1	32	36	47	32
Hysteria	0	0	−1	−2	0	−1	1	1	0	0	0	2	0	0	0	2	28	29	43	26
Psychopathic	0	0	0	−1	0	−1	1	−1	1	0	0	−1	1	0	−1	2	32	32	48	29
Masculinity-femininity	1	0	1	0	0	0	−1	1	0	0	0	0	1	0	−1	2	25	33	38	29
Paranoia	−1	0	0	−1	0	0	1	0	1	0	0	−1	1	0	1	1	30	36	48	32
Psychasthenia	0	−1	−1	−1	0	−1	1	0	0	0	−1	1	0	0	−2	3	55	70	78	63
Schizophrenia	0	−1	−1	−1	1	0	1	1	0	1	0	1	0	0	2	2	48	66	75	58
Hypomania	−1	0	2	−1	1	0	−1	−1	1	1	1	−1	1	1	1	1	33	35	48	32
Social introversion	−1	0	−3	−1	1	1	−1	−1	1	1	0	2	0	2	0	1	47	52	64	47

The obvious conclusion to be drawn here is that high "D" factor may result in antisocial, impulsive behavior, although there is really no serious dynamic (antisocial tendency) distortion in character structure. On the other hand, if the individual has settled down to socially maladjusted behavior and, nevertheless, achieved high ego strength, the reconstruction of his modes of reaction is going to be more difficult because he has a well-formed ego and is experiencing comparatively little anxiety. The theories concerning the treatment of delinquency arising from this quantitative experimental approach, as stated by Pierson and Kelly, have turned out to be quite antithetical to those developed on previous purely clinical grounds. Theories based on clinical observation have treated the delinquent essentially as a neurotic who is acting out. As such, he was considered a candidate for the same therapeutic approach, including the reduction of anxiety. The experimental results that showed that delinquents were actually deficient in anxiety led Pierson to argue, instead, that the first task in therapy is to increase the anxiety level of the delinquent, and his results seem to justify this approach.

Precise practical applications of the intersection model theories will require far more survey research than has yet been accomplished, research that focuses on discovering specification equations for a wide variety of pathological behaviors. That is, we need to know which personality source traits are involved and to what quantitative extent in response to a wide variety of standard life situations, such as occupation, clinical settings, marriage and the family. This is a very considerable undertaking and can only be accomplished if psychiatrists provide more extensive encouragement in getting systematic measurements than they have to date. Specific theories about the role of particular source traits in certain disorders already exist, but the cautious therapist is not going to feel that he can depend on them until the necessary measurement relations have been cross-validated by larger samples.

OBSERVATION OF INDIVIDUAL CONFLICTS AND MEASUREMENT OF COMMON SOURCE TRAITS

This is not the only reason for current difficulties in applying source trait theory. There is also a real theoretical difficulty in reconciling observations of conflicts and fixations that are obviously quite specific and idiosyncratic to the patient with measures of source traits that are by definition common forms. Is Patient X's symptom formation to be related to a sexual trauma at age 3 or to a low score on the ego strength factor ("C"), and what bearing does the answer to the question have on therapeutic techniques?

When the factor analyst studies individual differences and correlates behavior measures, essentially he is developing concepts of common traits. That is to say, the intelligence or the anxiety he is measuring is considered to have the same typical pattern for all people as a measure of mass does for all objects; therefore, he ignores certain variations in form in the individual. He does not ignore them completely, however, for to a great extent the peculiarity of expression visible in one source trait is due to the fact that it is combined in particular measures with some other source trait. For example, in the expression of dominance of an individual rated high on the common dominance trait who is also high on the common measure of anxiety, there will be some measure of anxiety, some qualities of rigidity, etc., that will not be present in the person who scores at the same level on the dominance trait but at a far lower level on the anxiety trait. In short, a great deal of what we recognize as the uniqueness of the individual can be very adequately represented by his unique combination of scores on absolutely common traits.

On the other hand, we must also recognize absolutely unique traits, particularly in the dynamic field and in regard to the patient's interests. For example, the interest of an individual in the house in which he was born and in the sexual life of his grandmother are continua on which other people cannot be given any real score. At best, we can say that the rest of humanity has a zero score on this scale, and a scale that is useful to only one person is not very useful. One of the most common causes of misunderstanding between the psychometrician and the psychiatrist is the fact that the psychometrician is rarely concerned with unique traits, and the psychiatrist has not grasped the conceptual distinction between a common trait and a unique trait. It happens that a good deal of clinical work is concerned with the immediate observation of unique traits, and this is apt to obscure the fact that in the long run the psychiatrist may have to give more attention to common traits. For example, initially, the clinician may be interested in the specific dynamic conflicts and personal history fixations indicated above, but his ultimate objective is to raise the level of the common trait of ego strength and to reduce, say, the level of the common trait of anxiety. Obviously, he must attend to the idiosyncratic and cultural attachments in which a common trait, such as the sex drive or the superego, has become entangled; but his final concern is with a general economics of energy that will produce changes that can be recognized by measurements of the massive common traits.

Parenthetically, there exist potent but costly ways of objectively exploring and measuring individual unique trait structure, dynamic or otherwise —notably, through what has been called "P technique." P technique repeats a battery of measures on the patient for, say, 100 days; his scores are then correlated over time, revealing the functionally unitary factors. When ways can be found to simplify these research approaches for routine application, one hopes that there will be a more extensive use of measurement in psychiatry in regard to the structure and strength of the unique traits. Meanwhile, psychiatry can go a long way in terms of common traits alone, provided the psychiatrist recognizes that both unique and common patterns exist and that the direct manipulation of the unique trait may frequently contribute to change in the common trait measurement.

SPECIFICITY OF INDIVIDUAL CONFLICTS

In principle, the specificity of conflicts and fixations in the individual patient is no different from the specificity of form of a house. A unique dwelling does not prevent the builder or carpenter from using his knowledge of common materials to construct or manipulate the structure of the house. Similarly, we can account for much of a unique psychological structure in terms of different quantitative combinations of common traits. In the last resort we find attachments, it is true, that are absolutely unique to the individual and his history; the handling of these attachments is discussed below.

APPLICATION OF DYNAMIC CALCULUS TO CONFLICT MEASUREMENT

If the universal applicability of mathematical-statistical methods to the discovery of structure is valid, then the dynamic, interest-motivation aspects of personality, which have not yet been discussed, should also admit of an analysis at least equal in precision to that based on clinical methods. Developments from such research, under the name of the "dynamic calculus," have fully justified these expectations.

The two main devices for dynamic analysis that were developed primarily in the clinical field—namely, free association and hypnotism—have been based mainly on the verbal report of the patient. This is true of the early contributions of the psychometrists as well. Tests of interest, such as the Strong or the Kuder, and approaches to conflict evaluation through such devices as the ordinary questionnaire have also depended on the patient's verbal self-evaluation. It is true that, in principle, the evaluation in free association is at a more sophisticated level than are the self-statements about occupational interests in the Strong Interest Test, for example; but, ultimately, both depend on verbal and self-directed evaluation.

More recently, in projective tests, the psychologist has offered the psychiatrist an avenue to dynamic trait measurement that is somewhat more sophisticated. Unfortunately, it has also proved very unreliable, as numerous studies of the Thematic Apperceptions Test (TAT) and other projective tests have shown. A fundamentally different approach from all these began when some 90 different objective devices for measuring motivational strength—ranging from measures of perceptual distortion to ego defense mechanisms through information and physiological responses, such as blood pressure and galvanic skin reflex—were subjected to factor analysis in order to identify their components. One cannot assume that all motivational manifestations will have a single underlying factor. Actually, the results show seven types of motivation components that appear regularly, no matter how diverse the content of interest may be. This has permitted the measurement of motivational factors by tests that can themselves be construct-validated against the factors. It is from such objective measures that the generalizations commonly called the dynamic calculus have emerged.

At present, the nature of the seven distinct primary motivational components is not fully understood. One theory considers them to be the contributions to any interest, emanating from the id, the ego, the superego, physiological (autonomic) response, complexes, and certain other sources—that is, the sum total of interest in any response or course of action. For example, wanting to succeed in one's profession is analyzed by such a battery of tests as the MAT into relative strengths in these components. However, more recent investigations have shown that for both adults and children the seven components fall into two groups; or, to be precise, they are organized by two second-order factors. From their nature these have been called, respectively, the integrated and the unintegrated components in interest. Thus a "U" and an "I" score can be assigned by the battery to the strength of any interest in any given course of action. Such subtests as autism, perceptual distortion, and galvanic skin reflex are found to contribute to the unintegrated component; and such responses as word association, information, and penetrating perception of jumbled sentences contribute to the integrated component.

Current theory in this area favors the view that the unintegrated component, though not wholly unconscious, corresponds to many manifestations that have been clinically described as emanating from the unconscious and has to do with that component of interest that has never found any reality-testing. On the other hand, the integrated component in the battery corresponds to interest that has been tested out, invested in adjusted performances, educated, and integrated with the self-concept. These two components show relatively little correlation in any individual, but Sweney's work suggests that, in general, a high magnitude of the unintegrated relative to the integrated component score occurs whenever there is conflict in that particular drive or need area. The validities of these batteries are not yet raised to the same level as those familiar in ability batteries, and their reliabilities are lower, but experiment is broad enough to show that these factor structures exist, and promising beginnings have been made toward their theoretical interpretation.

Being able to measure interest strength by objective tests is, however, only a beginning. The next step is to apply such a battery over a wide array of the typical citizen's life interests in order to attempt to correlate the grouping and structuring of action-interests.

DYNAMIC STRUCTURE FACTORS

Suppose a battery of half a dozen objective subtests to give a single intensity-of-interest score, applied to about 300 normal subjects, is made for each of about 50 attitudes and interest areas. The 50 widely sampled attitudes, each measured by a score on the total battery, are then correlated. Through factor analysis one then has the basis for discovering empirically the way in which interests are commonly interrelated in our culture. The factor analysis of such matrices has yielded about 20 distinct factors, which we shall call "dynamic structure factors" to differentiate them from the motivational component factors just described. The reader will recall that the motivational component factors are *groupings within measurement devices*, which hold over *all* areas of interest, whereas the dynamic structure factors are statements about the way in which our interests fall into some functional unities.

The main result of the dynamic calculus research, as applied to dynamic structure factors, has been the finding that interest factors are essentially biological drives on the one hand and sentiments or aggregates of interests acquired by education about certain objects and institutions on the other. These two distinct kinds of dynamic structure factors must be taken into account in almost any area in which one works. One consequence of this work has been that the theorizing about the nature of drives in man is no longer on a speculative basis; it is now based on experimental verification by suitable calculation. This work appears to have verified the psychoanalytic rather than the biological position that there are two distinct sexual needs, which Freud described: One, which is directed toward object love, is mainly heterosexual in character; the other is narcissistic in character.

On the other hand, this research has not supported the list of drives hypothesized by Murray. In actual fact, among the schemas adopted in various historically important writings, McDougall's analysis is closest to the experimentally based structures. In particular, it disagrees with the Freudian reduction of all drives to merely two or three instincts. It may be that libido, thanatos, etc., will yet appear as patterns at a higher order of factor analysis, but initially we certainly get no less than nine or ten drives —including the two sex drives mentioned above, fear, gregariousness, curiosity, parental protective behavior, self-assertiveness, pugnacity—and a picture that is more closely akin to what the ethologists have observed in the primates. To avoid confusion with instincts, these new, empirical patterns have been called ergs, and the measures that have subsequently been set up for them in terms of the objective motivational devices have been called measures of ergic tension level.

In terms of the mathematical model, these findings can be brought into exactly the same framework as the general personality source traits. Thus, a particular attitude-interest—that is, a strength of interest as evidenced by responding with a particular course of action in a particular situation, such as "I want so much to go out with X"— can be translated into the specification form as before, namely

$$I_j = b_{j1}E_1 + \cdots + b_{jk}E_k + b_{jm1}M_1 + \cdots + b_{jmp}M_p$$

where I is strength of interest in course of action j; E_1 to E_k are strengths on k ergs; M_1 to M_p are scores on p sentiments; and the b's are the usual appropriate behavioral indices, found by correlation, which express the involvement of the drive in the action, etc.

It will be seen that the factoring of objective dynamic measures to reveal these b values amounts to a quantitative psychoanalysis. By this method we are able to say how much, though still in terms of common traits of *all* people, a given interest derives from certain ergic roots. Some interesting findings have resulted in this field, and, again, several of them confirm psychoanalytic positions. For example, interest in smoking is found to be loaded in sex interest, fitting the oral erotic explanation. Some new insights into the nature of drives (ergs) have also emerged, in that a fair number of aggressive attitudes are found to be more loaded by the fear drive than by a pugnacity or sadistic erg as such.

Clinical research with these instruments—the factored MAT, etc.—and theory construction have only just begun. As indicated above, ergs and sentiments, including self-sentiment, can be measured, and equations can be stated in two distinct forms—by the integrated component strength and the unintegrated component strength—and there are many indications that differences in these will have special significance for understanding the dynamic make-up of the individual, notably in regard to conflict.

Conflict

One of the most important propositions arising from the above theorems is that conflict over a given course of action should be recognizable by the coexistence of positive and negative signs in the specification equation. For example, in equation 4, below, the negative behavior of indices of E_2 and E_4 show that, to follow the interest I_j, one must lose satisfactions on E_2 and E_4, though gaining on E_1 and E_3.

$$I_j = .4E_1 - .3E_2 + .5E_3 - .4E_4 \tag{4}$$
$$I_k = .4E_1 + .2E_2 + .3E_3 - .1E_4 \tag{5}$$

Furthermore, the model supposes that the severity of conflict is measurable, in theory, by the magnitude of the amount of canceled (negative) behavioral index variance relative to the total magnitude loading. Thus, in equation 4, there would be decidedly more conflict than in equation 5, indicating that the interest in equation 4 is an interest that, for most people, involves conflict, whereas the other has presumably developed in a less conflictful atmosphere and situation. The second equation offers .9(+) to .1(−), whereas the first equation offers only .9(+) to .7(−), a balance of satisfaction of +.8 versus +.2.

It would also follow from this theory that, if we took a broad, representative array of the typical individual's total life interest, determined the amount of conflict in each, and then added the scores for the whole field of self-expression, an individual who showed a high conflict score would be expected to be in a more frustrated and conflictful psychiatric state. In practice, to check this by experimentally determining the values for such a calculation is costly because the behavioral indices must be determined by a separate experiment on each individual. It requires the use of the factor analytic method called P technique, described above. That is, it is necessary to do a factor analysis of the single individual by scoring him on a wide array of interests each day for perhaps 100 days and then correlating the changes in these interests over time and identifying the factors that define the influences behind the day-to-day variation of symptoms. Here, again, it will be observed that, in principle, the multivariate experimentalist is doing something very similar to what the clinician does. The two main differences between them are that the experimenter actually *measures* the changing strength of the symptoms from day-to-day and *calculates* covariation to see what is connected with what instead of forming his judgments about connections on the basis of chance observation and mere intuition. Yet the multivariate experimentalist has the same goal as the clinician who tries to establish interconnections by observing the covariation of symptoms with the impact of daily events and the clinical interaction of psychiatrist and patient.

A few years ago, J. Williams undertook the monumental task of doing factor analyses on as many as a dozen subjects, each measured daily over months. Six of the subjects were patients in a mental hospital; the remaining six were normal controls. The results of this research clearly supported the theory. The behavioral indices derived from the specification equations for the psychotics indicated a much higher level of internal conflict—disagreement of algebraic sign— than did those for the normals. Promising as this theoretical advance is, it may be several years before the methods just described on which it is based can be applied to everyday clinical practice.

Fortunately, the demand for extensive calculation has now been overcome by the computer, so that it would not be impossible for a psychiatrist to hand his measurements to a technician, who could then translate the dynamic structure of an individual patient into quantitative form within the hour. The difficulty lies in collecting the data; it has not proved possible statistically to get clear results after less than about 100 days of repeated measurement. This is a lot of time to devote to one patient, but perhaps before long we can hope that a short-cut will be found. The advantage of P technique and its associated diagnostic methods lies not only in the objectivity of the findings and in the fact that it provides an index of total conflict in the way just indicated but also in its ability to locate conflict by measures of severity of conflict in particular areas. Certain valid objections can be anticipated at this point. Obviously, it is not enough for the psychiatrist on the basis of classical psychoanalysis, but not behavior therapy, to identify clearly the areas of conflict. The patient must also achieve insight and awareness of his conflicts and their origins. But if the therapist can from an early stage in treatment see more exactly where the tensions lie, surely this will be a great aid to him in bringing the patient to the point of achieving such awareness by the best chosen routes.

Let us summarize briefly the potential advantages of the dynamic calculus theory and measurement. First, they equip the psychiatrist with a set of objective measurements in a field where the psychologist and psychometrist previously had little but loose, projective devices to offer. Second and more important, they offer a theoretical foundation for calculations based on these measurements to guide diagnostic and therapeutic decisions. In general, the dynamic calculus concepts do not differ radically from those that have been presented in a variety of psychiatric theories. That is, they describe a series of drives (redefined with the special properties of ergs), a series of acquired dynamic structures (such as sentiment with regard to parents, to occupation, and, above all, to self), notions of conflict, and integrated attitudes. What is new in dynamic calculus is the possibility it provides for measurement of the properties and the existence of formulas for calculation and prediction in conformity with these concepts. An interesting difference from the traditional psychoanalytic conceptualization appears at certain points, notably in the discovery of two structures regulating morals and manners—the superego and self-sentiment—instead of just the superego. This inference is supported by the fact that the self-sentiment structure is elicited both through the medium of the questionnaire ("Q_3") and through the medium of objective measures of motivation in the MAT. Similarly, these independent instrumentalities agree on the superego factor ("G" in the 16 P.F. Test).

Third, the findings derived from application of the dynamic calculus theory leave us less in doubt about the number and nature of ergs (constitutional drives). Typically, the dynamic specification equations would also take into account about eight or nine sentiment structures, but it would give predominant weight to self-sentiment and to the superego among these learned structures. Measurement of ergic tension levels over time enables the psychiatrist to evaluate the patient's progress in terms of whether there is a building-up or reduction of tension levels and drives, and the same instruments throw light on development in dynamic structures. At present, the MAT actually measures ten factors—five ergs and five sentiments. It confines itself to these factors because it is unlikely that clinicians will be prepared to handle a more complex predictive system than ten variables initially. While the clinical usefulness of these is being explored, research should continue to focus on the remaining ergs and drives to improve the validity of their measurement.

Space limitations preclude a detailed presentation of the advantages of the dynamic calculus theory. The psychiatrist who is interested in exploring the full possibilities of this theoretical system is referred to the contributions by Bischof, Madsen, and Lindzey. In brief, the theory involves the concept of a dynamic lattice, which is a map of the way in which interests within the individual become subordinate to ultimate ergic goals through intermediate subgoals. Factor analysis is only one way of unraveling the structure of this lattice; however it is done, one cannot lose sight of the fact that it is really this lattice that the clinician seeks to understand as he attempts to bring about the individual's readjustment in terms of those interests and goals that will permit greater satisfaction. Using the model of a lattice enables the psychometrist to avail himself of some of the mathematical treatments applied by electricians to understanding complex electrical circuits as well as certain propositions in information theory. Another important adjunct of the dynamic calculus is the concept of a series of dynamic crossroads at which decisions are made in a necessary, typical sequence. These possibilities are discussed in further detail in the auxiliary reading references cited above.

ADDITIONS TO THE TRAIT MODEL: MEASUREMENT OF TEMPORARY STATES AND ROLE EFFECTS

The theoretical developments that have resulted from the use of correlational methods to locate functional unities in behavior have succeeded to the degree that experiments have continued to replicate about 20 factors in the general area of personality and some 10 to 15 in the motivational area, as discussed above. The ultimate aim of research, of course, is to clarify the individual nature of these factors by relation of them to specific criteria, by plots of the typical life course, by nature-nurture investigations, and by exploration of physiological relationships. However, some 20 years of basic research and much debate and refinement of methods with existing resources have been necessary before we reached the point where instruments could be given to the clinician. Consequently, this last phase in which, ideally, hypotheses would be developed about the nature of the factors according to various clinical criteria has been belated. Indeed, even while some armchair theorists continue to manufacture alleged unitary traits or concept and describe their predictive importance before they have even been confirmed as patterns, we have the spectacle of a dozen or more well-confirmed and measured factor patterns waiting to be employed and enriched in explanation.

Origins of factor patterns. Since it has become increasingly evident that the desire to interpret these confirmed, constantly reappearing unitary factor patterns is gathering momentum, we should inquire first about the general types of influence that can be expected to produce them. It is clear from the earlier description of schizothyme temperament, ego strength, ergs, and sentiments that some appreciable fraction can be considered to correspond to genetic endowments, probably with associated physiological variables, and that the pattern of behavior emanates from a gene or genes. For example, it would certainly seem from genetic research that the "H" factor (parmia—a toughness associated with predominance of the parasympathetic over the sympathetic reactivity) in the 16 P.F. Test can be so classified and possibly the "A" factor (the schizothyme temperament) as well. In both instances this interpretation is supported by physiological associations and the fact that they have high nature-nurture ratios, examined in studies of twins. Conceivably, we might look to a temperamental mechanism—such as autonomic, sympathetic high responsiveness as apparently shown in the threctic ("H —") pole of the "H" factor—for several such factors.

On the other hand, it is equally clear from the same initial nature-nurture studies that environmental influences must be largely responsible for other source trait patterns. Consequently, in these, the theorist will look to the family atmosphere, to traumatic experiences, and to associations with particular social institutions, such as school and church, as sources. Here we are presumably dealing with a set of habits laid down by systematic learning experience that appear in the same mold for everyone because of some standard social institution but to different degrees of intensity.

Like some RNA template, it fashions the trait to much the same form in the human molecules exposed to it. To appear as a factor, however, it is necessary that people be exposed to the same experiences and yet adopt the pattern to different degrees. Thus, although the factor pattern we are dealing with in these cases may not correspond to some presently active force but rather to a deposit of learned habit skills representing a force once active, the pattern is still worth scoring as a unitary entity, for it remains descriptively and predictively useful to score all people on the degrees to which they possess it. A well-known example of this is what is called the crystallized general ability factor, "G_c," which represents the extent to which intelligence has been channeled into scholastic work and skills and which enables us to define and measure the individual's cognitive apparatus by the traditional intelligence test in terms of the typical pattern of verbal and numerical skills that the bright child picks up in our school system.

These explanations do not exhaust the possible theoretical bases for source traits; other more subtle possible origins of discovered factor patterns are discussed elsewhere.

MEASUREMENT OF STATES

So far, we have assumed that factor patterns represent relatively permanent traits, but at this point we need to ask whether a particular pattern might represent some transient state, such as a state of excitement or of depression, or an adrenergic response. At the outset, the formal mathematic-statistical models included process. We are now asking how a process, a changing state, would appear in mathematical analysis. Note that, when we measure individual differences by testing 300 people at a given hour, we normally catch everyone in a transient mood. It is as if we took a snapshot that captured the deviations of that instant. Consequently, some factors thought to be traits when we subject them to individual factor analysis may actually be frozen states.

We are confronted here with complex statistical issues. The usual factor analytic search for structure across, say, 300 people is called R technique. Earlier, a different factoring, P technique, was described, where one measures one person across, say, 300 occasions. There is also a differential R technique (dR), in which the 300 people are measured once today and once next week, and their change scores on all the variables are then correlated. From such P and dR technique experiments, we are able to discover how many dimensions of change are necessary to account for the complex changes in emotional state that human beings experience. When this is done, some nine dimensions have been reasonably confirmed that represent state dimensions, such as anxiety, effort stress response, elation-depression, and general fatigue. Just as batteries can be set up for measuring traits, so collections of performance subtests, identified as highly loading such factors, can be built up into batteries for measuring the level at which an individual stands on a particular state at a given moment.

A complete description of an individual at a point in time requires not only scores on a set of coordinates corresponding to the common traits but also a position in the hyperspace defined by the coordinates for these nine states and others yet to be discovered. The measurement of relatively pure states that, when combined, describe the complex state of an individual at a given moment has considerable importance for both psychiatric therapy and pharmacology. Previously in ataractic drug research, the beautiful precision on the side of the chemist has been matched by a rather vague evaluation on the part of psychologists with regard to the nature and measurements of the states induced by drugs. Within this new framework, it becomes possible to assign to any drug administered in standard dose an exact vector describing in terms of states the unique combination of changes that it may produce. It also becomes possible for the therapist to use a state measurement, for example, on anxiety, in much the same way the internist uses a clinical thermometer—to study the patient's changing adaptations in response to various therapeutic measures.

Despite the fact that they are still in a psychometrically rudimentary form, some interesting theories have already begun to emerge in regard to these measures of states. For example, it has been pointed out that the newly acquired ability to differentiate the effort stress state dimension from the anxiety dimension offers a different interpretation of serum cholesterol changes. Scheier's simultaneous measurement of distinct effort stress and anxiety factors has also had some interesting results. For example, the anxiety level of students in relation to examinations was found to be higher two or three weeks before the examination, and it actually seems to fall during the examination itself, but the effort stress reaction rises as anxiety falls. Studies by Pawlik and others have related these behavioral state measurements to EEG records. And the interesting finding has emerged from other investigations that serum cholinesterase rises in an anxiety state. Work has also begun on motivational states in terms of particular ergic tensions, as measured by the MAT. This is only in its infancy, though it obviously has considerable potential importance for clinical work.

Role modulation. From the standpoint of a really adequate personality theory, consideration of trait factors alone is obviously not enough. One must consider the transforming effect of the situation as well as the inherent nature of the individual's traits. In the general class of transient states presently under consideration, it is particularly important to include those special transients that we call roles. How are we to know when a given piece of behavior is due to the essential personality and when it reflects an adopted role? The theoretical model we are discussing handles this by conceiving of role as a dynamic structure in the individual that is provoked only by a particular set of stimuli which are usually related to social situations. In all probability, such dynamic factors would be organized as facets of the self-sentiment, but just how this organization comes about has not been properly investigated experimentally. The theoretical possibility also exists that the role behaviors not only arise from the single factor but also evolve from some modulation it produces in certain personality factors. To illustrate, a policeman out of uniform might respond to a traffic violation according to his personality factor profile. But in uniform, under the same circumstances, a whole set of new habits appears, causing a response to an over-all situation rather than the original focal situation, which, in turn, might lead to an expression of personality that differs from the ordinary specification equation.

Whether we adopt the theory that a simple new role factor intrudes or move to this slightly more complex theory, which has been called the theory of personality modulators, we adopt a model that accounts for both temporary role action and the reaction of the states we discussed above. Although it is a technical point, it should be mentioned that role modulator action would be likely to appear as a second-order factor among personality factors, one that will appear only in the analysis of certain types of situations.

It is still too early to judge the extent to which this temporary modulation device in personality theory will prove of practical importance to the psychiatrist. However, the recent factoring of psychiatrist and patient interaction by Rickels points to the existence of a quite substantial role reaction factor that simultaneously affects both patient and psychiatrist in the interview situation. According to this evidence, certain patients adopt the patient role more completely than others, and their dependent, demanding behavior evokes a more concerned reaction from the therapist. This, in turn, affects his rating of the severity of the patient's symptoms to the extent, as shown by our results, that about as much statistical variance in the ratings of anxiety arises from the intensity of this role factor as from the actual patient differences in anxiety and symptom level, as revealed by objective tests. It would seem, therefore, that a personality theory without any model and mode of measurement of temporary states and situation-provoked role effects—that is, one based only on traits—is unnecessarily crude. At a time when chemotherapy is coming into its own, these additional techniques for locating and measuring state components have their most obvious application in giving precision to our understanding of the psychological effects of pharmacological agents.

PERSONALITY LEARNING THEORY AND PSYCHOTHERAPY

Personality learning theory has been distinguished from learning theory because the latter has been based almost entirely on atomistic bits of reflex behavior. Eventually, both approaches must merge in a general learning theory, but it would be anything but scientific to assume that reflexology can explain the structural personality phenomena that reflexologists have never studied. Psychoanalysis, to name just one body of opinion, has rejected the claims of reflexology to explain its complex phenomena. From the viewpoint of the intersection theory of personality, a noncommittal attitude toward present reflexological learning theory is most appropriate. Meanwhile, intersection theory, working with its well-defined and measurable personality and motivation traits, takes the experimental position that personality learning theory must explain changes that have been accurately measured according to these trait dimensions. Two important new models have been introduced for the formulation of laws in these areas: adjustment path analysis and the matrix treatment of multidimensional learning.

Adjustment path analysis. The aim of adjustment path analysis and analytical adjustment theory is to set up a standard paradigm to analyze the possible outcomes from a basic, universal psychological situation. This most elementary situation is one that begins with stimulation of a particular drive in a particular situation. Cattell and Scheier have described this elsewhere in some detail in connection with neurosis; however, such adjustment path analysis theory could apply to any kind of dynamic learning. The paradigm is one of a series of choice points, at each of which two or more standard possibilities exist. It is not possible to describe these series of dynamic crossroads in detail, but one can easily see that they will include such outcomes as whether or not the drive is frustrated, whether or not the barrier is attacked, and whether or not the barrier is overcome. A decision at one point leads to other possible choice points. Thus, in the event that the barrier is not overcome, the alternative is suppression or repression or continual nonadjustive behavior. From these possible adjustment paths only a certain combination of choices will eventually terminate in the neurotic end path.

Granted this adjustment path theory assigns certain consequences to certain experimental adjustments, one can proceed to an adjustment analysis theory, in which assumptions are made regarding the effects of particular choices on the dynamic and general personality structure. Indeed the whole aim of the analytical adjustment theory, which includes these and other concepts, is to provide a framework within which personality learning, particularly the personality learning that has to do with the acquisition of a neurosis and its resolution by relearning, can be brought to experimental study through quantification.

Thus, this adjustment theory provides a framework of analysis and matrix calculations (described below) that is intended to furnish guidance in research designs and to permit statistical analysis of life record data that can serve as the basis for the formulation of laws about personality factor change in learning. Incidentally, it does not merely assume that exposure to a frustrating, traumatic, repressive, anxiety-provoking, or similar unfavorable experience influences personality; it maintains that personality may exert a reciprocal influence over the choice of such experiences at the various chiasms or dynamic crossroads that the organism encounters in the adjustment process. Admittedly, analytical adjustment theory is only a model that expresses in final form the mass of clinical and other evidence that has been accumulated as to the general manner in which personality and situation interact. But if, as hoped, it should prove an effective model in the gathering and reduction of quantitative data, it will further enhance development of personality theories based on functionally unitary traits.

Let us examine more closely the way in which personality learning change in these adjustment paths can best be considered. According to the model described above, analytical adjustment theory arises from the conceptual analysis of personality into functionally unitary traits and considers that they interact with the environment. Unlike the reflexological approach, it assumes that any experience produces a multiple change in personality, potentially affecting any and all of the scores in the personality profile. This brings us to consideration of the aspect of analytical adjustment theory that is called path transformation theory and that introduces, by means of matrix algebra, the concept that the effect of any path in the adjustment path diagram provides a certain total pattern of changes in the personality factor profile.

The contributions to such volumes as the *Kentucky Symposium on Learning Theory and Personality Theory* illustrate only too clearly that attempts by psychologists over the past twenty years to unify learning theory and personality theory have been far from successful, especially from the standpoint of the clinician. The central but perhaps insufficiently appreciated reason for this is that most learning theorists have conceived of learning purely in terms of a reflexological and atomistic model. By this we mean reflexology in the classical, Pavlovian sense, not in the sense of punishment and reward for various drive expressions. Some of the latter behavior, by a feat of semantic acrobatics, has been subsumed by some reflexologists under reflexology.

There are perhaps two major reasons why reflexological learning theory has also been justifiably rejected in principle by clinicians. First, it deals with changes in highly specific bits of behavioral reflexes, whereas the clinician defines his task as the handling of major dimensions of total personality. Second, the type of bivariate, manipulative experiment that learning theory employs most frequently has proved to be inept in relation to human learning, primarily because, as pointed out earlier, human beings cannot be subjected to sufficiently strong manipulative stimulus situations in the laboratory to bring about noticeable changes in personality. Only life itself provides these situations, and only the clinician has an opportunity to watch their action. Consequently, even when laboratory work is directed to important aspects of personality, rather than the eye-blink reflex or something of that kind, it has failed conspicuously to produce significant laws, and the clinician may rightly suspect whether entirely new principles will emerge from adjustment path analysis research.

Here, once more, the technical potency of the multivariate method is revealed. It can hope to elicit from actual life behavior, without manipulation, evidence of the causal sequences through which personality is affected by environmental learning. To date, this goal has only produced the statement of a theoretical position—namely, that new and different learning principles remain to be unearthed—for, as yet, virtually no concrete experimental evidence has emerged from this proposal.

Meanwhile, an attempt has been under way for some time to apply the more obvious reflexological principles to relearning in the clinical situation under the name of behavior therapy. The work of such leaders as Wolpe, Rachman, and Costello has resulted in an impressive array of evidence of removal of symptoms by reflexological extinction methods. As yet, there is no clear indication of what this does to the measurements of functionally unitary traits as such. Provided this approach utilizes a broader concept of learning theory than that stated above, it may either proceed to greater successes or at least provide clear evidence as to the areas in which it is not succeeding. Definite evidence of that kind would be an advance over any therapeutic technique currently available. It will almost certainly be open to criticism, however, if it is used merely—as it is now being used, for the most part—to remove some specific symptom, such as a phobia to a particular object. Most clinicians are thoroughly familiar with the phenomenon of one symptom disappearing and another appearing when there has not been a fundamental change in personality structure. The implication of the theoretical position on personality that runs through this chapter is that whole source traits must be modified if therapy is to be considered successful. This does not rule out the possibility that the amelioration of a weak ego structure ("C" factor), for example, or the reduction of the general ergic tension level ("Q_4" factor) may be affected by the cumulative effect of a number of highly specific readjustments. But, certainly, any general personality learning theory must operate on the basis of the measurement of source traits as a whole.

MATRIX ANALYSIS OF MULTIDIMENSIONAL LEARNING

The matrix analysis that is needed for research expresses the central feature of the intersection theory in that it brings together personality and situation, each in its multiple dimensionality. On the one hand, we have the natural complexity of life experiences over an interval of time, analyzed according to an adjustment process diagram. On the other, we have the equally complex and composite personality change over the period of interaction with the situation, expressed and measured as change in profile on the measured source traits. From these two matrices (see Figure 2), the possibility exists of arriving by statistical analysis at an understanding of the specific effects that particular situations have on particular source traits. Although it is impossible to describe this in detail in this brief space, its general principle will be clear to anyone familiar with matrix algebra from Figure 2.

CHIEF MATRIX CALCULATIONS IN ANALYTICAL ADJUSTMENT

1. Calculation of Expected Personality Profiles from Record of Path Frequencies (Experience)

Formula (i) C = AB, which can be set out in detail as follows:

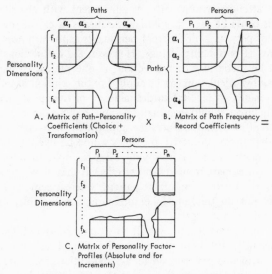

A. Matrix of Path–Personality Coefficients (Choice + Transformation)

X

B. Matrix of Path Frequency Record Coefficients

=

C. Matrix of Personality Factor-Profiles (Absolute and for Increments)

2. Calculation of Path Frequency Experience from Personality Profile

Formula (ii) $B = A^{-1}D^{-1}C$, where $D = AA'$

3. Calculation of General Path–Personality Coefficients from Experimental Data

Formula (iii) $A = CB'D^{-1}$, where $D = BB'$

FIGURE 2. *Chief matrix calculations in analytical adjustment theory.* (*From Cattell, R. B., and Scheier, I. H.* The Meaning and Measurement of Neuroticism and Anxiety, *p. 341. Ronald Press, New York, 1961.*)

Let us suppose that there exists, as shown in the figure, a matrix that relates the fate of a particular choice to the change in a particular personality factor. In addition, we have a record of the person's historical associations with such choices. The causal direction, as stated above, is presumed to be both from personality to choice and from choice to personality. But the two together can, if necessary, be considered simply as an empirical association. The second matrix in Figure 2, which is called a path frequency matrix, aims to express by numbers in the cells the frequency with which particular subjects—p_1, p_2, etc.—involved in the research have followed and repeated certain paths of attempted adjustment.

From these two matrices we can, by multiplication, produce a third, as shown, which will indicate the extent to which a certain personality profile is likely to be associated with particular persons in view of this history.

On the whole, this mathematical expression of analytical adjustment theory is nothing more than a means of recognizing that the experience of a particular path of adjustment will simultaneously affect several personality dimensions in characteristic ways and that different persons will characteristically attempt certain paths of adjustment with characteristic frequency. This could be used, primarily, as a means of calculating what the associations of persons with different personality paths will eventually produce in terms of personality change. However, the calculations and inferences could be made in either direction. If one prefers to make certain assumptions, this calculation can be applied to the solution of unknowns in original personality to facilitate a desirable set of therapeutic experiences. Thus, the therapist should eventually be able to consider therapy or various alternatives in therapy as possible adjustment paths and to work out the effects that these alternative therapies would be likely to have on the average personality or a given personality. For example, there is some indication that, quite apart from any other effect it may have, group therapy may increase the extroversion of the patient, whereas some other mode of therapy may not do this, and chemotherapy, for example, may reduce anxiety and raise ego strength.

Whereas, in relation to the over-all structural theory outlined here, objective personality measurement and its clinical applications constitute an immediately available practical aid today, applications from the analysis of personality learning are entirely a matter for the future. No experimental use of the design yet exists; consequently, certain technical problems remain to be solved. But it is described as a development that is consistent with the theoretical position, one that would give new power to therapeutic procedure and planning if implemented.

FUNCTIONAL TESTING IN CLINICAL DIAGNOSIS AND THERAPY

There is a widespread illusion on the part of both psychiatrist and psychometrist that the increasingly liberal use of psychological testing by psychiatrists in this generation implies a real use of true quantitatively based theory as here described. Useful though psychological testing practices have been, their application has often had a nonorganic and even patchwork quality. This has been due to the fact that psychiatric theory itself originates from quite different sources from that of test theory. Consequently, tests have tended to be extraneous gadgets, such as special-purpose tests like Rorschach, subordinated as diagnostic instruments to concepts that originated within a different frame of reference.

One can now hope that this relatively ineffective, scientifically unsatisfactory compromise is likely to change radically in the near future as psychologists trained in functional testing, related to personality theory from experimental origins, become more active in clinical practice and theory. Although much of the new, quantitative theory has turned out to be consistent with earlier clinical impressions, which have thereby been extended and made more precise, it has also produced radically new theory and created a demand that theory and measurement now enter into a truly fruitful relationship.

To get the most out of these possibilities, perhaps the average psychiatrist needs to get over the inferiority complex—or, at least, the diffidence—with which he has often approached the technical aspects of psychological testing. In fact, he has no need to apply advanced statistics, such as factor analysis; he must only apply a logical principle that is close to his own, the concept of a unitary trait. He needs only the simple algebraic formula that sees traits as acting in additive fashion and linearly in the specification equation. Similarly, although he uses his knowledge of chemistry to get a general idea of the composition of pharmacological products he prescribes, he would be quite unprepared to understand the steps of synthesis or the abstruse issues of stereochemistry.

Effective use of the proposed measures of anxiety, ego strength, surgency, intelligence, and schizothymia does, however, require that he comprehend the logical properties of the source trait concepts with which he is dealing and the theoretical setting in which they are embedded. That is, he needs to understand that these source traits derive from factors obtained by correlational methods; that they have a demonstrated functional independence; that they can be considered to interact additively, at least at first approximation, according to weightings that are decided by the situation in which the action takes place. It would help, too, if he had some idea of second-order factors as influences that modify first-order factors and if he would undertake to become as thoroughly familiar with the nature of 20 or so factors, their typical nature-nurture origins and life history, as he is with anatomy or the action of the principal organs in the body.

It has been asserted for some years, partly on the basis of Meehl's interesting work, that six independent bits of information constitute about as much as the human mind can effectively handle in forming a composite judgment. This is supported in the clinical field by the fact that there is no appreciable increase in predictive power when more than six bits are added to the clinician's basic information.

However, as will be pointed out below in connection with the possible harnessing of computers to clinical work, this conclusion that information on more than six factors is lost must depend on the way in which clinical work is conducted. Certainly, in terms of how many trait descriptions can be absorbed in psychiatric education, no one is going to make the absurd claim that instruction has to be restricted to half a dozen concepts. Still less, one hopes, will convenience and acceptability be allowed to dictate that nature be simplified to the trinity id, ego, and superego, which is for some the main attraction of Freudian theory. In factor analysis, too, there have been oversimplifications of the real personality factor position that we have tried to describe in a more complete way here. If biochemists can keep 21 amino acids in mind and chemists can remember more than 100 elements, it is surely no harsh dictum that the psychiatrist should be well aware of the properties of some 20 general personality factors and perhaps an equal number of factors in the motivational structure field. He may not be able to keep the scores on all of them aptly in mind in making a particular diagnosis, but certainly his psychological theory should include them all. As mentioned earlier, his quantitative and diagnostic use of them can be augmented and assisted by computational aids in ways we can now discuss, beginning with the choice of tests themselves.

The choice of psychological tests is difficult for the psychologist and perhaps even more difficult for the psychiatrist, but their bewildering array is brought into some order by the standard Buros' *Mental Measurements Yearbook*, which, like a pharmacopoeia, condenses evaluative research evidence. Actually, the number of tests based on replicated oblique simple structure factor analyses is perhaps 5 per cent of the published total, and if this is one's criterion, the choice is much simplified. However, as pointed out above, in making a measurement of a factor, one has a choice of several media. For example, the superego strength factor ("G" in the 16 P.F. Test) can be measured by questionnaire, by objective motivation measure (in the MAT), or by objective tests (including projective, stylistic, and many other varieties of performance) in the O-A. The psychiatrist can also take his choice as to whether he will operate at the primary factor level, as in the factors in the 16 P.F. tests and the HSPQ, or at the second-order factor level, using such concepts as anxiety, extroversion, and cortertia. Secondaries can be derived from primary scores by suitable weighting. The second orders enable one to use fewer scores but give rougher results, and for most purposes, especially with clerical or computer aid, primaries are better.

In using factors that psychologists have currently been able to incorporate in their tests, the psychiatrist may well ask whether the methods of investigation have been such as to *guarantee* an inclusion of most dimensions of theoretical and practical importance. The basing of the first sweep on the personality sphere concept has done much to ensure this, but undoubtedly some factors are not yet included in available tests. Research now under way in this area of personality theory is almost certain to add a few new testable dimensions. For example, preliminary work suggests that there are no fewer than eight factors in the area of depression, and a pathology supplement of several new scales for psychiatric deviations is consequently now being added to the 16 P.F. Test to expand its clinical coverage. As pointed out above, there is also some value in measuring certain surface traits (symptom strengths) directly, as by the MMPI, while getting at the general personality source traits by such tests as those just discussed through psychometric depth analysis. There is, of course, room for improvement in all these tests, but the techniques for progressively moving to more valid factor measurements have been mastered to an increasing extent.

Granted a certain adequacy in source trait measurements themselves, the practice of clinical measurements will also require procedural revisions. The psychiatrist must expect that the time allotted to testing will have to increase. At the present stage of psychometric research, it is simply not possible to cover 20 or 30 personality factor measurements in an hour or two. Even so, the efficiency will be much higher; for testing, as it is traditionally carried out in mental hospitals and clinics today, is definitely wasteful in terms of the number of demonstrably independent pieces of information it yields per hour. Typically, the psychologist spends as much as an hour in getting just one factor, intelligence, and then spends only 5 minutes on some two or three other personality factors, each of greater clinical importance than intelligence. Whereas with tests of the prefactor era he gets 2 dimensions in, say, 80 minutes, the 16 P.F. Test. which takes about 40 minutes, gives a score on no fewer than 16 dimensions, including intelligence. Of course, one could not recommend such an extreme condensation as measuring a factor in 2½ minutes by about 12 items. Indeed, it is strongly recommended that no less than 5, and preferably no less than 10 minutes be given to one factor. The compromise presented by the former would result in the practice of using the 80 minutes to give *both* A and B forms of the 16 P.F. test; the latter would enable the use of the full quota of forms (A, B, C, and D), thus giving about 8 to 10 minutes to each of 16 factors, including intelligence. No adequate reliabilities can be expected unless several equivalent forms are used, for the period of testing is simply too short. Furthermore, there is considerable unnecessary duplication of areas in traditional practices with unfactored tests, whereas any kind of factoring approach, even though it may not be oriented to functional unitary traits, does at least guarantee that the various dimensions are given approximately equal representation in any battery.

USE OF THE COMPUTER IN CLINICAL PRACTICE

Not infrequently, psychiatrists have been known to complain that training in physical medicine has done them a disservice because it has set up the model of a definite disease, whereas the pathological phenomena with which they are concerned usually do not fit this model and, instead, correspond to a tangle in the functioning of traits and processes that are, in themselves, as normal as those in any normal individual. There may be instances where a disease process, as abnormal and specific as some germ disease, may play a role in psychiatric illness, as in the organic psychoses. But over the past twenty years, there has been a definite attempt on the part of psychiatrists to emancipate themselves from the incubus of the sickness prejudice. They have become disposed to question sharp-line disease categories drawn between normality and pathology and even to regard the behaviors of the psychotic as essentially normal processes that are merely exaggerated and out of control and context. The whole of the intersection model and the dynamic calculus theory that forms part of it are in accord with this view of psychopathology as a problem of disequilibrium and loss of adjustment rather than one of the appearance of specifically malignant disease processes.

The factor analytic studies of mental hospital populations, as carried out by Dubin with Cattell some 20 years ago and with Tatro recently, showed quite early that essentially the same personality dimensions can be found in psychotic as in control groups, even though they stand at significantly different absolute levels of score. Theoretically, we would take the position that pathology is either an extreme deviation in particular source traits on a normal continuum or, probably with greater frequency, an extreme combination of malfunctioning source traits that are not so deviant individually. Empirical evidence that could give a decision on the latter has not been accumulated in sufficient quantity. However, one constantly sees suggested indications. For example, in the paranoiac it is not acute anxiety alone or rigidity alone but a particular combination of acute anxiety with acute addiction to the reduction of tension by the projective mechanism that seems to characterize this profile. Also, although the source traits of anxiety (U.I. 24) and regression (U.I. 23) are uncorrelated in the general population, they show specific correlation in neurotics. That is, there is not only the repeated evidence, notably from the work of Eysenck and the Maudsley group but also from Rickels at Philadelphia and from Cattell's laboratory, that neurotics are highly deviant on each of these factors; there is also evidence that anxiety and regression become highly correlated. Surely, the most promising indication for these findings is that some spiral of interaction between them is setting in. Still another empirical indication that we are dealing with a functional type of disorder rather than the appearance of a disease due to some foreign agent lies in the evidence, as yet sparse but significant, that under therapy the deviant measurements retreat toward normal values. If the process is reversible in this way and if grades of deviation can be found in our population, surely we are dealing with something best described as maladaptive or having to do with the economics of energy rather than with some qualitatively distinct disease entity.

If a theory properly consists of a model plus a set of laws about its operation, then the intersection therapy and the dynamic calculus concepts represent only the beginnings of a theory. It is true that the model is clear and that it fits the facts closely enough to permit a great deal of effective research to be done. For example, it has sufficed to produce experiments that reveal the nature of several source traits, and it has been demonstrated that their interactions fit reasonably closely to the additive model. But all this has occurred too recently for the measurement devices to have been very widely circulated among psychiatrists, so that only a brief early harvest from the use of the concepts and the measurements that arise from them is available as yet. Consequently, the body of laws about the way in which these factors behave is quite fragmentary. Compared with many other theories discussed in this book, the present structure, therefore, inevitably lacks several necessary floors. To see the theory in its proper perspective, one may, on the other hand, claim that its foundation is such as to admit in the long run a far higher and more effective architectonic growth than is possible from the nonexperimental and unquantitative theories. The latter is still pre-eminent in the field of psychiatry in terms of a sheer count of its adherents, but it is to be hoped that a progressive minority can appreciate what the radical difference of method here means in long-term promise. The architectonic growth believed possible will occur most readily if we can bring about the dissolution of the communication barriers between the psychological model theorist and statistician working with the computer in the backroom and the psychiatrist working with the patient in the clinic. The writings of such psychiatrists as Werry and Rickels and such psychologists as Cohen and Lorr do much to convey a sense of the gains possible from such communication. What the theoretical development most needs at the present moment is a clear grasp of the particular source trait concepts (temperamental and dynamic) by psychiatrists and an application of these concepts in relation to the rich clinical criteria to which they alone have ready access and in relation to which new intuitive leads for confirmatory research are needed.

Two important matters have found little or no space in this chapter: the blending of a scientific theory with psychiatric art and the specific aids that a quantitative theory can gain from the electronic computer. If little has been said about the art of psychiatry and if little space is given to illustration by individual cases here, it is because our primary purpose was to provide a highly condensed statement of a still tentative theoretical structure with very wide ramifications to be followed up. In the application of any theory, however precise and complete, there must, of course, ultimately be art and intuition. However, the theories described here are as different from the most common species of clinical theory in their scientific structure as they are in their suggestions for the art of application. Essentially, these developments imply that the psychiatrist might advantageously be using his art and intuition at a very different level from that of direct observation and interaction with the patient. Effective interaction at the human level with the patient is, of course, absolutely necessary. But the more developed model here presented means that the psychiatrist can be presented with an array of quantitative evidence of a hitherto unprecedented richness and precision and that he will need to develop his artistic judgment especially in inferring from this evidence what steps are to be taken in his immediate relation with the patient. He is being asked, so to speak, to stand off for a moment from immediate impressions about the patient and view his make-up and his environmental problem in the perspective of a complex quantitative model.

This will be seen by some as a threat and by others as a remarkable opportunity. The opportunity is inherent in the fact that, if the theories are truly quantitative theories, then they should admit of all kinds of actual computations helpful in the diagnostic and therapeutic action with individual patients. This fortunate conjunction of the scientific advent of quantitative theories with the social advent of electronic computers needs to be recognized and seized upon. Here we have an opportunity to inaugurate a very sensitive use of our theoretically required computations without involving the time and brain power of the psychiatrist in the more routine phases of it. We have been accustomed to an engineer needing mathematics and to a physician getting along without any at all. But as physical medicine and psychological medicine assume more and more the status of advanced sciences, they will necessarily require quantitative methods to be applied to the individual case for their most outstanding feats. Already this is becoming evident in the use of technicians' estimates on hormone concentrations, on basal metabolic rates, and in calculations in physical medicine in which the doctor either has some calculation carried out for him or makes a rough estimate as he proceeds. Since a human being has a more complicated organization than a bridge or an automobile engine, the psychiatrist of the future is likely to need to have more subtle calculations carried out for him than those carried out in engineering.

At a simple level, this impact of our theoretical position can be seen in the use of the specification equation above. It should be possible to store in a computer the weights reached by research for a considerable array of behavioral predictions and prognoses. Profiles can also be stored for an array of patterns needed in diagnosis. However, the psychiatrist may be in need of something more than a service in which the data is sent to the computer and comes back in tomorrow's mail. The psychiatrist is surely almost as much in need as the surgeon is of information and analyses fed back very swiftly. Practical decisions have to be made in therapy in the light of information appearing at the same session or test results made an hour or two before. Fortunately, the physicists have given their answer to this type of need in the Telstar satellite, which potentially is capable of instantly feeding back answers from a considerable bank of information to any location.

Probably, the practical use of such an information bank in computer calculations of diagnoses and dynamic probabilities is still one or two decades away. In recognizing this radical new direction as an important and likely one, we must also recognize that, as an organic outgrowth from quantitative personality theory, its effective development must depend on the shaping of theories and effectively predictive laws. What has been described in this chapter is only a clearing of the foundations, a statement of principles, and some fragmentary beginnings of the superstructure yet to be built. The computer technological development will follow easily enough. The more difficult task is to call psychiatrists and psychologists from their verbal theorizing to the quantitative methods that can give us this superstructure of behavioral science.

REFERENCES

Berg, I. A., and Pennington, L. A., editors. *An Introduction to Clinical Psychology*, ed. 3. Ronald Press, New York, 1966.

Buros, O. K., editor. *The Sixth Mental Measurements Yearbook*. Gryphon Press, Highland Park, N.J., 1966.

Cattell, R. B. P-technique, a new method of analyzing the structure of personal motivations. Trans. N. Y. Acad. Sci., Ser. II, 14: 29, 1951.

Cattell, R. B. *Personality and Motivation Structure and Measurement*. Harcourt, Brace and World, New York, 1957.

Cattell, R. B. *The Scientific Analysis of Personality*. Penguin Books, Baltimore, 1965.

Cattell, R. B., and Eber, H. J. *The Sixteen Personality Factor Questionnaire*, ed. 3. Institute for Personality and Ability Testing, Champaign, Ill., 1966.

Cattell, R. B., et al. The O-A (Objective-Analytic) Personality Factor Battery, ed. 2. Institute for Personality and Ability Testing, Champaign, Ill., 1961.

Cattell, R. B., and Scheier, I. H. The Meaning and Measurement of Neuroticism and Anxiety. Ronald Press, New York, 1961.

Cattell, R. B., Stice, G. F., and Kristy, N. F. A first approximation to nature-nurture ratios for eleven primary personality factors in objective tests. J. Abnorm. Soc. Psychol., 54: 143, 1957.

Cattell, R. B., and Tatro, D. F. The personality factors, objectively measured, which distinguish psychotics from normals. Behav. Res. Ther., 4: 39, 1966.

Cohen, J. The impact of multivariate research in clinical psychology. In Handbook of Multivariate Experimental Psychology, R. B. Cattell, editor. Rand McNally, Chicago, 1966.

Eysenck, H. J. The Dynamics of Anxiety and Hysteria. Routledge and Kegan Paul, London, 1957.

Eysenck, H. J. A rational system of diagnosis and therapy in mental illness. In Progress in Clinical Psychology, vol. 4. Grune & Stratton, New York, 1960.

Freud, S. A General Introduction to Psychoanalysis. Doubleday, New York, 1917.

Horn, J. L., Cattell, R. B., and Sweney, A. B. The Motivational Analysis Test (MAT). Institute of Personality and Ability Testing, Champaign, Ill., 1964.

Hundleby, J. D., Pawlik, K., and Cattell, R. B. Personality Factors in Objective Test Devices. R. R. Knapp, San Diego, 1965.

Kentucky Symposium on Learning Theory, Personality Theory and Clinical Research. Wiley, New York, 1954.

Kretschmer, E. Physique and Character, ed. 2. Routledge, London, 1936.

Lindzey, G. Assessment of Human Motives. Rinehart, New York, 1958.

Lorr, M., Rubenstein, E., and Jenkins, R. L. A factor analysis of personality ratings of outpatients in psychotherapy. J. Abnorm. Soc. Psychol., 48: 511, 1953.

McDougall, W. An Outline of Abnormal Psychology. Methuen, London, 1926.

Meehl, P. E. Clinical versus Statistical Prediction. University of Minnesota Press, Minneapolis, 1954.

Murray, H. A. Explorations in Personality. Oxford University Press, New York, 1938.

Pierson, G. R., and Kelly, R. F. Anxiety, extraversion, and personality idiosyncrasy in delinquency. J. Psychol., 56: 441, 1963.

Rickels, K., and Cattell, R. B. The clinical factor validity and trueness of the IPAT verbal and objective batteries for anxiety and regression. J. Clin. Psychol., 21: 257, 1965.

Scheier, I. H. The 8-Parallel Form Battery. Institute of Personality and Ability Testing, Champaign, Ill., 1962.

Sweney, A. B., and Cattell, R. B. Components measurable in manifestations of mental conflicts. J. Abnorm. Soc. Psychol., 68: 749, 1964.

Werry, J. S. Automation and Medicine: The View from a 19th Century Window. University of Illinois Press, Urbana, 1965.

CHAPTER SIXTEEN

Other Psychological Personality Theories

RAYMOND B. CATTELL, Ph.D., D.Sc., &

GERALD M. MEREDITH, Ph.D.

INTRODUCTION

THE AIM OF THIS CHAPTER is to provide an eclectic picture of personality theory derived from psychological theory by presenting a survey of all activities in the field. For obvious reasons, such an attempt to integrate so many different levels of methodological sophistication and types of approach can only be made at the sacrifice of internal consistency. Our guiding thread is one of historical narrative, and our common focus is on those activities and writings that are concerned with some aspect of personality theory.

Nevertheless, an attempt will be made to present a comprehensive, albeit only one, survey of personality theories derived from all sources as viewed from the standpoint of the discipline of psychology. No framework for such a wide comparative treatment would be equally suitable for all theories; however, the main categories for this discussion of personality include the concepts of personality structure, motivation (dynamics of action), developmental sequences, and environmental determinants (classification of environmental as opposed to constitutional forces).

The family resemblance to these various theories, with respect to the concepts within the categories delineated above, would not have been so evident fifty years ago. Furthermore, although it is possible to distinguish constitutional theories as postulated by Sheldon or sociological theories as formulated by Sarbin, it is no longer customary, nor is it actually possible, for a sociologist to deny completely the role of heredity; nor can a constitutional psychologist deny the importance of interpersonal expression or the relationship between personality and social institutions. Emphases differ, but the conceptual framework is becoming increasingly uniform.

HISTORICAL PERSPECTIVE

For the Greeks, a consanguineous relationship existed between man and nature. According to the philosopher Collingwood, a prominent view of nature held that earth, air, fire, and water (the Empedoclean elements) constituted the basic units of composition for all things. The commingling and the separation (syncrisis and diacrisis) of these irreducible elements, Hippocrates reasoned, produced different vital fluids (humors)—such as phlegm, blood, and black and yellow bile—which constituted the basic determinants of individual temperament and personality types. Thus, in Hippocrates' typology of the sanguine, melancholic, phlegmatic, and choleric personalities, a fusion of physics and psychology may be witnessed. The specific theory of temperament types sought a congruence between personality organization and distal determinants of the physical world.

Western man has continued to think in terms of types. However, although they permit an orderly view of the universe, typologies remove us from specific consideration of individual personality. Typologies may be simple, such as that of Hippocrates, or highly stylized, as seen in the Jungian system, which permutates the conscious-unconscious dimension with the attitudes of introversion-extroversion and the functions of thinking, feeling, sensing, and intuiting. In either case, the finer grains of individual differences are sacrificed for broader nomothetic description.

There is some indication of a countertrend in the contributions of Theophrastus, the founder of literary characterology. In *The Characters*, Theophrastus focused on human traits as they develop to give color and flavor to the life of the individual. The slightest nuance of behavior was woven into a composite view of the individual's life style. In his description of the flatterer, for example, Theophrastus described the machinations of the person whose primary life goal is to ingratiate himself with others. For the most part, however, the esthetic tradition of literary characterology has been confined to the writing field and has failed to penetrate the boundaries of academic psychology. One is reminded here of Lord Dunsany's remark that the excavations of psychologists, like those of road menders, extend for only two inches, whereas those of poets, like miners, extend for a mile.

Consider another relevant contribution from the past. In *The Republic*, Plato conceived of an ideal society consisting of commoners, warriors, and philosopher-kings. Within the framework of this global sociology, he further postulated that the individuals who form these ordered classes are motivated by three distinct categories of impulses. The philosopher-king is propelled by strivings for truth and knowledge (for Good); the warrior is motivated by courage and strength; the commoner is motivated by desire and baser needs. Thus, we have the concept of a sociology sustained by a psychology of individual motivation. On closer study, one finds that Plato went beyond these formulations to link these motivations to somatic structural determinants. He speculated that the philosopher-king was well developed in the cerebral region (the locus of reason), the warrior excelled in thoracic development (the locus of courage), and the commoners were characterized by an overly developed visceral zone (the locus of desire; see *Philebus*). In Plato, the stage is set for a theory of man that pays due respect to sociological and biological as well as psychological determinants.

Preoccupation with change and development within living structure may be traced back to ancient Greece. In Aristotle one finds an interesting notion of process. In reply to the question "What is an acorn?" Aristotle observed that one must look not only at what something appears to be but what it tends to become—being-in-capacity versus being-in-perfection.

The following set of questions, which derive from the intellectual climate of the third century, B.C., may be formulated to assess contemporary theories of personality:

What Are the Basic Units of Individual Personality Organization?

The problem of how the person is constructed intrapsychically, the proper elements in theory building, constitutes the structural problem.

What Are the Wants, Needs, and Desires That Propel a Man into Action?

In contemporary psychology we phrase this issue in terms of instigation, regulation, and maintenance. Essentially, it constitutes the problem of motivation.

What Is the Relationship Between Early Personality Development and Personality Structure in Later Life?

How does change take place, and how is the person modified over time? Investigations of changes over time (diachronic processes) seek to elucidate developmental sequences.

What Is the Relationship Between Environmental Events (Stimuli) and Personality Organization? What Are the Forces That Mold and Modify Behavior in Everyday Life?

This concern with the role of immediate (synchronic) influences on personality focuses on identification of the environmental determinants of behavior.

Within the framework provided by these four broad rubrics (structure, motivation, developmental sequences, and environmental determinants), this chapter briefly outlines several of the outstanding approaches to contemporary personality theory.

HENRY MURRAY

PERSONALITY STRUCTURE

Henry Murray, who is a psychoanalyst as well as a professor of psychology at Harvard University, has adopted Freud's schematic model and formulated his theory around the central structural elements of id, ego, and superego, with some theoretical differences. For Murray, the id is not only the repository of asocial and antisocial impulses; nor does the ego function solely as an inhibitor and repressor. The id is the source of all psychic energy, but this energy derives from instincts that are acceptable to both the self and society as well as those that are not. To quote Murray: "It seems best to think of the id as consisting of all the basic energies, emotions, and needs (value-vectors) of the personality, some of which are wholly acceptable." Murray conceives of the superego as a cultural implant that represents an internalized subsystem of inner directions that regulate the person's behavior in much the same way external agents once acted. And he includes peer and literary and mythological figures as well as parents among the external agents who can contribute to the formulation of the superego. The ego-ideal is related to the superego and represents an idealized picture of the self. It represents the person "at his future best, realizing all his ambitions."

MOTIVATION

Murray has insisted that, if we are to achieve adequate understanding of the individual, our investigations must include a sufficiently large number of variables in keeping with the basic complexity of the subject matter under study. And the elaborate theory of needs that he has evolved to explain the problem of motivation supports this viewpoint. Numerous variables have been proposed to permit description of the nature of these motivating forces. For example, needs may be viscerogenic—that is, linked to organic events—or psychogenic in origin. They may be expressed in overt behavior or revealed in covert phenomena, such as fantasy and dream. Specific needs do not function in isolation within the organism but interact to produce fusion, conflict, prepotency, and subsidization. Murray fully accepts the pervasive and powerful role of unconscious needs, as postulated by classical psychoanalytic theory. Although Murray's formulations in this area have incorporated some experimental findings, notably those derived from the Thematic Apperception Test (TAT) and from the psychoanalytic research conducted by Rosenzweig and others, basically it rests on clinical observations, almost to the same extent as the purely clinical theories reviewed earlier in this book.

DEVELOPMENTAL SEQUENCES

Consideration of the development of personality over time is of crucial importance in Murray's theory. In this area, he has elaborated on the psychoanalytic view of the various stages of development to hypothesize the formulation of five complexes. The sequelae of experiences involving five areas of the body form the nuclei of the claustral, oral, anal, urethral, and castration complexes.

ENVIRONMENTAL DETERMINANTS

Murray has conceptualized two sets of behavioral determinants—press and social-cultural variables. A press is defined as the property or attribute of an environmental object or person that facilitates or impedes the individual's efforts to reach a given goal. These press forces may be objectively discovered (alpha press) or function as subjective, anticipated obstacles in the environment (beta press). Murray draws an interesting distinction between cathexis and sentiment in this connection: Cathexis is the capacity of an environmental object to attract or repel an individual; sentiment refers to the capacity of the individual to be attracted or repelled by these objects. In any event, need and press generally interact and ultimately form a thema, a molar and interactive behavioral unit. Murray and his colleagues have been extremely inventive in their attempts to develop projective devices to uncover the major themas in human personality.

THEODORE R. SARBIN

PERSONALITY STRUCTURE

Theodore R. Sarbin, of the University of California at Santa Cruz, has developed a theory that is multidisciplinary, derived from studies of culture, society, and personality. In addition, the theory is presented within an interactional framework. Personality is conceived of as the integration of role and self. A role is a patterned sequence of learned actions or deeds performed by the individual in interaction with a given situation. The position of the person in a social structure is a function of a set of expectations or acquired anticipatory reactions. That is, an organized system of role expectations is equivalent to a position in the social structure. Varying degrees of organismic involvement accompany various role enactments. For example, level I, which is labeled "role and self differentiations," is the lowest stage of interactional involvement: level VI, the highest stage of involvement, is exemplified by ecstasy and *rites de passage*. The second important component of personality, the self, is a cognitive structure that develops as a result of the interaction between the organism and various stimuli (objects and events). The personality word card (PWC), consisting of 200 trait terms, has been developed to quantify dimensions of the self, such as self-acceptance versus self-criticism.

MOTIVATION

In early life the motivating conditions that lead to action arise from disturbances in the steady state of the organism. In the neonate, the steady state is maintained by means of chemical equilibrium or homeostasis. In the process of maintaining equilibrium, trace residuals are deposited within the nervous system to form the earliest cognitions. The application of the equilibrium principle from chemical homeostasis to conceptual constancy in Sarbin's theory is extended to all cognitive substructures. This parallels Lecky's thesis of self-consistency.

DEVELOPMENTAL SEQUENCES

The self is an organization of qualities that are unverbalized and unverbalizable at first and are verbalized in part later by gestural devices, such as self-drawing, or linguistic devices, such as naming, the use of adjectives, "I" sentences, etc. The self has its origins in the interaction between two series of events: the maturational series and the personal-social series. The first series, the maturational series, is assumed to remain fairly constant from culture to culture. In contrast, the personal-social series, which is of paramount significance, is characterized by specific modes of interaction at particular times. The self evolves on the basis of the interaction between these series of events through various stages, including the somatic self (S_1), the receptor-effector self (S_2), the primitive construed self (S_3), the introjecting-extrojecting self (S_4), and the social self (S_5).

ENVIRONMENTAL DETERMINANTS

The extensive influence of sociological concepts on Sarbin's theory has led to an emphasis on the social-interactional determinants of personality. Associated with this concept of role as a structural component of personality are hypotheses concerning role expectation. These represent the basic determinants of human behavior. Concomitantly, since personality is defined as the integration of self and role, Sarbin has elaborated on self-role and role-role conflicts as the basis of personality disorganization.

GARDNER MURPHY

PERSONALITY STRUCTURE

Gardner Murphy, former director of research at the Menninger Clinic, has delineated the basic components of personality to include: (1) physiological dispositions, which stem from genetic and embryological dispositions; (2) canalizations, which are formed early in life; (3) conditioned responses, which are ingrained through repeated reinforcement; and (4) cognitive and perceptual habits, which are the joint products of canalization and conditioning. Another structural component of personality is the self, which Murphy defines as "the individual as known to the individual."

The ego, which represents still another component, refers to a system of habits that enhance or defend the self and therefore serve the same function as the mechanisms of defense described in classical psychoanalytic theory. In addition, habits, values, attitudes, percepts, images, and character are cited in Murphy's theory as structural elements of personality.

MOTIVATION

Murphy has stated that "the ultimate elements in personality structure are the needs or tensions." A tension is described as a concentration of energy in a particular tissue or group of tissues. Intercommunication among various motives is achieved by the transmission of energy—that is, tension—from one region to other regions of the body. As a consequence of this intercommunication, a network of motivation develops. An important feature of Murphy's theory of motivation is his emphasis on sensory and physical needs. For example, the transmission of tensions that have their locus in the sense organs and muscles are the basis for esthetic motivation and for the individual's delight in a variety of esthetic experiences.

DEVELOPMENTAL SEQUENCES

Murphy contends that there are three distinct stages of personality development. The first stage is one of undifferentiated wholeness—for example, the mass activity of the newborn. The second stage is marked by a differentiation of functions. The third stage is characterized by a blending of functions into organized, coordinated activity. These stages have been termed globality, differentiation, and integration, respectively.

ENVIRONMENTAL DETERMINANTS

Murphy conceives of the learning process as the interaction between an organism and a specific environment. Through the learning process, connections are formed between needs and responses. These connections are established by means of two processes, canalization and conditioning. The concept of canalization is similar to the psychoanalytic concepts of cathexis and fixation. It is the process by which a motive or energy pool finds an outlet by discharging itself in behavior. An important concomitant to early canalizations involving one's own body is the emergence of the concept of self. Since canalization cannot fully explain all learning, Murphy introduces the idea of conditioning to implement this theory. He also recognizes the influences of socialization and the impact of cultural expectations on behavior. Murphy's emphasis on the immediate stimulus field as a determinant of behavior finds expression in his concept of situationism.

GORDON W. ALLPORT

PERSONALITY STRUCTURE

Possibly more than any other personality theorist, Allport attempted to construct a personality theory that would take into account the complexity and uniqueness of individual human behavior. And this view is reflected in his definition of personality as the "dynamic organization within the individual of those psychophysical systems that determine his unique adjustments to his environment." The central structural element in Allport's theory is the trait, which may be defined as a determining tendency or a predisposition to act. In reality, no two individuals ever have exactly the same trait, but biological and cultural similarities allow for "a limited number of roughly comparable modes of adjustment." Thus, an individual trait stands in opposition to a common trait. A number of other distinctions also merit consideration, such as trait versus habit, trait versus attitude, and trait versus type. A trait represents the result of the combination or integration of two or more habits. An attitude is related to a trait; but an attitude is linked to a specific object or referent, and a trait is not. Allport regarded a type as a construction that man is fitted to. A person may possess a trait but not a type.

MOTIVATION

On close inspection, one finds a fusion of structure and motivation in Allport's theory. Traits not only serve as a basis of personality description but also refer to generalized predispositions to behavior. For example, a cardinal trait is "so dominant that there are few activities that cannot be traced directly or indirectly to its influence." In *Becoming*, Allport described the propriate functions of the personality that form the basis of all attitudes, intentions, and evaluations. This concept of the proprium, which is pivotal in Allport's theory, includes all the aspects of personality that make for inward unity: body image, self-identity, ego enhancement, ego extension, rational agent, self-image, propriate striving, and the knower.

DEVELOPMENTAL SEQUENCES

Allport's theory minimizes the importance of the individual's history. His goals and strivings provide more important clues for the understanding of an individual than the early child-rearing practices to which he was subjected. To support his theoretical position, Allport proposed the principle of the functional autonomy of motives. Basically, this principle states that a given activity or form of behavior may become an end or goal in itself, in spite of the fact that it was originally initiated to serve some other purpose. In Allport, the extent to which an individual's motivation pattern is autonomous is a measure of his maturity.

ENVIRONMENTAL DETERMINANTS

Allport's learning theory is an eclectic one. His emphasis on an idiographic approach and the central role accorded the proprium (propriate motives) leaves little room for consideration of environmental influences.

KURT LEWIN

PERSONALITY STRUCTURE

The basic ingredients of personality structure in Lewin's theory are the person and the psychological environment. The life space (L) may be defined as P (the person) $+ E$ (the psychological environment). Thus, the life space contains the totality of facts capable of determining behavior. Behavior (B) is defined as a function (F) of the life space—that is, $B = F (L)$. Facts that exist outside and adjacent to the boundary of the life space form a region referred to as the foreign hull. However, there is two-way communication between the life space and the foreign hull; and this permeability between the two means that facts in the external world may influence the inner world. The person is differentiated into two zones: the perceptual-motor region $(P\text{-}M)$ and the inner-personal region $(I\text{-}P)$. The psychological environment (E) is articulated and divided into regions. The characteristics of the psychological environment are nearness-remoteness, firmness-weakness, and fluidity-rigidity.

MOTIVATION

Lewin subscribes to the theory that each person is a complex energy system. The kind of energy that performs psychological work is called psychical energy. An increase of tension or the release of energy within the $I\text{-}P$ region is caused by the arousal of need, either biological or quasibiological. This produces disequilibrium within the system. Tensions in the $I\text{-}P$ system are described in Lewin's theory as vectors or forces operating on the person as he is represented in the life space. These vectors have strength, direction, and point of application and propel the person to a valenced (valued) region of the psychological environment. Tension may be reduced and equilibrium restored either by direct locomotion or by purely imaginary locomotion.

DEVELOPMENTAL SEQUENCES

Although Lewin does not reject the idea that heredity and maturation play a role in development, the extent of their influence is not elaborated. Rather, he discusses three important concepts in relation to the developmental process—namely, differentiation, boundary properties, and integration. Differentiation refers to an increase in the number of parts of a whole. With age, the psychological environment becomes increasingly differentiated. Boundary properties change in respect to permeability from childhood to adulthood. The subsystems within the adult show greater organizational interdependence than they do in the child. Since development is conceived of as a continuous process, the delineation of fixed, discrete stages is not developed in the Lewinian theory.

ENVIRONMENTAL DETERMINANTS

Lewin did not develop an elaborate learning theory to account for modifications of behavior. Influenced by the Gestalt school, Lewin discusses learning in such terms as cognitive restructuring, differentiation, and organization.

ANDRAS ANGYAL

PERSONALITY STRUCTURE

Organismic theories of personality, such as that proposed by Andras Angyal, are characterized by their emphasis on the unity of functioning of the normal personality. The concept of the biosphere is proposed to describe the holistic entity, which includes both the individual and the environment. The biosphere has two poles: The social pole refers to the individual's interpersonal interactions in society; the psychological pole refers to his symbolic functions. An important property of the system is the extent of its rigidity. Plasticity in a system may result in a wide array of functional variations; a rigid system reacts in a uniform and stereotyped manner. Angyal has described three important dimensions of the biosphere—the vertical, the transverse, and the progressive. The vertical dimension refers to a graduated series of actions that lead to a goal; the transverse refers to the coordination of activities into unified behavior units. Since man can form symbolic ideas about himself, the sum total of these perceptions defines the symbolic self. Behavior is a function of a person's self-image.

MOTIVATION

Typical of the organismic penchant for sovereign drive theory, Angyal maintains that system energy comes from the tensions that arise between the social pole and the psychological pole. In this sense, disequilibrium creates the energy necessary for self-expansion. Two phases of self-expansion are autonomy, movement by the organism to master the environment, and homonomy, which is the submerging of individuality within the social group. These two trends within the biosphere constitute the dynamic elements of Angyal's theory.

DEVELOPMENTAL SEQUENCES

Angyal has not evolved a theory of learning but relies on the language of Gestalt psychology. Development of the organism is viewed as a unified process in time. Such theoretical terms as differentiation, reorganization, and shifting are employed to cover the changes that take place in the evolving personality system. Inherent in the biosphere is a central design or pattern that gives coherence to the individual.

ENVIRONMENTAL DETERMINANTS

The major source of environmental determinants is the biospheric occurrence—that is, the dynamic interplay of the environment-organism unit. Experiences that inhibit or impede the total functioning of the organism, such as anxiety, are termed bionegative.

KURT GOLDSTEIN

PERSONALITY STRUCTURE

Strongly influenced by the Gestalt school, Kurt Goldstein viewed the organism as an entity that possesses differentiated factors. The concepts of figure and ground, borrowed from the perceptual domain, are used to describe the primary organization of organismic functioning. A figure is defined as any process that emerges to stand out against a background, with properties similar to those described by Rubin. Goldstein differentiated between natural figures, which are functionally embedded in a background consisting of the total organism, and unnatural figures, which are isolated from the total organism and stand out against backgrounds that are also isolated parts of the organism. A figure emerges in response to demands made on the organism, and natural figures are orderly, flexible, and appropriate to the situation. Although there is a potent dynamic emphasis in Goldstein's formulation, he recognized that many activities of the organism remain relatively constant. To handle this contingency, Goldstein introduced the concept of constancy, analogous to perceptual constancies in the visual system, to explain the issue of invariance in behavior over changes in the stimulus situation. There is little explication of subsystems within the organism, but Goldstein drew distinctions with regard to behavior between performances (which are conscious, willed activities), attitudes (which are moods, feelings, and elements of the inner life of the organism), and processes (which are bodily functions).

MOTIVATION

The major concepts employed by Goldstein to deal with the dynamic properties of the organism are (1) the equalization process or centering of the organism and (2) self-actualization. In the equalization process an available energy supply is postulated within the personality that is relatively constant and evenly distributed throughout the system. The absolute amount of energy available may vary from one person to another, but there is an average parameter for each individual system. When states of tension (disequilibrium) occur, the organism automatically attempts to return to its average state. The compensatory shift to a psychological plumb line defines the centering process and explains the coherence, consistency, and orderliness on the part of the organism faced with a constantly changing environment. The second dynamic property of the organism, self-actualization, is the sovereign motive in the Goldstein theory. The various phenotypic drive states are all manifestations of this single system drive. The fulfillment of any void within the organism is a manifestation of self-actualization. Although this is a universal principle, each person has different innate potentialities, and therefore people strive for self-actualization along different paths.

DEVELOPMENTAL SEQUENCES

Although the self-actualization concept might suggest various stages of organismic development, Goldstein did not elaborate a developmental sequence except for some generalities suggesting that behavior becomes more even and orderly as the individual matures.

ENVIRONMENTAL DETERMINANTS

Goldstein clearly recognized the influence and interplay of hereditary and environmental influences. Many of the constancies, for example, are viewed as inborn. The concept of reorganization is used, but no systematic account of the learning process is developed. The effects of environmental determinants are heavily weighted in his concept of coming to terms with the environment. The environment produces imbalances in the organismic system; at the same time it sets the stage that enables the individual to find or construct an environment that will fulfill his destiny. Essentially, coming to terms with the environment means mastering it, for only in this manner can the obstacles to self-actualization be overcome.

ABRAHAM H. MASLOW

PERSONALITY STRUCTURE

Maslow developed a theory of personality that focuses on the psychiatrically healthy man. In contrast to many personality theories—especially those in the Freudian tradition, which are primarily concerned with pathology—Maslow argued for a reorientation to a concern for a formulation built around the positive view of man. The structural position of his holistic theory parallels the Gestalt-organismic theories described earlier in this chapter. On the whole, less attention is devoted to structure than to dynamics.

MOTIVATION

Maslow's theory of human motivation assumes that needs are arranged according to a hierarchy of priority or potency. When the needs that have the greatest priority for satisfaction are dealt with, the next stratum of needs emerges and presses for fulfillment. The needs of the individual are arranged on a continuum that ranges from physiological needs (linked to somatic processes) to higher-order esthetic needs.

DEVELOPMENTAL SEQUENCES

Although he did not elaborate a theory of developmental sequences, Maslow recognized that the young organism is dominated by physiological and tissue needs. As the organism matures, the needs for safety and security become potent. In the optimally adjusted adult, the higher-order needs are prepotent.

ENVIRONMENTAL DETERMINANTS

Maslow's studies of self-actualized individuals and his speculations concerning organized societies constitute a unique contribution to personality theory. Maslow believed that man is essentially good. Society may foster antisocial behavior by denying the individual the opportunity to fulfill his inborn needs. However, institutions can be developed that will contribute to self-actualization.

STIMULUS-RESPONSE THEORY

PERSONALITY STRUCTURE

In the tradition of Pavlov, Watson, and Thorndike, S-R theory attempts to provide a rigorous, scientific approach to personality. The work of Dollard and Miller typify this orientation, which derives from reinforcement learning theory. The major structural element in S-R theory is the habit, which is a link of association between a stimulus (cue) and a response. The concept of habit replaces the earlier Thorndikian notion of the S-R bond.

MOTIVATION

The dynamic component in S-R theory is the concept of drive. Generally defined, a drive is any stimulus strong enough to instigate the organism into action. Drives are divided into two categories: primary and secondary. The primary drives are unlearned and innate and are linked to physiological processes. The secondary drives are acquired on the basis of association with primary drive stimulation. The latter account for a large segment of behavior in the socialized adult.

DEVELOPMENTAL SEQUENCES

Dollard and Miller handle the problem of development and change in terms of a survey of the innate equipment of the organism and the learning process. At birth, the child is equipped with an array of specific reflexes, an innate hierarchy of responses, and a set of primary drives. Although these authors have not elaborated a theory of crucial stages, attention is directed toward the ability to use language and early learning conditions.

ENVIRONMENTAL DETERMINANTS

A great amount of attention is devoted by Dollard and Miller to the four elements of the learning process: drive, cue, response, and reinforcement or reward. The basic premise of S-R theory is that learning only takes place under conditions of drive reduction. To buttress the theory, the concepts of spontaneous recovery, gradient of stimulus, and response generalization are discussed in detail. Recently, Mowrer has extended the boundaries of the original S-R position to deal with the broader crises in psychiatry and religion as well.

O. HOBART MOWRER

PERSONALITY STRUCTURE

Mowrer, who is on the faculty of the University of Illinois, has developed an original and important theory of personality. However, its originality does not reside in its structural concepts, which are essentially eclectic. In general, Mowrer subscribes to the psychoanalytic structural model of ego, id, and superego. But in contrast to psychoanalysts such as Freud and Murray and to experimentalists such as Cattell, he makes no attempt to specify the number and nature of hypothesized instincts or drives. Rather, his concepts introduce modifications in regard to the dynamic relation of these structural components. Moreover, one must recognize a quality in these structures that differs from the comparatively loose descriptions of the psychoanalysts, for example. Mowrer has brought to learning the concepts of habit formation, of the defense mechanisms, and an attempt to translate structures into classical reflex learning theory, couched in Hullian formulations at first and later in his own. The translation hinges on concepts of internal stimuli and expectation.

MOTIVATION

As indicated, drives are recognized as the primary motivators, but no specific list has been proposed in his scheme. However, he is specific to the degree that he reflects a set of simple biological goals—such as hunger, thirst, and sex—with which other animal experimenters have been content, and states that social needs (gregariousness), avoidance of loss of honor, and various relatively intangible nonviscerogenic needs must be considered. Drive-instigated activity, then, is controlled by ego and superego, strengthened in the course of the learning process.

DEVELOPMENTAL SEQUENCES

Mowrer has outlined four main stages of development, which are not derived from zones of the body, as is the libido theory: (1) infantile indulgence, which embodies such psychoanalytic concepts as narcissism and infantile omnipotence; (2) the onset of socialization, beginning with toilet-training and similar impositions of social standards; (3) a phase of negativism, involving conflict both with society and with the developing superego; and (4) the outcome of such conflict at adolescence, which may take the form of delinquency, neurosis, or successful adult integration.

ENVIRONMENTAL DETERMINANTS

It is in this area that Mowrer has made his most creative contribution to clinical psychology. Whereas the classical psychoanalytic position sees conflict principally as occurring between ego and id impulses, which lead in practice to attempts to mitigate the repressive acts of a too severe superego, Mowrer believes that the core conflict stems from an alienation from society and from a superego that is too lenient rather than too strict.

Although many clinicians think of the delinquent and the neurotic as deviating from the normal—the former toward excessive and the latter toward defective impulse expression—Mowrer sees both as cheating and as refractory in meeting the role expectations of society and the demands of the superego. The refractory phase in development becomes outright revolt in the delinquent; in the neurotic it is expressed as a defect and results in the repression of superego urges. Translated into the language of learning theory, the neurotic is making a two-fold error in punishment avoidance. First, he seeks to hide his misdemeanors, an attempt that is rarely successful; second, he turns his back on guilt, using various defenses, escape into hyperactivity, alcoholism, hysteric or compulsive symptoms.

In what Mowrer defines as integrity therapy, the neurotic is encouraged to confess his deviance and duplicity, which usually refers to his actual behavior, past or present, not merely his imagined sins; to recognize that even then society may not accept him again until he has served penance; to satisfy the demands of his superego by social service; and to sever inconsistent ties and seek new alignments. In contrast to the Freudian position, Mowrer has succinctly stated his belief that "the super-ego knows best."

MULTIVARIATE PERSONALITY THEORY

The theories derived from experimental psychology and particularly the application of multivariate statistical procedures are fundamentally different in origin from the theories described above. The concepts and procedures of this approach have been set out in the preceding chapter. Nevertheless, they should be represented in this context as well, however briefly. For one thing, the presentation of these rather complex hypotheses within the simple framework adopted throughout this section may contribute to their further clarification. Second, it will permit comparative evaluation of this rather revolutionary approach to personality theory as opposed to other, more traditional theoretical systems. There have been relatively few researchers in this complex field, and this discussion rests largely on the work of Cattell and Eysenck and the less systematic and comprehensive investigations of Baggaley, Burt, Digman, Goldberg, Guilford, Horn, Hundleby, Meredith, Messick, Pawlik, Peterson, Scheier, Sweney, Warburton, and Wiggins.

PERSONALITY STRUCTURE

Depending on whether the discovered personality factors are described at the primary level (Burt, Cattell, Guilford, Scheier) or only at the second order (Eysenck, Peterson), more or fewer structures will be listed. Typically, however, some 30 factors in questionnaire response and objective tests are recognized as primary personality components that, in turn, give rise to perhaps six to ten higher-order components. Some of the primary factors—such as ego strength, schizothymia, superego strength—serve to facilitate experimental mental confirmation of clinical theory; others such as cortertia and parmia proceed to new concepts.

These unitary structures comprise three modalities—abilities, temperament dimensions, and dynamic traits—and have been shown to be determined to varying degrees by heredity and environment. In the dynamic field they proved to be primary drives (nine of them, including sex, fear, and curiosity), acquired social sentiment structures (to home, to religion, to self), and defense mechanisms.

Because they are simple structure factors, these factors are measurable mathematically on the 16 P.F. Test, the MMPI, O-A Batteries, and the Motivation Analysis Test (MAT). The basic theory of their interaction assumes that they are simply summative in action, although speculations regarding complex curvilinear relations are also entertained, so that the magnitude of any particular action or symptom may be accounted for by a specification equation, as follows:

$$\text{Response} = b_1 T_2 + b_2 T_2 \cdots + b_k T_k$$

where T_1 to T_k are k source traits (factors) with values appropriate for the given individual and the b's or behavioral indices are peculiar to that response and the situation in which it occurs. The b values for each situation are obtained by correlation methods and express the extent to which the given response involves the given trait.

MOTIVATION

Besides the T's, which are abilities, there are others that, as stated, represent drives and sentiments (acquired attachments). The former are the primary motivators, stabilized in expression by the sentiments and governed and directed by self-sentiment and the superego, with characteristics defined by the discovered factor loadings.

Objective devices for measuring motivation prove to separate into I (integrated) and U (unintegrated) components, and a good many inferences about conflict, suppression, and repression can be drawn from their relationship in a particular case. Factoring of motivation data by Cattell and his co-workers has confirmed the existence of repression, projection, and other Freudian mechanisms as well as the existence of complexes. Eysenck, however, has rejected psychoanalytic terminology in regard to any resemblances found.

DEVELOPMENTAL SEQUENCES

Twenty years of work by correlational methods have been devoted largely to determining temperamental and dynamic structures and demonstrating that they hold true across different ages and cultures. Recently, through Eysenck's application of extroversion-introversion to concepts of inhibition in learning and through Cattell's reduction of personality change or observations to algebraic matrix analyses in adjustment process analysis, this theory of personality structure has become increasingly related to learning theory. Both authors stress the reality of constitutional and genetic components and the methods that enable their identification. They have also accorded the generalization of learning, experience, and specific social molds a significant role in determining the observed structures.

ENVIRONMENTAL DETERMINANTS

Cattell has suggested three classes of learning experiences: classical conditioning, reward learning, and integration learning. Eysenck has focused on the application of conditioning principles to personality change in behavior therapy. One of the main learning issues in multivariate experimental theory at the moment concerns the manner in which specific learning experiences generate the general factor dimensions found structurally. Ferguson, Tucker, and Fleishman have investigated this in relation to ability. Similarly, Cattell's adjustment process analysis represents an attempt to account for the impact of sociological institutions and acquired social roles.

REFERENCES

Allport, G. W. *Pattern and Growth in Personality*. Holt, Rinehart and Winston, New York, 1961.

Angyal, A. *Foundations for a Science of Personality*, Commonwealth Fund, New York, 1941.

Cattell, R. B., editor. *Handbook of Multivariate Experimental Psychology*. Rand McNally, Chicago, 1966.

Collingwood, R. G. *The Idea of Nature*. Clarendon Press, Oxford, 1945.

Deutsch, M. Field theory in social psychology. In *Handbook of Social Psychology*, G. Lindzey, editor, p. 181. Addison-Wesley, Reading, Mass., 1954.

Dollard, J., and Miller, N. E. *Personality and Psychotherapy: An Analysis in Terms of Learning, Thinking and Culture*, McGraw-Hill, New York, 1950.

Eysenck, H., and Rachman, S. *The Causes and Cures of Neurosis: An Introduction to Modern Behavior Therapy Based on Learning Theory and the Principles of Conditioning.* R. R. Knapp, San Diego, 1965.

Goldstein, K. *The Organism.* American Book Company, New York, 1939.

Lewin, K. *A Dynamic Theory of Personality.* McGraw-Hill, New York, 1935.

Maslow, A. H. *Motivation and Personality.* Harper & Row, New York, 1954.

Mowrer, O. H. *The New Group Therapy.* D. Van Nostrand, New York, 1963.

Murphy, G. *Human Potentialities.* Basic Books, New York, 1958.

Murray, H. A., Barrett, W. G., and Homburger, E. *Explorations in Personality.* Oxford University Press, New York, 1938.

Sarbin, T. R., Taft, R., and Bailey, D. E. *Clinical Inference and Cognitive Theory.* Holt, Rinehart and Winston, New York, 1960.

Wepman, J. M., and Heine, R. W. *Concepts of Personality.* Aldine Publishing Company, Chicago, 1963.

Contributors

RAYMOND B. CATTELL, Ph.D., D.Sc.
Research Professor of Psychology and Director, Laboratory of Personality and Group Analysis, University of Illinois, Urbana, Illinois

HOWARD DAVIDMAN, M.D.
Director, Out-Patient Services, Essex County Hospital Center, Newark, New Jersey

ALFRED M. FREEDMAN, M.D.
Professor of Psychiatry and Chairman of the Department of Psychiatry, New York Medical College; Director of Psychiatric Services, Flower and Fifth Avenue Hospitals, Metropolitan Hospital, and Bird S. Coler Memorial Hospital and Home, New York, New York

HAROLD I. KAPLAN, M.D.
Professor of Psychiatry and Director of Psychiatric Education and Training, New York Medical College; Attending Psychiatrist, Flower and Fifth Avenue Hospitals; Visiting Psychiatrist, Metropolitan Hospital and Bird S. Coler Memorial Hospital and Home, New York, New York

JOHN E. MACK, M.D.
Associate Clinical Professor of Psychiatry, Harvard Medical School, Boston, Massachusetts; Chief of Psychiatry, The Cambridge Hospital, Cambridge, Massachusetts

GERALD M. MEREDITH, Ph.D.
Evaluation Officer, Office of the Dean for Academic Development, University of Hawaii, Honolulu, Hawaii

GEORGE MORA, M.D.
Assistant Clinical Professor of Psychiatry, New York Medical College; Lecturer, Department of Psychiatry, Columbia University College of Physicians and Surgeons, New York, New York; Clinical Associate Professor of Psychiatry, Albany Medical College, Albany, New York; Research Associate, Department of History of Medicine, Yale University School of Medicine, New Haven, Connecticut; Medical Director, Astor Home for Children, Rhinebeck, New York

SIMON H. NAGLER, M.D.
Clinical Professor of Psychiatry, New York Medical College; Attending Psychiatrist, Flower and Fifth Avenue Hospitals; Visiting Psychiatrist, Metropolitan Hospital and Bird S. Coler Memorial Hospital and Home, New York, New York

HELENE PAPANEK, M.D.

Dean and Director, Alfred Adler Institute; Adjunct Psychiatrist Emeritus, Lenox Hill Hospital; Faculty Member, Postgraduate Center for Mental Health, New York, New York; Consultant, Veterans Administration, Brooklyn, New York

JACK L. RUBINS, M.D.

Associate Clinical Professor of Psychiatry, New York Medical College; Associate Attending Psychiatrist, Flower and Fifth Avenue Hospitals; Associate Visiting Psychiatrist, Metropolitan Hospital; Lecturer, Training Analyst, and Assistant Dean, American Institute of Psychoanalysis; Director, Day-Care Center for Schizophrenia, Karen Horney Clinic, New York, New York

LEON SALZMAN, M.D.

Deputy Director, Bronx State Hospital; Clinical Professor of Psychiatry, Albert Einstein College of Medicine of Yeshiva University, Bronx, New York

ELVIN V. SEMRAD, M.D.

Professor of Psychiatry, Harvard Medical School; Director of Psychiatry, Massachusetts Mental Health Center; Faculty, Boston Psychoanalytic Institute, Boston, Massachusetts

EDITH WEIGERT, M.D.

Chairman of Faculty, Washington School of Psychiatry; Training Psychoanalyst, Washington Psychoanalytic Institute, Washington, D.C.

EDWARD C. WHITMONT, M.D.

Training Psychoanalyst and Professor, C. G. Jung Institute for Analytical Psychology of New York, New York, New York

Index

Alfred M. Freedman

Alfred M. Freedman received his A.B. from Cornell University and his M.D. from the University of Minnesota Medical School. After Army service in World War II, he engaged in neurophysiological and neurochemical research, and trained in general and child psychiatry at Bellevue Hospital. He received his certificate in psychoanalysis from the William Alanson White Institute for Psychoanalysis, and is a Diplomate of the American Board of Psychiatry and Neurology. Since 1960 he has been Professor and Chairman of the Department of Psychiatry at the New York Medical College. Dr. Freedman is Director of the Metropolitan Community Mental Health Center, and Director of Psychiatry at Flower and Fifth Avenue Hospitals, Metropolitan Hospital, and Bird S. Coler Hospital; in addition, he is President of the American Psychopathological Association and President-elect of the American College of Neuropsychopharmacology. He has published over a hundred scientific papers, and is co-editor of the *Comprehensive Textbook of Psychiatry* (1967) and of *Psychopathology of Adolescence* (1970).

Harold I. Kaplan

Harold I. Kaplan received an undergraduate degree from Columbia University and an M.D. from the New York Medical College in 1949. He trained in psychiatry at the Kingsbridge Veterans Hospital and Mount Sinai Hospital in New York and became a Diplomate of the American Board of Psychiatry and Neurology in 1957; presently he is an Associate Examiner of the American Board. He began the practice and teaching of psychiatry and was certified in psychoanalytic medicine at the New York Medical College in 1954. He became Professor of Psychiatry and Director of Psychiatric Training and Education at the New York Medical College in 1961. He is Attending Psychiatrist at Metropolitan Hospital Center, Flower and Fifth Avenue Hospitals and Bird S. Coler Hospital. He is the Principal Investigator of ten National Institute of Mental Health training programs, specializing in the areas of undergraduate and graduate psychiatric education as well as the training of women in medicine. He is the author of over seventy scientific papers and co-editor of the *Comprehensive Textbook of Psychiatry* (1967) and of *Comprehensive Group Psychotherapy* (1971).

Interpreting Personality:

A Survey of Twentieth-Century Views

No one theory of personality adequately explains normal or abnormal functioning. Nevertheless, the practice of psychiatry exists, and its insights into the causes of mental illness and into the methods of cure rest on the various theories discussed in this volume.

The first section deals with orthodox Freudian psychoanalytic theories, and includes a chapter on that notable expounder of ego psychology, Erik Erikson. The second area covers the major cultural and interpersonal psychoanalytic theories, as represented by Alfred Adler, Carl Jung, Karen Horney, Harry Stack Sullivan, Erich Fromm, and Sandor Rado. The theories of Adolph Meyer, Otto Rank, Melanie Klein, Wilhelm Reich, and Jules H. Masserman are examined in the third section, which concludes with a chapter on existential psychoanalysis. Last is a close look at quantitative measurement and other personality theories derived from psychology, including those of Henry Murray, Theodore Sarbin, Gardner Murphy, Gordon W. Allport, Kurt Lewin, Andras Angyal, Kurt Goldstein, Abraham Maslow, and O. Hobart Mowrer.